MATHEMATICS
FOR LEAVING CERTIFICATE

ORDINARY LEVEL

FOURTH EDITION

GEORGE HUMPHREY

Gill & Macmillan

Gill & Macmillan Ltd
Hume Avenue
Park West, Dublin 12
with associated companies throughout the world

© George Humphrey 1996, 2000, 2001, 2007, 2008, 2009

978 0 7171 4151 7

Print origination by Macmillan India

The paper used in this book is made from the wood pulp of managed forests.
For every tree felled, at least one tree is planted, thereby renewing natural resources.

CONTENTS

All of the material covered in this book is relevant for students taking the Leaving Certificate Ordinary Level Examination in **2011.**

For students preparing for the Leaving Certificate Ordinary Level Examination in **2012** the following chapters will no longer be examined in the way they are dealt with in this book: 8, 9, 10, 11, 12, 13. The content of these chapters will be replaced by the new Project Maths syllabus.

Preface

This book was written to help you revise for the Leaving Certificate Ordinary Level Mathematics Examination. Chapters 1 to 6 deal with Paper 1 and Chapters 7 to 14 deal with Paper 2. This book has been developed to help you to achieve the best result you can in the examination. Unlike a textbook, this book has been organised to make your revision easier.

Throughout your course you can use the book to:

- remind you of what you have been taught
- help you with your homework
- do some extra practice at the kind of questions you will meet in the examination
- sort out things you did not quite follow in class
- focus on the essential points in each topic
- organise your revision and preparation for the actual examination.

To make the best use of this book, attempt to solve the problems yourself before looking at the solutions given. Redo any questions you answer incorrectly. Get into the habit of making your own notes as you work throughout the book and use these notes in later revision sessions.

I would like to thank Clare O' Dea, Dublin City University, who read the entire manuscript and made many valuable suggestions which I have included in the final text and greatly reduced my errors!

I also wish to express my thanks to the staff at Gill & Macmillan for their advice, guidance and untiring assistance in the preparation and presentation of the text.

George Humphrey
St Andrew's College
Booterstown Avenue
Blackrock
Co. Dublin

Dedicated to the memory of my brother Larry

Tips on Revision and the Examination in Mathematics

It is very important to realise that you are your own best teacher. Revision is when you begin to teach yourself. Thus, it is very important that you start your revision as soon as possible. Make notes while you are revising. If you are having difficulty with a particular question seek help from your teacher, a friend or a member of your family. As with all subjects, the best examination preparation is to work through past examination or sample papers so that you are familiar with the layout and style of questions.

There is no such thing as rough work in Maths – all work is relevant. Therefore any such work should be done beside the question, so that the examiner can see it. If the examiner doesn't know how you reached an answer, even a correct answer, then full marks will usually not be awarded. Thus, show all your work. Make sure to give your answers to the correct degree of accuracy (for example, correct to two decimal places) and include the appropriate units of measurements (for example, m^2) when relevant.

One-third of the marks will be awarded for any step in the right direction. Therefore make an attempt at each part of the question. Even if you do not get the correct answer, you can still pick up most of the marks on offer if you show how you worked it out. Also, draw a diagram where possible, because this can help in seeing the solution.

If you cannot finish part of a question, leave a space and come back to it later. Never scribble out any work or use Tipp-Ex. Put a single line through it so that the examiner can still read it. In many cases work that had a line through it received more marks. Avoid using pencil because the writing can be very faint and difficult to read.

Familiarise yourself with your calculator. Also, it is a good idea to show each stage of a calculation when using a calculator (in case you press a wrong key). Know all your formulas – your own formula dictionary can be useful – and don't forget to write down any formula that you use.

There is an attempt to divide each question into 3 parts, part A, part B and part C.

Part A – Straightforward, testing only one or two basic concepts and carrying a total of 10 marks.

Part B – More difficult, but still straightforward and carrying a total of 20 marks.

Part C – Much more challenging and may have several parts, carrying a total of 20 marks.

Therefore it is important to get the 'marks : time' ratio correct.

> The 'marks : time' ratio in mathematics is 2 : 1.
>
> A part 'A', worth 10 marks, should be given 5 minutes.
>
> A part 'B', worth 20 marks, should be given 10 minutes.
>
> A part 'C', worth 20 marks, should be given 10 minutes.

Structure of the examination

Paper 1

Time: $2\frac{1}{2}$ hours   Marks: 300

Attempt any 6 questions from a choice of 8

Q1.	Arithmetic
Q2,3.	Algebra
Q4.	Complex Numbers
Q5.	Sequences and Series
Q6,7,8.	Functions, Graphing Functions and Differentiation

Paper 2

Time: $2\frac{1}{2}$ hours   Marks: 300

Section A: Attempt any 5 questions from a choice of 7

Q1.	Perimeter, Area and Volume
Q2.	Coordinate Geometry of the Line
Q3.	Coordinate Geometry of the Circle
Q4.	Geometry
Q5.	Trigonometry
Q6.	Permutations, Combinations and Probability
Q7.	Statistics

Section B: Attempt any 1 question from a choice of 4

Q8.	Further Geometry
Q9.	Vectors
Q10.	Further Sequences and Series
Q11.	Linear Programming

Glossary of the words used on the examination paper

Write down, State
You can write down your answer without showing any work. However, if you want you can show some working.

Calculate, Find, Show that, Determine, Prove
Obtain your answers by showing all relevant work. Marks are available for showing the steps leading to your final answer or conclusion.

Solve
Find the solution, or root, of an equation. The solution is the value of the variable that makes the left-hand side balance with the right-hand side.

Evaluate
Usually to work out, or find, a numerical value by putting in numbers for letters.

Plot
Indicate the position of points on a graph, usually on the x- and y-planes.

Construct
Draw an accurate diagram, usually labelled, using a pencil, ruler, set square, compass and protractor. Leave all constructions on your diagram.

Sketch
Make a rough diagram or graph, labelled if needed.

Hence
You **must** use the answer, or result, from the previous part of the question.

Hence or otherwise
It is recommended that you use the answer, or result, from the previous part of the question, but other methods are acceptable.

Chapter 1. ARITHMETIC

Proportional Parts
(Dividing Quantities in a Given Ratio)

Ratios can be used to divide, or share, quantities.

To divide, or share, a quantity in a given ratio, do the following:

> 1. Add the ratios to get the total number of parts.
>
> 2. Divide the quantity by the total of the parts (this gives one part).
>
> 3. Multiply this separately by each ratio.

Example 1

Express 35 cm as a fraction of 1 m. Give your answer in its simplest form.

Solution:

Express both in cm.

1 m = 100 cm

$$\frac{35 \text{ cm}}{1 \text{ m}} = \frac{35 \text{ cm}}{100 \text{ cm}} = \frac{35}{100} = \frac{7}{20}$$

Example 2

€112 is divided between two pupils, A and B, in the ratio 11 : 3. How much does each pupil get?

Solution:

Number of parts = 11 + 3 = 14.   11 parts = €8 × 11 = €88

$1 \text{ part} = \dfrac{€112}{14} = €8$ 3 parts = €8 × 3 = €24

Thus, A gets €88 and B gets €24.

Example 3

(i) Express as a ratio of whole numbers $\frac{1}{2} : \frac{2}{3} : \frac{3}{4}$

(ii) Hence, or otherwise, divide €920 in the ratio $\frac{1}{2} : \frac{2}{3} : \frac{3}{4}$

Solution:

(i) $\frac{1}{2} : \frac{2}{3} : \frac{3}{4}$

       $\frac{1}{2} : \frac{2}{3} : \frac{3}{4}$

       $= 6 : 8 : 9$

(multiply each part by 12)

(ii) $\frac{1}{2} : \frac{2}{3} : \frac{3}{4} = 6 : 8 : 9$

       $6 + 8 + 9 = 23$

$\therefore$ there are 23 parts altogether

1 part $= \dfrac{€920}{23} = €40$

6 parts $= €40 \times 6 = €240$

8 parts $= €40 \times 8 = €320$

9 parts $= €40 \times 9 = €360$

$\therefore$ €920 in the ratio $\frac{1}{2} : \frac{2}{3} : \frac{3}{4}$

$=$ €240, €320, €360

Sometimes we are given an equation in disguise.

Example 4

€320 is $\frac{4}{9}$ of a prize fund.   Find the total prize fund.

Solution:

Given: €320 is $\frac{4}{9}$ of a prize fund.

$\frac{4}{9}$ of the prize fund $= €320$ (equation given in disguise)

$\frac{1}{9}$ of the prize fund $= €80$ (divide both sides by 4, $\frac{4}{9} = 4 \times \frac{1}{9}$)

$\frac{9}{9}$ of the prize fund $= €720$ (multiply both sides by 9)

Thus, the total prize fund is €720.

Example 5

A glass rod falls and breaks into 3 pieces whose lengths are in the ratio $8 : 9 : 5$. If the sum of the lengths of the two larger pieces is 119 cm, find the length of the third piece.

Solution:

$8 + 9 + 5 = 22$

$\therefore$ there are 22 parts altogether

Given: sum of two larger lengths is 119 cm

$\therefore$ $(8 + 9)$ parts $= 119$ cm

           17 parts $= 119$ cm

             1 part $= 7$cm

third piece

$=$ smallest piece

$= 5$ parts

$= 5 \times 7$ cm

$= 35$ cm

Example 6

A, B, C and D shared €493. B and C each received twice as much as A while D received 350% of what A received. Calculate how much each received.

Solution:

A received the smallest amount.

Let A receive one part.

$\therefore$ B and C receive two parts each (as B and C received twice as much as A) and D receives $3\frac{1}{2}$ parts (as D received $3\frac{1}{2}$ times as much as A).

(**Note:** $350\% = 3\frac{1}{2}$ as a fraction)

$\therefore$ $A : B : C : D = 1 : 2 : 2 : 3\frac{1}{2}$

                $= 2 : 4 : 4 : 7$ (multiply each part by 2)

In other words, we are asked to divide €493 in the ratio $2 : 4 : 4 : 7$.

$2 + 4 + 4 + 7 = 17$

$\therefore$ there are 17 parts altogether

one part $= \dfrac{€493}{17}$

         $= €29$

A's share $= 2$ parts $= €29 \times 2 = €58$

B's share $= 4$ parts $= €29 \times 4 = €116$

C's share $= 4$ parts $= €29 \times 4 = €116$

D's share $= 7$ parts $= €29 \times 7 = €203$

Distance, Speed and Time

There are three formulas to remember when dealing with problems involving distance (D), speed (S), and time (T). It can be difficult to remember these formulas; however, the work can be made easier using a triangle and the memory aid 'Dad's Silly Triangle'.

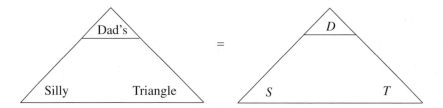

1. Speed $= \dfrac{\text{Distance}}{\text{Time}}$	2. Time $= \dfrac{\text{Distance}}{\text{Speed}}$	3. Distance $=$ Speed $\times$ Time

Consider the triangle on the right. By covering the quantity required, D, S or T, any of the three formulas above can be found by inspection. Speed here means 'average speed'.

Example 1

(i) A train travelled 201.6 km at an average speed of 134.4 km/h. How long does the journey take?

(ii) A car travels for 2 hours and 45 minutes at an average speed of 84 km/h. How far does it travel?

Solution:

(i) Time $= \dfrac{\text{Distance}}{\text{Speed}}$

$\quad\; = \dfrac{201.6}{134.4}$

$\quad\; = 1\frac{1}{2}$ hours

(ii) 45 mins $= \dfrac{45}{60} = \dfrac{3}{4}$ hour

$\qquad$ Distance $=$ Speed $\times$ Time

$\qquad\qquad = 84 \times 2\frac{3}{4}$

$\qquad\qquad = 231$ km

Example 2

A train leaves Cork at 09.05 and arrives in Dublin at 12.25.
The distance from Cork to Dublin is 250 km.
Find the average speed of the train in km/h.

Solution:

Average speed

$= \dfrac{\text{Distance}}{\text{Time}}$

$= \dfrac{250}{3\frac{1}{3}}$

$= 75$ km/h

Time $= 12.25 - 09.05$

$= 3$ hours 20 mins

$= 3\frac{1}{3}$ hours

$(20$ min $= \dfrac{20}{60} = \dfrac{1}{3}$ hour$)$

Example 3

The time taken by Jack to travel from Derry to Waterford, a distance of 378 km, is 6 hours.

His return journey from Waterford to Derry, by the same route, takes an extra 45 mins.

By how many km/h is his average speed slower on the return journey?

Solution:

(i) Derry to Waterford

Average speed

$= \dfrac{\text{Distance}}{\text{Time}}$

$= \dfrac{378}{6}$

$= 63$ km/h

(ii) Waterford to Derry

Average speed

$= \dfrac{\text{Distance}}{\text{Time}}$

$= \dfrac{378}{6\frac{3}{4}}$

$= 56$ km/h

$(45$ mins $= \dfrac{45}{60} = \dfrac{3}{4}$ hour$)$

Difference $= 63 - 56 = 7$ km/h.

Thus, his average speed on the return journey was 7 km/h slower.

Percentages

Example 1

A woman travelled 52.8 km of a journey of 160 km.

What percentage of the journey had been completed?

Solution:

$$\text{Percentage completed} = \frac{\text{Actual distance travelled}}{\text{Total journey}} \times \frac{100}{1}$$

$$= \frac{52.8}{160} \times \frac{100}{1}$$

$$= 33\%$$

In many questions dealing with percentages we will be given an equation in disguise. The best way to tackle this type of problem is to write down the equation given in disguise. From this we can find 1%, and, hence, any percentage we like. Consider the next examples.

Example 2

A solicitor's fee for the sale of a house is $1\frac{1}{2}\%$ of the selling price.

If the fee is €8,700, calculate the selling price.

Solution:

Given: Solicitor's fee is €8,700

$$1\tfrac{1}{2}\% = €8,700 \qquad \text{(equation given in disguise)}$$

$$3\% = €17,400 \qquad \text{(multiply both sides by 2)}$$

$$1\% = €5,800 \qquad \text{(divide both sides by 3)}$$

$$100\% = €580,000 \qquad \text{(multiply both sides by 100)}$$

$\therefore$ the selling price of the house was €580,000

Example 3

The selling price of a car was €26,250 which includes 25% VAT. Before being sold the VAT rate was reduced from 25% to 15%. Find:

(i) the new selling price of the car

(ii) the cost to the customer if the salesman allowed a 7% discount on this new selling price.

Solution:

(i) Given: Cost of car, including VAT of 25%, is €26,250

$\therefore$ $125\% = €26,250$ (equation given in disguise)

         $1\% = €210$ (divide both sides by 125)

        $115\% = €24,150$ (multiply both sides by 115)

$\therefore$ the new selling price, including VAT at 15%, is €24,150

(ii) Discount of 7%

        $100\% = €24,150$ (equation given in disguise)

          $1\% = €241.50$ (divide both sides by 100)

        $93\% = €22,459.50$ (multiply both sides by 93, i.e. $100 - 7 = 93$)

$\therefore$ Cost to the customer, including a 7% discount, is €22,459.50

Relative Error and Percentage Error

When calculations are being made errors can occur, especially calculations which involve rounding. It is important to have a measure of the error.

Definitions

> Error = |True value – Estimated value| and is always considered positive.

> Relative error $= \dfrac{\text{Error}}{\text{True Value}}$

> Percentage error $= \dfrac{\text{Error}}{\text{True Value}} \times \dfrac{100}{1}$

Example 1

It is estimated that the cost of building a table will be €360. The actual cost was €350. Calculate (i) the relative error (as a fraction) and (ii) the percentage error, correct to two decimal places.

Solution:

Error = |Actual cost − Estimated cost| = |€350 − €360| = | − €10| = €10

(i) Relative error = $\dfrac{\text{Error}}{\text{True cost}} = \dfrac{10}{350} = \dfrac{1}{35}$

(ii) Percentage error = Relative error $\times \dfrac{100}{1} = \dfrac{1}{35} \times \dfrac{100}{1} = \dfrac{100}{35} = 2.86\%$

(correct to two decimal places)

Example 2

When using a calculator to add 1.7 and 2.2, a student strikes the multiplication key instead of the addition key.
Calculate the percentage error in the result, correct to one decimal place.

Solution:

Correct value = 1.7 + 2.2 = 3.9

Incorrect value = 1.7 × 2.2 = 3.74

Error = |Correct value − Incorrect value| = |3.9 − 3.74| = |0.16| = 0.16

Percentage error = $\dfrac{\text{Error}}{\text{Correct value}} \times \dfrac{100}{1}$

$= \dfrac{0.16}{3.9} \times \dfrac{100}{1} = 4.1\%$ \qquad (correct to one decimal place)

Foreign Exchange

In Ireland the euro, €, is the basic unit of currency.

Example 1

If €1 = 109 Japanese yen, how much in € would a person receive for 17,222 Japanese yen, if the commission is $1\frac{1}{2}\%$?

Solution:

It is good practice to put the units of currency we require on the RHS.

$$109 \text{ yen} = €1 \qquad \text{(put what you want on the RHS)}$$

$$1 \text{ yen} = €\frac{1}{109} \qquad \text{(divide both sides by 109)}$$

$$17,113 \text{ yen} = €\frac{17,222}{109} \qquad \text{(multiply both sides by 17,113)}$$

$$= €158$$

Now, $1\frac{1}{2}\%$ commission must be paid on this.

$$\text{Commission} = 1\frac{1}{2}\% \text{ of } €158 = €2.37$$

Thus the person will receive $= €158 - €2.37 = €155.63$

Example 2

A person changes €1,200 into SF (Swiss francs). A charge is made for this service. The exchange rate is €1 = 2.2 SF. If the person receives 2,593.8 SF, calculate the percentage charge.

Solution:

First express €1,200 in SF

$$€1,200 = 1,200 \times 2.2 \text{ SF} = 2,640 \text{ SF}$$

$$\text{Amount received} = 2,593.8$$

$$\therefore \qquad \text{Charge} = 2,640 - 2,593.8 = 46.2 \text{ SF}$$

$$\text{Percentage charge} = \frac{\text{Charge}}{\text{Original amount}} \times \frac{100}{1}$$

$$= \frac{46.2}{2,640} \times \frac{100}{1}$$

$$= 1.75\%$$

Example 3

If €1 = 9 Norwegian krone and €1 = 2.25 SF, how many Swiss francs would you get for 1,388 krone?

Solution:

Our answer is to be in SF, $\therefore$ put SF on the RHS.

Given: €1 = 9 krone and €1 = 2.25 SF

$\therefore$

$$9 \text{ krone} = 2.25 \text{ SF} \qquad \text{(as both equal €1)}$$

$$1 \text{ krone} = \frac{2.25}{9} \text{ SF} \qquad \text{(divide both sides by 9)}$$

$$1,388 \text{ krone} = \frac{1,388 \times 2.25}{9} \text{ SF} \quad \text{(multiply both sides by 1,388)}$$

$$= 347 \text{ SF}$$

Thus, you would get 347 Swiss francs for 1,388 krone.

Income Tax

The following is called the income tax equation:

Gross tax − Tax credits = Tax payable

Gross tax is calculated as follows:

Standard rate on all income **up to** the standard rate cut-off point	+	A higher rate on all income **above** the standard rate cut-off point

Example 1

The standard rate of income tax is 20% and the higher rate is 42%.
Colm has weekly tax credits of €50 and a standard rate cut-off point of €240.
Until recently, Colm had a gross weekly income of €900.

(i)   Calculate the tax Colm paid each week.

(ii) After getting a pay rise, Colm's weekly after-tax income increased by €20.30.
Calculate the increase in Colm's gross weekly income.

Solution:

(i) Income tax equation:

Gross tax − Tax credits = Tax payable

Gross tax = 20% of €240 + 42% of €660 ⟵

$$= €240 \times 0.2 \quad + \quad €660 \times 0.42$$

$$= €48 \quad\quad\quad + \quad €277.20$$

$$= €325.20$$

> Income **above** the standard rate cut-off point
>
> = €900 − €240
>
> = €660

Income tax equation: Gross tax − Tax credits = Tax payable

$$€325.20 \quad - \quad €50 \quad = €275.20$$

Thus, Colm paid €275.20 in tax each week.

(ii) Any increase Colm gets in his income is taxed at 42%.
Thus, he only receives 58% of any increase in income.
Equation given in disguise:

58% of increase in income = €20.30

1% of increase in income = €0.35   (divide both sides by 58)

100% of increase in income = €35   (multiply both sides by 100)

Thus, the increase in Colm's gross weekly income is €35.

Example 2

Jill has a gross income of €50,000.

Her total income tax payable amounts to €10,460.

The standard rate cut-off point is €32,000.

The standard rate of tax is 20% and the higher rate is 42%.

What are Jill's tax credits for the year?

Solution:

Income tax equation:

Gross tax − Tax credits = Tax payable

Gross tax:

$$= 20\% \text{ of } €32,000 + 42\% \text{ of } €18,000 \quad ⟵$$

$$= €32,000 \times 0.20 + €18,000 \times 0.42$$

$$= €6,400 + €7,560$$

$$= €13,960$$

> €52,000 − €32,000
>
> = €18,000
>
> = income **above** the standard rate cut-off point

Gross Tax − Tax credits = Tax payable   (Income tax equation)

€13,960   − Tax credits = €10,460

€13,960   − €10,460   = Tax credits

€3,500   = Tax credits

Thus, Jill's tax credits for the year were €3,500.

Example 3

A woman paid €6,820 in tax for the year. She had a tax credit of €1,974 and a standard rate cut-off point of €24,800. The standard rate of tax is 16% of income up to the standard rate cut-off point and 38% on all income above the standard rate cut-off point. Calculate:

(i) the amount on income taxed at the rate of 38%
(ii) the woman's gross income for the year.

Solution:

(i) Income tax equation:

$$\text{Gross tax} - \text{Tax credits} = \text{Tax payable}$$

16% of €24,800 + 38% of (income above cut-off point) − €1,974 = €6,820

€3,968 + 38% of (income above cut-off point) − €1,974 = €6,820

38% of (income above cut-off point) + €1,994 = €6,820

38% of (income above cut-off point) = €4,826

1% of (income above cut-off point) = €127

divide both sides by 38

100% of (income above cut-off point) = €12,700

multiply both sides by 100

Therefore, the amount of income taxed at the higher rate of 38% was €12,700.

(ii) Gross income

= standard rate cut-off point + income above the standard rate cut-off point

= €24,800 + €12,700 = €37,500

Interest

Interest is the sum of money that you pay for borrowing money, or that is paid to you for lending money. When dealing with interest we use the following symbols:

P = the '**principal**', the sum of money borrowed or invested, at the beginning of the period.

T = the '**time**', the number of years for which the sum of money is borrowed or invested.

R = the '**rate**', the percentage rate per annum at which interest is charged.

A = the '**amount**', the sum of money, including interest, at the end of the period.

Note: per annum = per year.

Compound Interest

Very often when a sum of money earns interest, this interest is added to the principal to form a new principal. This new principal earns interest in the next year and so on. This is called '**compound interest**'.

When calculating compound interest, do the following:

Method 1:

Calculate the interest for the **first** year and add this to the principal to form the new principal for the next year. Calculate the interest for **one** year on this new principal and add it on to form the principal for the next year, and so on. The easiest way to calculate each stage is to multiply the principal at the beginning of each year by the factor:

$$\left(1 + \frac{R}{100}\right)$$

This will give the principal for the next year, and so on.

Method 2:

Use the formula: $A = P\left(1 + \frac{R}{100}\right)^{T}$

Note: The formula does **not** work if:

1. the interest rate, R, is changed during the period.
2. money is added or subtracted during the period.

Example 1

€2,500 is invested for 8 years at 6% per annum compound interest.

Find (i) the amount and (ii) the compound interest after 8 years, to the nearest cent.

Solution:

(i) Given: $P = 2{,}500$, $R = 6$ and $T = 8$, find A.

$$A = P\left(1 + \frac{R}{100}\right)^T$$

$$= 2{,}500\left(1 + \frac{6}{100}\right)^8$$

$$= 2{,}500\left(1 + 0.06\right)^8$$

$$= 2{,}500\left(1.06\right)^8$$

$$= 3{,}984.620186$$

Thus, the amount is €3,984.62   (to the nearest cent).

(ii) Compound interest $= A - P = $ €3,984.62 $-$ €2,500 $=$ €1,484.62

Example 2

A machine bought for €8,000 depreciates at a compound rate of 8% per annum.

Find its value after 6 years, correct to the nearest €.

Solution:

When dealing with depreciation, the formula becomes $A = P\left(1 - \dfrac{R}{100}\right)^T$

Given: $P = 8{,}000$, $R = 8$ and $T = 6$, find A.

$$A = P\left(1 - \frac{R}{100}\right)^T$$

$$= 8{,}000\left(1 - \frac{8}{100}\right)^6$$

$$= 8{,}000(1 - 0.08)^6$$

$$= 8{,}000(0.92)^6$$

$$= 4{,}850.840011$$

Thus, the machine is worth €4,851 after 6 years (to the nearest €).

Example 3

€5,000 was invested for 3 years at compound interest.

The rate for the first year was 4%. The rate for the second year was $4\frac{1}{2}\%$.

(i) Find the amount of the investment at the end of the second year.

At the beginning of the third year a further €4,000 was invested.
The rate for the third year was $r\%$.
The total investment at the end of the third year was €9,669.85.

(ii) Calculate the value of r.

Solution:

(i) $\left(1 + \dfrac{R_1}{100}\right) = \left(1 + \dfrac{4}{100}\right) = (1 + 0.04) = 1.04$

$\left(1 + \dfrac{R_2}{100}\right) = \left(1 + \dfrac{4\frac{1}{2}}{100}\right) = (1 + 0.045) = 1.045$

Method 1

$P_1 = 5,000$

$A_1 = 5,000 \times 1.04 = 5,200$

$P_2 = 5,200$

$A_2 = 5,200 \times 1.045 = 5,434$

Method 2

In one calculation:

$A_2 = 5,000 \times 1.04 \times 1.045$

$A_2 = 5,434$

Thus, the amount of the investment at the end of the second year is €5,434.

(ii) At the begining of the third year a further €4,000 was invested.

Thus, the principal at the begining of the third year, P_3, is €5,434 + €4,000 = €9,434

Thus, $P_3 = 9,434$

Given: $A_3 = 9,669.85$

Interest for the third year $= I_3 = A_3 - P_3 = 9,669.85 - 9,434 = 235.85$

Interest rate for the third year $= \dfrac{\text{Interest for the third year}}{\text{Principal for the third year}} \times \dfrac{100}{1}$

$\qquad\qquad = \dfrac{235.85}{9,434} \times \dfrac{100}{1}$

$\qquad\qquad = 2.5\%$

Example 4

At the start of the year 2005 the population of a particular town was P.
During the year 2005 the population of the town increased by 10%.

(i) Express, in terms of P, the population of the town at the end of the year 2006.

(ii) During the year 2006 the population of the town increased by 8%.
During the year 2007 the population increased by 5%.
Find the total percentage increase in the population of the town over the three years.

(iii) The actual increase in the population was 7,422. Find the value of P.

Solution:

$$\left(1 + \frac{R_1}{100}\right) = \left(1 + \frac{10}{100}\right) = (1 + 0.1) = 1.1$$

$$\left(1 + \frac{R_2}{100}\right) = \left(1 + \frac{8}{100}\right) = (1 + 0.08) = 1.08$$

$$\left(1 + \frac{R_3}{100}\right) = \left(1 + \frac{5}{100}\right) = (1 + 0.05) = 1.05$$

(i) $P_1 = P$

$A_1 = P \times 1.1 = 1.1\,P$

Thus, in terms of P, the population at the end of year 2005 was $1.1\,P$.

(ii) $A_3 = P \times 1.1 \times 1.08 \times 1.05$

$A_3 = 1.2474P$

$1.2474 \times 100 = 124.74\%$

Thus, the total percentage increase in the population of the town over the three years $= 124.74 - 100 = 24.74\%$.

(iii) Given: The actual increase in the population, P, was 7,422.

$\therefore$ 24.74% of $P = 7,422$	(equation given in disguise)
1% of $P = 300$	(divide both sides by 24.74)
100% of $P = 30,000$	(multiply both sides by 100)

Thus, $P = 30,000$.

Example 5

A sum of money was invested at compound interest for two years.

The interest rate for the first year was 5% and the interest rate for the second year was 4%. After two years the sum amounted to €8,954.40.

Calculate the original sum of money invested.

Solution:

Method 1   (working backwards)

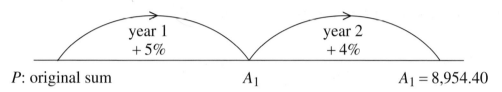

P: original sum A_1 $A_1 = 8,954.40$

End of year 1	**End of year 2**
A_1: $105\% = 8,610$	A_2: $104\% = 8,954.40$
$1\% = 82$	$1\% = 86.1$
$100\% = 8,200$	$100\% = 8,610$
(P_1 original sum of money)	(A_1 amount after one year)

Thus, the original sum of money invested was €8,200.

Method 2

Calculate what €1,000 will amount to after two years. Divide this into 8,954.40 and multiply by 1,000.

$€1,000 \times 1.05 \times 1.04 = €1,092$

$$\frac{8,954.40}{1,092} = 8.2$$

Thus, the original sum of money invested was €1,000 × 8.2 = €8,200.

Method 3

Original sum of money invested

$$= \frac{8,954.40}{1.05 \times 1.04} = \frac{8,954.40}{1.092} = €8,200$$

Sometimes we are given the amount, A, and asked to find the principal, P. To do this we rearrange the formula to get P on its own.

Example 6

A certain sum of money, invested for 9 years at 5% per annum compound interest, amounted to €6,000. Find this sum of money, correct to the nearest cent.

Solution:

Given: $A = 6{,}000$, $R = 5$ and $T = 9$,   find P.

$$\left(1 + \frac{R}{100}\right) = \left(1 + \frac{5}{100}\right) = (1 + 0.05) = 1.05$$

$$A = P\left(1 + \frac{R}{100}\right)^{T}$$

$$P\left(1 + \frac{R}{100}\right)^{T} = A \qquad\qquad \text{(swop sides)}$$

$$P(1.05)^{9} = 6{,}000 \qquad\qquad (A = 6{,}000,\ R = 5,\ T = 9)$$

$$P = \frac{6{,}000}{(1.05)^{9}} \qquad\qquad \text{(divide both sides by } (1.05)^{9})$$

$$P = 3{,}867.653497 \qquad\qquad \left(\boxed{}\ 6{,}000\ \boxed{\div}\ 1.05\ \boxed{y^{x}}\ 9\ \boxed{=}\right)$$

Thus, the sum of money invested was €3,867.65.

Index Notation

Index notation is a shorthand way of writing very large or very small numbers. For example, try this multiplication on your calculator: $8{,}000{,}000 \times 7{,}000{,}000$.

The answer is 56,000,000,000,000.

It has fourteen digits, which is too many to show on most calculator displays.

Your calculator will display your answer as $\boxed{5.6^{\,13}}$ or $\boxed{5.6\ 13}$ or $\boxed{5.6\text{E}13}$.

This tells you that the 5.6 is multiplied by 10^{13}.
This is written:

$$5.6 \times 10^{13}$$

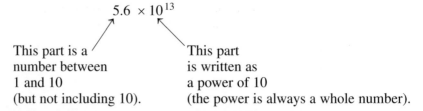

This part is a
number between
1 and 10
(but not including 10).

This part
is written as
a power of 10
(the power is always a whole number).

This way of writing a number is called **index notation** or **exponential notation,** or sometimes **standard form.** (It was formerly called **'scientific notation'**.)

Index notation gives a number in two parts:

| Number between 1 and 10 (but not 10) | $\times$ | power of 10 |

This is often written as $a \times 10^n$, where $1 \leqslant a < 10$ and $n \in \mathbf{Z}$.

Keying in Numbers in Index Notation into a Calculator

Numbers given in index notation can be keyed into your calculator by using the 'exponent key'. It is marked $\boxed{\text{EXP}}$ or $\boxed{\text{EE}}$ or $\boxed{\text{E}}$.

To key in a number in index notation, do the following:

> 1. Key in 'a', the 'number part', first.
> 2. Press the exponent key next.
> 3. Key in the index of the power of 10.

To enter 3.4×10^6, for example, you key in 3.4 $\boxed{\text{EXP}}$ 6.

Note: If you press $\boxed{=}$ at the end, the calculator will write the number as a natural number, provided the index of the power of 10 is not too large.

Addition and Subtraction

To add or subtract two numbers in index notation, do the following:

> 1. Write each number as a natural number.
> 2. Add or subtract these numbers.
> 3. Write your answer in index notation.
>
> Alternatively, you can use your calculator by keying in the numbers in index notation and adding or subtracting as required.

Multiplication and Division

To multiply or divide two numbers in index notation, do the following:

1. Multiply or divide the 'a' parts (the number parts).

2. Multiply or divide the powers of 10 (add or subtract the indices).

3. Write your answer in index notation.

Alternatively, you can use your calculator by keying in the numbers in index notation and multiplying or dividing as required.

Example 1

(i) Express $\dfrac{1{,}512}{0.36}$ in the form $a \times 10^n$, where $1 \leqslant a < 10$ and $n \in \mathbf{Z}$.

(ii) Find x if $\dfrac{560}{0.008} = 7 \times 10^x$.

Solution:

(i)
$$\frac{1{,}512}{0.36} = 4{,}200$$
$$= 4.2 \times 1{,}000$$
$$= 4.2 \times 10^3$$

(ii)
$$\frac{560}{0.008} = 7 \times 10^x$$
$$\frac{560}{0.008} = 70{,}000$$
$$= 7 \times 10{,}000$$
$$= 7 \times 10^4$$
$$\therefore \ x = 4$$

Example 2

Express   **(i)** $5.328 \times 10^5 - 2.8 \times 10^3$ **(ii)** $6.28 \times 10^{-2} + 3.2 \times 10^{-3}$

in the form $a \times 10^n$, where $1 \leqslant a < 10$, and $n \in \mathbf{Z}$.

Solution:

(i) $5.328 \times 10^5 - 2.8 \times 10^3$

$$5.328 \times 10^5 = 532,800$$

$$2.8 \times 10^3 = \frac{2,800}{530,000} \quad \text{(subtract)}$$

$$= 5.3 \times 10^5$$

🖩 5.328 | EXP | 5 | $-$ | 2.8 | EXP | 3 | $=$ |

$$= 530,000 \quad \text{(on the display)}$$

$$= 5.3 \times 10^5$$

(ii) $6.28 \times 10^{-2} + 3.2 \times 10^{-3}$

$$6.28 \times 10^{-2} = 0.0628$$

$$3.2 \times 10^{-3} = \frac{0.0032}{0.066} \quad \text{(add)}$$

$$= 6.6 \times 10^{-2}$$

🖩 6.28 | EXP | +/− | 2

| $+$ | 3.2 | EXP | +/− | 3 | $=$ |

$$= 0.066 \quad \text{(on the display)}$$

$$= 6.6 \times 10^{-2}$$

Example 3

Express   **(i)** $(6.5 \times 10^3) \times (2.4 \times 10^2)$ **(ii)** $(3.91 \times 10^4) \div (1.7 \times 10^{-1})$

in the form $a \times 10^n$, where $1 \leqslant a < 10$, and $n \in \mathbf{Z}$.

Solution:

(i) $(6.5 \times 10^3) \times (2.4 \times 10^2)$

$$= 6.5 \times 10^3 \times 2.4 \times 10^2$$

$$= 6.5 \times 2.4 \times 10^3 \times 10^2$$

$$= 15.6 \times 10^{3+2}$$

(multiply the 'a' parts, add the indices)

$$= 15.6 \times 10^5$$

$$= 1.56 \times 10^1 \times 10^5$$

$$= 1.56 \times 10^{1+5}$$

$$= 1.56 \times 10^6$$

🖩 6.5 | EXP | 3 | $\times$ | 2.4 | EXP | 2 | $=$ |

$$= 1,560,000 \quad \text{(on the display)}$$

$$= 1.56 \times 10^6$$

(ii) $(3.91 \times 10^4) \div (1.7 \times 10^{-1})$

$$= \frac{3.91 \times 10^4}{1.7 \times 10^{-1}}$$

$$= \frac{3.91}{1.7} \times \frac{10^4}{10^{-1}}$$

$$= 2.3 \times 10^{4-(-1)}$$

$$= 2.3 \times 10^{4+1}$$

(divide the 'a' parts, subtract the index on the bottom from the index on top)

$$= 2.3 \times 10^5$$

🖩 3.91 | EXP | 4 | $\div$ | 1.7 | EXP | +/− | 1 | $=$ |

$$= 230,000 \text{ (on the display)}$$

$$= 2.3 \times 10^5$$

Example 4

(a) Calculate the value of $\dfrac{3.1 \times 10^5 - 1.5 \times 10^4}{5.9 \times 10^6}$

and write your answer as a decimal number.

(b) Write your answer in the form:

(i) $\dfrac{a}{b}$, where $a, b \in \mathbf{Z}$ **(ii)** $a \times 10^n$, where $1 \leqslant a < 10$ and $n \in \mathbf{Z}$.

(a) Top:

$3.1 \times 10^5 - 1.5 \times 10^4$

$3.1 \times 10^5 = 310{,}000$

$\underline{1.5 \times 10^4 = 15{,}000}$

$295{,}000$ (subtract)

$= 2.95 \times 10^5$

Bottom: 5.9×10^6

$\therefore \quad \dfrac{\text{Top}}{\text{Bottom}}$

$= \dfrac{2.95 \times 10^5}{5.9 \times 10^6}$

$= \dfrac{2.95}{5.9} \times \dfrac{10^5}{10^6}$

$= 0.5 \times 10^{5-6}$

(divide the 'a' parts, subtract the index on the bottom from the index on top)

$= 0.5 \times 10^{-1}$

$= 0.05$

[( ] [3.1] [EXP] [5] [−] [1.5] [EXP] [4] [ )] [÷] [( ] [5.9] [EXP] [6] [ )] [=]

(it is essential to separate the top and bottom with brackets)

$= 0.05$

(b) **(i)** 0.05

$= \dfrac{5}{100} = \dfrac{1}{20}$

(ii) 0.05

$= 5 \times 10^{-2}$

Chapter 2. ALGEBRA

Evaluating Expressions (Substitution)

A **substitute** is used to replace something. In football, a substitute replaces another player. In algebra, when we replace letters with numbers when evaluating expressions, we call it **substitution**. When you are substituting numbers in an expression, it is good practice to put a bracket around the number that replaces the letter. (Remember: **BEMDAS**.)

Example

(i)   Find the value of $5x - 3y$ when $x = \dfrac{5}{2}$ and $y = \dfrac{2}{3}$.

(ii) Find the value of $\dfrac{ab - c}{2}$ when $a = 5$, $b = \dfrac{2}{5}$ and $c = 1$.

(iii) Find the value of $\dfrac{p - q + 1}{p + q + 1}$ when $p = \dfrac{1}{8}$ and $q = 2$.

Solution:

(i) $5x - 3y$

$\quad 5\left(\dfrac{5}{2}\right) - 3\left(\dfrac{2}{3}\right) \qquad \left(x = \dfrac{5}{2}, y = \dfrac{2}{3}\right)$

$\quad = 12\dfrac{1}{2} - 2$

$\quad = 10\dfrac{1}{2}$

(ii) $\dfrac{ab - c}{2}$

$\quad \dfrac{5\left(\frac{2}{5}\right) - 1}{2} \qquad \left(a = 5, b = \dfrac{2}{5}\right)$

$\quad = \dfrac{2 - 1}{2} = \dfrac{1}{2}$

(iii) $\dfrac{p - q + 1}{p + q + 1}$

$\quad \dfrac{\frac{1}{8} - 2 + 1}{\frac{1}{8} + 2 + 1} \qquad \left(p = \dfrac{1}{8}, q = 2\right)$

$\quad = \dfrac{-\frac{7}{8}}{\frac{25}{8}}$

$\quad = -\dfrac{7}{25}$

Addition and Subtraction of Algebraic Fractions

Algebraic fractions can be added or subtracted in exactly the same way as in arithmetic, i.e. we express the fractions using the lowest common denominator.

Algebraic fractions are added or subtracted with the following steps:

1. Put brackets in where necessary.
2. Find the LCM of the expressions on the bottom.
3. Proceed in exactly the same way as in arithmetic.
4. Simplify the top (add and subtract terms which are the same).

Note: If a part of the expression is not a fraction, it can be changed into fraction form by putting it over 1.

For example, $7 = \dfrac{7}{1}$, $3x = \dfrac{3x}{1}$, $2x - 5 = \dfrac{2x - 5}{1}$.

Example

Write: (i) $\dfrac{3}{2x} - \dfrac{4}{3x - 1}$ (ii) $\dfrac{5}{x} - \dfrac{3}{x - 2} + \dfrac{1}{3}$

as a single fraction in its lowest terms.

Solution:

(i) $\dfrac{3}{2x} - \dfrac{4}{3x - 1}$

$= \dfrac{3}{2x} - \dfrac{4}{(3x - 1)}$ (put brackets on $3x - 1$)

                     (the LCM is $2x(3x - 1)$

$= \dfrac{3(3x - 1) - 4(2x)}{2x(3x - 1)}$ (do the same as in arithmetic)

$= \dfrac{9x - 3 - 8x}{2x(3x - 1)}$ (remove the brackets on top)

$= \dfrac{x - 3}{2x(3x - 1)}$ (simplify the top)

(ii) $\dfrac{5}{x} - \dfrac{3}{x - 2} + \dfrac{1}{3}$

$= \dfrac{5}{x} - \dfrac{3}{(x - 2)} + \dfrac{1}{3}$ (put brackets on $x - 2$)

                     (the LCM is $3x(x - 2)$)

$= \dfrac{5(3)(x - 2) - 3(3x) + x(x - 2)}{3x(x - 2)}$ (do the same as in arithmetic)

$$= \frac{15(x-2) - 3(3x) + x(x-2)}{3x(x-2)} \qquad (5(3) = 15)$$

$$= \frac{15x - 30 - 9x + x^2 - 2x}{3x(x-2)} \qquad \text{(remove the brackets on top)}$$

$$= \frac{x^2 + 4x - 30}{3x(x-2)}$$

Note: It is common practice **not** to multiply out the expressions on the bottom.

Single Variable Linear Inequalities

The four inequality symbols:

1. > means 'greater than'	2. ⩾ means 'greater than or equal to'
3. < means 'less than'	4. ⩽ means 'less than or equal to'

Algebraic expressions that are linked by one of the four inequality symbols are called **'inequalities'**.

For example, $3x - 1 \leqslant 11$ and $1 - 2x \geqslant 5$ are inequalities.

Solving inequality is exactly the same as solving equations, with the following exception:

Multiplying or dividing both sides of an inequality by a **negative** number **reverses** the direction of the inequality.

That is:

$$> \text{ changes to } < \qquad \geqslant \text{ changes to } \leqslant$$
$$< \text{ changes to } > \qquad \leqslant \text{ changes to } \geqslant$$

For example, $4 > -7$ is true. If we multiply both sides by -1, it gives $-4 > 7$, which is **not** true. Thus, $-4 < 7$ is true; multiplying both sides by -1 and reversing the direction of the inequality keeps the inequality true.

Solving an inequality means finding the values of x that make the inequality true.

The following rules apply to graphing inequalities on a number line:

Number line for $x \in \mathbf{N}$ or $x \in \mathbf{Z}$, use dots.

Number line for $x \in \mathbf{R}$, use a 'full' heavy line.

Example 1

Find the solution set of $11 - 2x > 3$, $\quad x \in \mathbf{N}$.
Graph your solution on the number line.

Solution:

$$11 - 2x > 3$$

$\quad\quad -2x > -8$ $\quad\quad\quad$ (subtract 11 from both sides)

$\quad\quad\quad 2x < 8$ $\quad\quad\quad$ (multiply both sides by -1 and reverse the inequality)

$\quad\quad\quad\quad x < 4$ $\quad\quad\quad$ (divide both sides by 2)

This is the set of natural numbers less than 4 (4 not included).
Therefore, the values of x are 0, 1, 2, 3.

Number line:

Example 2

Solve the inequality $3x - 2 < 7x + 6$ $\quad x \in \mathbf{R}$ and illustrate the solution on the number line.

Solution:

$$3x - 2 < 7x + 6$$

$\quad\quad 3x < 7x + 8$ $\quad\quad\quad$ (add 2 to both sides)

$\quad\quad -4x < 8$ $\quad\quad\quad$ (subtract $7x$ from both sides)

$\quad\quad\quad 4x > -8$ $\quad\quad\quad$ (multiply both sides by -1 and reverse the inequality)

$\quad\quad\quad\quad x > -2$ $\quad\quad\quad$ (divide both sides by 4)

This is the set of real numbers greater than -2 (-2 is **not** included).

Number line:

A circle is put around -2 to indicate that it is **not** part of the solution.

Example 3

(i) Find A, the solution set of $7x - 1 \leqslant 27$, $x \in \mathbf{R}$.

(ii) Find B, the solution set of $\dfrac{5 - 3x}{2} < 4$, $x \in \mathbf{R}$.

(iii) Find $A \cap B$, and graph your solution on the number line.

Solution:

(i) A: $7x - 1 \leqslant 27$

$\qquad 7x \leqslant 28$

$\qquad\quad x \leqslant 4$

(ii) B: $\dfrac{5 - 3x}{2} < 4$

$\qquad 5 - 3x < 8$

(multiply both sides by 2)

$\qquad\quad -3x < 3$

$\qquad\quad 3x > -3$

$\qquad\quad\; x > -1$

(iii) Combining the two inequalities:

$$-1 < x \leqslant 4$$

This is the set of real numbers between -1 and 4 but not including -1.

Number line:

A circle is put around -1 to indicate that it is **not** part of the solution.

Changing the Subject of a Formula

When we rearrange a formula so that one of the variables is given in terms of the others we are said to be '**changing the subject of the formula**'. The rules in changing the subject of a formula are the same as when solving an equation, that is we can:

1. **Add** or **subtract** the same quantity to both sides.

2. **Multiply** or **divide** both sides by the same quantity.

3. **Square** both sides.

4. Take the **square root** of both sides.

Note: Whatever letter comes after the word 'express' is to be on its own.

Example 1

(i)   Given that $px - q = r$, express x in terms of p, q and r, where $p \neq 0$.

(ii) Given that $u^2 + 2as = v^2$, express s in terms of v, u and a and, hence, calculate the value of s when $v = 20$, $u = 10$ and $a = 5$.

Solution:

(i) $px - q = r$

$px = r + q$ (add q to both sides)

$$\frac{px}{p} = \frac{r + q}{p}$$ (divide both sides by p)

$$x = \frac{r - q}{p}$$ (simplify the left-hand side)

(ii) $u^2 + 2as = v^2$

$2as = v^2 - u^2$ (subtract u^2 from both sides)

$$\frac{2as}{2a} = \frac{v^2 - u^2}{2a}$$ (divide both sides by $2a$)

$$s = \frac{v^2 - u^2}{2a}$$ (simplify the left-hand side)

$$s = \frac{(20)^2 - (10)^2}{2(5)}$$ (put in $v = 20$, $u = 10$ and $a = 5$)

$$= \frac{400 - 100}{10}$$

$$= \frac{300}{10} = 30$$

Example 2

(i) Express x in terms of r and s when $r - \dfrac{x}{s} = 1$, $s \neq 0$.

(ii) Express t in terms of p and q when $p = \dfrac{q-t}{3t}$, $t \neq 0$.

Calculate the value of t when $p = 0.5$ and $q = 25$.

Solution:

(i) $\qquad r - \dfrac{x}{s} = 1$

$\qquad\quad sr - \dfrac{sx}{s} = s(1)$ $\qquad\qquad$ (multiply each part by s)

$\qquad\qquad sr - x = s$ $\qquad\qquad\quad$ $\left(\dfrac{sx}{s} = x \text{ and } s(1) = s \right)$

$\qquad\qquad\quad -x = s - sr$ $\qquad\qquad$ (subtract sr from both sides)

$\qquad\qquad\quad\; x = -s + sr$ $\qquad\qquad$ (multiply both sides by -1)

(ii) $\qquad\qquad p = \dfrac{q-t}{3t}$

$\qquad\qquad 3tp = \dfrac{3t(q-t)}{3t}$ $\qquad\qquad$ (multiply both sides by $3t$)

$\qquad\qquad 3tp = q - t$ $\qquad\qquad\quad$ (simplify the right-hand side)

$\qquad\quad 3tp + t = q$ $\qquad\qquad\qquad$ (add t to both sides)

$\qquad\; t(3p + 1) = q$ $\qquad\qquad\qquad$ (take out common factor t on the left-hand side)

$\qquad \dfrac{t(3p+1)}{3p+1} = \dfrac{q}{3p+1}$ $\qquad$ (divide both sides by $(3p + 1)$)

$\qquad\qquad\quad t = \dfrac{q}{3p+1}$ $\qquad\qquad$ (simplify the left-hand side)

$\qquad\qquad\quad t = \dfrac{25}{3(0.5)+1}$ $\qquad\quad$ (put in $p = 0.5$ and $q = 25$)

$\qquad\qquad\qquad = \dfrac{25}{1.5+1}$

$\qquad\qquad\qquad = \dfrac{25}{2.5} = 10$

Example 3

If $r = \dfrac{1}{p} + \dfrac{1}{q}$, express p in terms of q and r.

Solution:

$$r = \frac{1}{p} + \frac{1}{q}$$

$$pqr = pq\,\frac{1}{p} + pq\,\frac{1}{q} \qquad \text{[multiply each part by } pq]$$

$$pqr = q + p \qquad\qquad\quad \text{[simplify right-hand side]}$$

$$pqr - p = q \qquad\qquad\quad \text{[subtract } p \text{ from both sides]}$$

$$p(qr - 1) = q \qquad\qquad \text{[take out common factor } p \text{ on left-hand side]}$$

$$\frac{p(qr - 1)}{qr - 1} = \frac{q}{qr - 1} \qquad \text{[divide both sides by } (qr - 1)]$$

$$p = \frac{q}{qr - 1} \qquad\qquad \text{[simplify the left-hand side]}$$

Example 4

If $\dfrac{x - y}{y} = \dfrac{r}{s}$, express y in terms of r, s and x.

Solution:

$$\frac{x - y}{y} = \frac{r}{s}$$

$$\frac{ys(x - y)}{y} = ys\,\frac{r}{s} \qquad\quad \text{[multiply both sides by } ys]$$

$$s(x - y) = yr \qquad\qquad \text{[simplify both sides]}$$

$$sx - sy = yr \qquad\qquad \text{[remove brackets on the left-hand side]}$$

$$-sy - yr = -sx \qquad\quad \text{[terms with } y \text{ on the left-hand side]}$$

$$sy + yr = sx \qquad\qquad \text{[multiply each part by } -1]$$

$$y(s + r) = sx \qquad\qquad \text{[take out common factor } y \text{ on left-hand side]}$$

$$\frac{y(s + r)}{s + r} = \frac{sx}{s + r} \qquad\quad \text{[divide both sides by } (s + r)]$$

$$y = \frac{sx}{s + r} \qquad\qquad \text{[simplify the left-hand side]}$$

Example 5

If $a = \dfrac{3bc}{b+c}$, express c in terms of a and b.

Solution:

$$a = \frac{3bc}{b+c}$$

$$a(b+c) = \frac{(b+c)3bc}{(b+c)} \qquad \text{[multiply both sides } (b+c)\text{]}$$

$$a(b+c) = 3bc \qquad \text{[simplify the right-hand side]}$$

$$ab + ac = 3bc \qquad \text{[remove brackets on the left-hand side]}$$

$$-3bc + ac = -ab \qquad \text{[terms with } c \text{ on the left-hand side]}$$

$$3bc - ac = ab \qquad \text{[multiply each part by } -1\text{]}$$

$$c(3b - a) = ab \qquad \text{[take out common factor } c \text{ on the left-hand side]}$$

$$\frac{c(3b-a)}{3b-a} = \frac{ab}{3b-a} \qquad \text{[divide both sides by } (3b-a)\text{]}$$

$$c = \frac{ab}{3b-a} \qquad \text{[simplify the left-hand side]}$$

Sometimes we have to remove a square root. We do this by squaring both sides.

Example 6

If $v = \sqrt{\dfrac{u-s}{ut}}$, express t in terms of u, v and s.

Solution:

$$v = \sqrt{\frac{u-s}{ut}}$$

$$(v)^2 = \left(\sqrt{\frac{u-s}{ut}}\right)^2 \qquad \text{(put in brackets and square both sides)}$$

$$v^2 = \frac{u-s}{ut} \qquad \text{(remove square root symbol)}$$

$$utv^2 = \frac{ut(u-s)}{ut} \qquad \text{(multiply both sides by } ut\text{)}$$

$$utv^2 = u - s \qquad \text{(simplify the right-hand side)}$$

$$\frac{utv^2}{uv^2} = \frac{u-s}{uv^2} \qquad \text{(divide both sides by } uv^2\text{)}$$

$$t = \frac{u-s}{uv^2} \qquad \text{(simplify the left-hand side)}$$

Quadratic Equations

A quadratic equation is an equation in the form:

$$ax^2 + bx + c = 0$$

where a, b and c are constants, but $a \neq 0$.

Solving a quadratic equation means 'finding the two values of the variable which satisfy the equation'. These values are called the **roots** of the equation. Sometimes the two roots are the same.

There are three types of quadratic equation we will meet on our course:

1. $3x^2 - 13x - 10 = 0$ (three terms)

2. $2x^2 + 3x = 0$ (no constant term)

3. $x^2 - 16 = 0$ (no x term)

Quadratic equations are solved with the following steps:

Method 1:

1. If necessary, arrange to have every term to the left-hand side.
   (If required multiply both sides by -1 to make the coefficient of x^2 positive.)

2. Factorise the left-hand side.

3. Let each factor $= 0$.

4. Solve each simple equation.

Method 2:

The roots of the quadratic equation $ax^2 + bx + c = 0$ are given by the formula:

$$x = \frac{-b \pm \sqrt{b^2 - 4ac}}{2a}$$

Notes:
1. The whole of the top of the right-hand side, including $-b$, is divided by $2a$.

2. It is often called the '$-b$' or 'quadratic' formula.

3. Before using the formula, make sure every term is on the left-hand side, i.e. write the equation in the form $ax^2 + bx + c = 0$.

Note: If $\sqrt{b^2 - 4ac}$ is a whole number, then $ax^2 + bx + c$ can be factorised.
The formula can still be used even if $ax^2 + bx + c$ can be factorised.

Type 1

Example

Solve $x(2x + 7) + 6 = 0$

Solution:

Method 1:

$$x(2x + 7) + 6 = 0$$
$$2x^2 + 7x + 6 = 0 \qquad \text{(write in the form } ax^2 + bx + c = 0\text{)}$$
$$(2x + 3)(x + 2) = 0 \qquad \text{(factorise the left-hand side)}$$
$$2x + 3 = 0 \quad \text{or} \quad x + 2 = 0 \qquad \text{(let each factor } = 0\text{)}$$
$$2x = -3 \quad \text{or} \quad x = -2$$
$$x = -\frac{3}{2} \quad \text{or} \quad x = -2$$

Method 2:

$$x(2x + 7) + 6 = 0$$
$$2x^2 + 7x + 6 = 0 \qquad \text{(write in the form } ax^2 + bx + c = 0\text{)}$$
$$a = 2, \; b = 7, \; c = 6$$

$$x = \frac{-b \pm \sqrt{b^2 - 4ac}}{2a}$$

$$x = \frac{-7 \pm \sqrt{(7)^2 - 4(2)(6)}}{2(2)}$$

$$x = \frac{-7 \pm \sqrt{49 - 48}}{4}$$

$$x = \frac{-7 \pm \sqrt{1}}{4}$$

$$x = \frac{-7 \pm 1}{4}$$

$$x = \frac{-7 + 1}{4} \quad \text{or} \quad x = \frac{-7 - 1}{4}$$

$$x = \frac{-6}{4} \quad \text{or} \quad x = \frac{-8}{4}$$

$$x = -\frac{3}{2} \quad \text{or} \quad x = -2$$

Type 2

Example

Solve for x,   **(i)** $x^2 + 3x = 0$ and   **(ii)** $2x^2 = 3x$

Solution:

(i) $x^2 + 3x = 0$

     $x(x + 3) = 0$ (factorise the left-hand side)

       $x = 0$ or $x + 3 = 0$ (let each factor $= 0$)

       $x = 0$ or $x = -3$

(ii) $2x^2 = 3x$

     $2x^2 - 3x = 0$ (subtract $3x$ from both sides)

     $x(2x - 3) = 0$ (factorise the left-hand side)

       $x = 0$ or $2x - 3 = 0$ (let each factor $= 0$)

       $x = 0$ or $2x = 3$

       $x = 0$ or $x = \dfrac{3}{2}$

Note: It is important not to divide both sides by x, otherwise you lose the root $x = 0$.

Type 3

Example

Solve for x: $x^2 - 9 = 0$

Solution:

We will use two methods to solve this quadratic equation.

Method 1: $x^2 - 9 = 0$ (every term is on the left-hand side)

          $(x)^2 - (3)^2 = 0$ (difference of two squares)

       $(x - 3)(x + 3) = 0$ (factorise the left-hand side)

         $x - 3 = 0$ or $x + 3 = 0$ (let each factor $= 0$)

            $x = 3$ or $x = -3$ (solve each simple equation)

Method 2: $x^2 - 9 = 0$

             $x^2 = 9$ (add 9 to both sides)

            $x = \pm\sqrt{9}$ (take the square root of both sides)

            $x = \pm 3$

         $x = 3$ or $x = -3$

Note: The examples of type 2 and type 3 could have been solved using the formula.

Quadratic Equations Where the Formula Must Be Used

Many quadratic equations cannot be resolved into factors. When this happens the formula **must** be used. To save time trying to look for factors, a clue that you must use the formula is often given in the question. When the question requires an approximate answer, e.g. 'correct to two decimal places', 'correct to three significant figures', 'correct to the nearest integer' or 'express your answers in surd form' (i.e. $a \pm \sqrt{b}$), then the formula must be used.

Example

Solve the equation, $3x^2 - 8x - 2 = 0$, giving your answers correct to two decimal places.

Solution:

$$3x^2 - 8x - 2 = 0 \qquad\qquad \text{(two decimal places } \therefore \text{ use formula)}$$

$$a = 3, \quad b = -8, \quad c = -2$$

$$x = \frac{-b \pm \sqrt{b^2 - 4ac}}{2a}$$

$$x = \frac{8 \pm \sqrt{(-8)^2 - 4(3)(-2)}}{2(3)}$$

$$x = \frac{8 \pm \sqrt{64 + 24}}{6}$$

$$x = \frac{8 \pm \sqrt{88}}{6}$$

$$x = \frac{8 + \sqrt{88}}{6} \qquad\qquad \text{or} \qquad\qquad x = \frac{8 - \sqrt{88}}{6}$$

$$x = \frac{8 + 9.38083152}{6} \qquad \text{or} \qquad x = \frac{8 - 9.38083152}{6}$$

$$x = \frac{17.38083152}{6} \qquad \text{or} \qquad x = \frac{-1.38083152}{6}$$

$$x = 2.896805253 \qquad\quad \text{or} \qquad\quad x = -0.230138586$$

$$x = 2.90 \quad \text{or} \quad x = -0.23 \text{ (correct to two decimal places)}$$

Quadratic Equations in Fractional Form

Quadratic equations in fractional form are solved with the following steps:

1. Multiply each part of the equation by the LCM of the expressions on the bottom.
2. Simplify both sides (no fractions left).
3. Proceed as in the previous section on solving quadratic equations.

Example 1

Solve for x: $\quad \dfrac{3}{2x-1} = 1 + \dfrac{2x}{x+2}$, $\quad x \neq \dfrac{1}{2}$ and $x \neq -2$.

Solution:

$$\frac{3}{(2x-1)} = 1 + \frac{2x}{(x+2)} \qquad \text{[put brackets on } 2x-1 \text{ and } x+2\text{]}$$

$$(2x-1)(x+2)\frac{3}{(2x-1)} = (2x-1)(x+2)(1) + (2x-1)(x+2)\frac{2x}{(x+2)}$$

[the LCM is $(2x-1)(x+2)$ multiply each part by$(2x-1)(x+2)$]

$$3(x+2) = (2x-1)(x+2) + 2x(2x-1) \quad \text{[simplify both sides]}$$

$$3x+6 = 2x^2 + 4x - x - 2 + 4x^2 - 2x \quad \text{[remove the brackets]}$$

$$3x + 6 = 6x^2 + x - 2 \qquad\qquad\qquad \text{[simplify the right-hand side]}$$

$$-6x^2 + 2x + 8 = 0 \qquad\qquad\qquad\quad \text{[every term on the left-hand side]}$$

$$6x^2 - 2x - 8 = 0 \qquad\qquad\qquad\quad \text{[multiply both sides by } -1\text{]}$$

$$3x^2 - x - 4 = 0 \qquad\qquad\qquad\quad\; \text{[divide both sides by 2]}$$

$$(3x - 4)(x + 1) = 0 \qquad\qquad\qquad \text{[factor the left-hand side]}$$

$$3x - 4 = 0 \quad \text{or} \quad x + 1 = 0 \qquad\quad \text{[let each factor} = 0\text{]}$$

$$3x = 4 \quad \text{or} \quad x = -1$$

$$x = \frac{4}{3} \quad \text{or} \quad x = -1 \qquad\qquad \text{[solve each simple equation]}$$

36

Example 2

Solve for x the equation: $\qquad \dfrac{3}{x+1} + \dfrac{1}{x-1} = 1, \qquad x \neq \pm 1.$

Give your answers in the form $a \pm \sqrt{b}$, where $a, b \in \mathbf{N}$.

Solution:

$$\dfrac{3}{(x+1)} + \dfrac{1}{(x-1)} = 1 \qquad \text{[put brackets on } x+1 \text{ and } x-1\text{]}$$

$$(x+1)(x-1)\dfrac{3}{(x+1)} + (x+1)(x-1)\dfrac{1}{(x-1)} = (x+1)(x-1)(1)$$

[the LCM is $(x+1)(x-1)$ multiply each part by $(x+1)(x-1)$]

$$3(x-1) + 1(x+1) = (x+1)(x-1) \quad \text{[simplify both sides]}$$

$$3x - 3 + x + 1 = x^2 - x + x - 1 \quad \text{[remove the brackets]}$$

$$4x - 2 = x^2 - 1 \qquad \text{[simplify both sides]}$$

$$-x^2 + 4x - 1 = 0 \qquad \text{[every term on the left-hand side]}$$

$$x^2 - 4x + 1 = 0 \qquad \text{[multiply each term by } -1\text{]}$$

$a = 1, b = -4, c = 1 \qquad$ (answers in the form $a \pm \sqrt{b}$, $\therefore$ use formula)

$$x = \dfrac{-b \pm \sqrt{b^2 - 4ac}}{2a}$$

$$x = \dfrac{4 \pm \sqrt{(-4)^2 - 4(1)(1)}}{2(1)} \qquad \text{(put in } a = 1, b = -4 \text{ and } c = 1)$$

$$x = \dfrac{4 \pm \sqrt{16 - 4}}{2}$$

$$x = \dfrac{4 \pm \sqrt{12}}{2}$$

$$x = \dfrac{4 \pm 2\sqrt{3}}{2}$$

$$\boxed{\begin{array}{l} \sqrt{12} \\ = \sqrt{4 \times 3} \\ = \sqrt{4}\,\sqrt{3} \\ = 2\sqrt{3} \end{array}}$$

$$x = 2 \pm \sqrt{3} \qquad \text{(divide \textbf{both} parts on top by 2)}$$

(in the form $a \pm \sqrt{b}$)

Simultaneous Linear Equations

Simultaneous linear equations in two variables are solved with the following steps:

1. Write both equations in the form $ax + by = k$ and label the equations ① and ②.

2. Multiply one or both of the equations by a number in order to make the coefficients of x or y the same, but of opposite sign.

3. Add to remove the variable with equal coefficients but of opposite sign.

4. Solve the resultant equation to find the value of the remaining unknown (x or y).

5. Substitute this value in equation ① or ② to find the value of the other unknown.

Example 1

Solve for x and y: $5x + 2y = 1$ and $x + 3y = 8$.

Solution:

Both equations are in the form $ax + by = k$. Label the equations ① and ②.

$$5x + 2y = 1 \qquad ①$$
$$\underline{x + 3y = 8 \qquad ②}$$
$$15x + 6y = 3 \qquad ① \times 3$$
$$\underline{-2x - 6y = -16 \qquad ② \times -2}$$
$$13x = -13 \qquad \text{(add)}$$
$$x = -1$$

Put $x = -1$ into ① or ②
$$5x + 2y = 1 \ ①$$
$$5(-1) + 2y = 1$$
$$-5 + 2y = 1$$
$$2y = 6$$
$$y = 3$$

$\therefore$ the solution is $x = -1$ and $y = 3$.

Example 2

Solve for x and y: $2(x - 3) = 5y + 13$ and $\dfrac{3x}{2} + \dfrac{4y}{3} = -1$.

Solution:

First write both equations in the form $ax + by = k$ and label the equations ① and ②.

$$2(x - 3) = 5y + 13$$
$$2x - 6 = 5y + 13$$
$$2x - 5y = 19 \quad ① \qquad \text{(in the form } ax + by = k\text{: label the equation ①)}$$

$$\frac{3x}{2} + \frac{4y}{3} = -1$$

$$6\left(\frac{3x}{2}\right) + 6\left(\frac{4y}{3}\right) = 6(-1) \qquad \text{(multiply each part by 6 to remove fractions)}$$

$$3(3x) + 2(4y) = -6 \qquad \text{(simplify both sides)}$$

$$9x + 8y = -6 \quad ② \qquad \text{(in the form } ax + by = k\text{: label the equation ②)}$$

$2x - 5y = 19$	①	Put $x = 2$ in	① or ②.
$9x + 8y = -6$	②	$2x - 5y = 19$	①
$16x - 40y = 152$	① × 8	$2(2) - 5y = 19$	
$45x + 40y = -30$	② × 5	$4 - 5y = 19$	
$61x = 122$	(add)	$-5y = 15$	
$x = 2$		$5y = -15$	
		$y = -3$	

$\therefore$ the solution is $x = 2$ and $y = -3$.

Solution containing fractions

If the solution contains fractions the substitution can be difficult.
If such cases the following method is useful:

> 1. Eliminate y and find x.
>
> 2. Eliminate x and find y.

Example 3

Solve for x and y: $3x + 5y = 7$ and $x - y = 1$

Solution:

Both equations are in the form $ax + by = k$. Number the equations ① and ②.

1. Eliminate y and find x.

$$3x + 5y = 7 \qquad ①$$
$$\underline{x - y = 1 \qquad ②}$$
$$3x + 5y = 7 \qquad ①$$
$$\underline{5x - 5y = 5 \qquad ② \times 5}$$
$$8x = 12 \qquad \text{(add)}$$
$$x = \frac{12}{8}$$
$$x = \frac{2}{3}$$

2. Eliminate x and find y.

$$3x + 5y = 7 \qquad ①$$
$$\underline{x - y = 1 \qquad ②}$$
$$3x + 5y = 7 \qquad ①$$
$$\underline{-3x + 3y = -3 \qquad ② \times -3}$$
$$8y = 4 \qquad \text{(add)}$$
$$y = \frac{4}{8}$$
$$y = \frac{1}{2}$$

$\therefore$ the solution is $x = \dfrac{2}{3}$ and $y = \dfrac{1}{2}$.

Note: This method can also be used if the solution does not contain fractions.

Simultaneous Equations, One Linear and One Quadratic

The **method of substitution** is used to solve between a linear equation and a quadratic equation.

The method involves three steps:

1. From the linear equation, express one variable in terms of the other.

2. Substitute this into the quadratic equation and solve.

3. Substitute separately the value(s) obtained in step 2 into the linear equation in step 1 to find the corresponding value(s) of the other variable.

Example 1

Solve for x and y: $x + 3 = 2y$ and $xy - 7y + 8 = 0$

Solution:

$x + 3 = 2y$ and $xy - 7y + 8 = 0$

1. $x + 3 = 2y$ (get x on its own from the linear equation)

$x = 2y - 3$ (x on its own)

2. $xy - 7y + 8 = 0$

$(2y - 3)y - 7y + 8 = 0$ (put in $(2y - 3)$ for x)

$2y^2 - 3y - 7y + 8 = 0$ (remove the brackets)

$2y^2 - 10y + 8 = 0$ (simplify the left-hand side)

$y^2 - 5y + 4 = 0$ (divide both sides by 2)

$(y - 1)(y - 4) = 0$ (factorise the left-hand side)

$y - 1 = 0$ or $y - 4 = 0$ (let each factor $= 0$)

$y = 1$ or $y = 4$ (solve each simple equation)

3. Substitute separately, $y = 1$ and $y = 4$ into the linear equation.

$$x = 2y - 3$$

$y = 1$	$y = 4$
$x = 2y - 3$	$x = 2y - 3$
$x = 2(1) - 3$	$x = 2(4) - 3$
$x = 2 - 3$	$x = 8 - 3$
$x = -1$	$x = 5$
$x = -1, \quad y = 1$	$x = 5, \quad y = 4$

$\therefore$ the solutions are $x = -1, y = 1$ or $x = 5, y = 4$

Example 2

Solve for x and y: $\qquad 2x - y + 1 = 0 \qquad$ and $\qquad y^2 - 2x^2 = 1.$

Solution:

1. $\quad 2x - y + 1 = 0$ $\qquad\qquad\qquad\qquad$ (set y on its own from the linear equation)

$\qquad\qquad -y = -2x - 1$

$\qquad\qquad y = (2x + 1)$ $\qquad\qquad\qquad\qquad$ (multiply each part by -1)

2. $\qquad\qquad y^2 - 2x^2 = 1$

$\qquad\qquad\;\;\searrow$

$\qquad (2x + 1)^2 - 2x^2 = 1$ $\qquad\qquad$ (put in $(2x + 1)$ for y)

$\quad 4x^2 + 4x + 1 - 2x^2 = 1$ $\qquad\qquad$ ($(2x + 1)^2 = 4x^2 + 4x + 1$)

$\qquad\quad 2x^2 + 4x + 1 = 1$ $\qquad\qquad$ (simplify the left-hand side)

$\qquad\qquad 2x^2 + 4x = 0$ $\qquad\qquad$ (subtract 1 from both sides)

$\qquad\qquad\;\; x^2 + 2x = 0$ $\qquad\qquad$ (divide each part by 2)

$\qquad\qquad x(x + 2x) = 0$ $\qquad\qquad$ (factorise the left-hand side)

$\qquad x = 0 \quad$ or $\quad x + 2 = 0$ $\qquad$ (let each factor $= 0$)

$\qquad x = 0 \quad$ or $\qquad x = -2$ $\qquad$ (solve each simple equation)

3. Substitute separately, $x = 0$ and $x = -2$ into the linear equation.

$$y = 2x + 1$$

$x = 0$	$x = -2$
$y = 2x + 1$	$y = 2x + 1$
$y = 2(0) + 1$	$y = 2(-2) + 1$
$y = 0 + 1$	$y = -4 + 1$
$y = 1$	$y = -3$
$x = 0, y = 1$	$x = -2, y = -3$

$\therefore\quad$ the solutions are $x = 0, y = 1$ $\qquad$ or $\qquad x = -2, y = -3$

Factor Theorem

If an algebraic expression is divided by one of its factors, then the remainder is zero. The expression $(x - k)$ is a factor of a polynomial $f(x)$, if the remainder when we divide $f(x)$ by $(x - k)$ is zero.
Generalising this:

> 1. If $f(k) = 0$, then $(x - k)$ is a factor of $f(x)$.
>
> 2. If $(x - k)$ is a factor of $f(x)$, then $f(k) = 0$.

Here are some examples:

Factor	Put factor $= 0$ and solve	Factor Theorem
$x + 2$	$x = -2$	$f(-2) = 0$
$x - 5$	$x = 5$	$f(5) = 0$

The factor theorem can be used to factorise polynomials or to find unknown coefficients in a polynomial.

Example 1

Verify that $x - 4$ is a factor of $x^3 - 2x^2 - 11x + 12$.

Solution:

Let $f(x) = x^3 - 2x^2 - 11x + 12$

$x - 4$ is a factor of $f(x)$ if:

(i) $f(4) = 0$ or   **(ii)** the remainder is 0 when $x^3 - 2x^2 - 11x + 12$ is divided by $x - 4$.

Method 1

$f(x) = x^3 - 2x^2 - 11x + 12$

$f(4) = (4)^3 - 2(4)^2 - 11(4) + 12$

$\quad = (64) - 2(16) - 11(4) + 12$

$\quad = 64 - 32 - 44 + 12$

$\quad = 76 - 76$

$\quad = 0$

$f(4) = 0$

$\therefore \quad x - 4$ is a factor of $x^3 - 2x^2 - 11x + 12$

Method 2

$$\begin{array}{r} x^2 + 2x - 3 \\[2pt] x-4 \enclose{longdiv}{x^3 - 2x^2 - 11x + 12} \end{array}$$

$\ominus x^3 \oplus 4x^2$

$\qquad 2x^2 - 11x$

$\ominus 2x^2 \oplus 8x$

$\qquad\qquad -3x + 12$

$\overset{\oplus}{-} 3x \overset{\ominus}{+} 12$

$\qquad\qquad\qquad 0 + 0$

Remainder $= 0$

43

Example 2

If $x - 5$ is a factor of $x^3 - kx^2 - 13x - 10$, find the value of k.

Solution:

$$\text{Let } f(x) = x^3 - kx^2 - 13x - 10$$

If $x - 5$ is a factor, then $x = 5$ is a root of $f(x) = 0$ and $f(5) = 0$

$$f(5) = 0$$
$$(5)^3 - k(5)^2 - 13(5) - 10 = 0 \qquad \text{(replace } x \text{ with 5)}$$
$$125 - 25k - 65 - 10 = 0$$
$$50 - 25k = 0$$
$$-25k = -50$$
$$25k = 50$$
$$k = 2$$

Example 3

If $(x + 1)$ and $(x - 2)$ are factors of $x^3 + 2x^2 + ax + b$, find the values of $a, b, \in \mathbf{R}$.

Solution:

Let $f(x) = x^3 + 2x^2 + ax + b$

If $(x + 1)$ is a factor, then $x = -1$ is a root of $f(x) = 0$ and $f(-1) = 0$

If $x - 2$ is a factor, then $x = 2$ is a root of $f(x) = 0$ and $f(2) = 0$

$f(-1) = 0$	$f(2) = 0$
$(-1)^3 + 2(-1)^2 + a(-1) + b = 0$	$(2)^3 + 2(2)^2 + a(2) + b = 0$
$-1 + 2 - a + b = 0$	$8 + 8 + 2a + b = 0$
$1 - a + b = 0$	$16 + 2a + b = 0$
$-a + b = -1$	$2a + b = -16 \quad ②$
$a - b = 1 \quad ①$	

We now solve the simultaneous equations ① and ②:

$a - b = 1 \qquad ①$	$a - b = 1 \qquad ①$
$\underline{2a + b = -16 \quad ②}$	$(-5) - b = 1$
$3a = -15 \quad \text{(add)}$	$-5 - b = 1$
$a = -5$	$-b = 6$
Put $a = -5$ into ① or ②	$b = -6$

$$\text{Thus, } a = -5 \text{ and } b = -6$$

Solving Cubic Equations

Any equation of the form $ax^3 + bx^2 + cx + d = 0$, $a \neq 0$, is called a cubic equation.
For example, $2x^3 - 3x^2 - x + 2 = 0$ is a cubic equation.

We use the factor theorem to find one root, and hence one factor. We divide the cubic expression by this factor to get a quadratic factor. We then let this quadratic factor $= 0$, factorise it and solve it to find the other two roots. Sometimes we have to use the ' $-b$ ' or 'quadratic' formula.

In mathematical terms, the steps in solving a cubic equation are:

1. Find the root k by trial and improvement, i.e. try $f(1), f(-1), f(2), f(-2)$, etc. (Only try numbers that divide evenly into the constant in the equation.)

2. If $x = k$ is a root, then $(x - k)$ is a factor.

3. Divide $f(x)$ by $(x - k)$, which always gives a quadratic expression.

4. Let this quadratic $= 0$ and solve by factors or formula.

Example 1

Show that $x = 3$ is a root of the equation $2x^3 - 3x^2 - 11x + 6 = 0$ and find the other two roots.

Solution:

Let $f(x) = 2x^3 - 3x^2 - 11x + 6$.

$x = 3$ is a root of $f(x) = 0$ if $f(3) = 0$ **or**   if $x - 3$ is a factor $f(x)$.

Method 1

$f(x) = 2x^3 - 3x^2 - 11x + 6$

$f(3) = 2(3)^3 - 3(3)^2 - 11(3) + 6$

$\quad = 2(27) - 3(9) - 11(3) + 6$

$\quad = 54 - 27 - 33 + 6$

$\quad = 60 - 60$

$\quad = 0$

Thus, $f(3) = 0$

Method 2 is better if you need
to find the other two roots as you
have to do the long division
to get the quadratic factor.

Method 2

$$\begin{array}{r} 2x^2 + 3x - 2 \\ x - 3 \overline{\smash{\big)}\, 2x^3 - 3x^2 - 11x + 6} \end{array}$$

$\ominus\ 2x^3 \oplus 6x^2$

$\qquad 3x^2 - 11x$

$\ominus\ 3x^2 \oplus 9x$

$\qquad\qquad -2x + 6$

$\overset{\oplus}{-}\ 2x \overset{\ominus}{+}\ 6$

$\qquad\qquad\qquad 0 + 0$

Remainder $= 0$, $\therefore$ $x - 3$ is a factor of $f(x)$

$\therefore$ $x = 3$ is a root of the equation $2x^3 - 3x^2 - 11x + 6 = 0$

Now let the quadratic factor $= 0$ and solve.

$$2x^2 + 3x - 2 = 0$$

$$(2x - 1)(x + 2) = 0$$

$2x - 1 = 0$	or	$x + 2 = 0$
$2x = 1$	or	$x = -2$
$x = \dfrac{1}{2}$	or	$x = -2$

$\therefore$ the other two roots are $x = \dfrac{1}{2}$ and $x = -2$.

Example 2

Solve the equation $2x^3 - 9x^2 + 7x + 6 = 0$

Solution:

We use the factor theorem to find the first root by trial and improvement. The first root will be a factor of 6. Thus, we try ± 1, ± 2, ± 3, ± 6.

(**Note:** There is no point in trying ± 4 or ± 5 as these are **not** factors of 6.)

Let $f(x) = 2x^3 - 9x^2 + 7x + 6$

$f(1) = 2(1)^3 - 9(1)^2 + 7(1) + 6 = 2 - 9 + 7 + 6 = 6 \neq 0$

$f(-1) = 2(-1)^3 - 9(-1)^2 + 7(-1) + 6 = -2 - 9 - 7 + 6 = -12 \neq 0$

$f(2) = 2(2)^3 - 9(2)^2 + 7(2) + 6 = 16 - 36 + 14 + 6 = 0$

$\therefore$ $x = 2$ is a root of the equation $2x^3 - 9x^2 + 7x + 6 = 0$

$\therefore$ $x - 2$ is a factor of $2x^3 - 9x^2 + 7x + 6$

Now divide $2x^3 - 9x^2 + 7x + 6$ by $x - 2$ to get the quadratic factor.

$$
\begin{array}{r}
2x^2 - 5x - 3 \\
x - 2 \enclose{longdiv}{2x^3 - 9x^2 + 7x + 6} \\
\underline{2x^3 \pm 4x^2} \\
-5x^2 + 7x \\
\underline{\pm 5x^2 \mp 10x} \\
-3x + 6 \\
\underline{\pm 3x \mp 6} \\
0 + 0
\end{array}
$$

Now let the quadratic factor $= 0$ and solve.

$2x^2 - 5x - 3 = 0$

$(2x + 1)(x - 3) = 0$

$2x + 1 = 0$ or $x - 3 = 0$

$2x = -1$ or $x = 3$

$x = -\dfrac{1}{2}$ or $x = 3$

$\therefore$ the roots of the equation $2x^3 - 9x^2 + 7x + 6 = 0$ are $x = 2$, $x = -\dfrac{1}{2}$, $x = 3$.

Constructing an Equation when Given its Roots

This is the reverse process of solving an equation by using factors.

Example

(i) Write down a quadratic equation with roots $\frac{1}{2}$ and -5.

(ii) Write down a cubic equation with roots -2, 1 and 3.

Solution:

(i) Roots $\frac{1}{2}$ and -5

$$\text{Let } x = \frac{1}{2} \quad \text{and} \quad x = -5$$

$$x = \frac{1}{2} \quad \text{and} \quad x = -5$$

$$2x = 1 \quad \text{and} \quad x = -5$$

$$2x - 1 = 0 \quad \text{and} \quad x + 5 = 0$$

$$\therefore \quad (2x - 1)(x + 5) = 0$$

$$2x^2 + 10x - x - 5 = 0$$

$$2x^2 + 9x - 5 = 0$$

(ii) Roots -2, 1 and 3

$$\text{Let } x = -2, \quad x = 1 \text{ and } x = 3$$

$$x + 2 = 0 \text{ and } x - 1 = 0 \text{ and } x - 3 = 0$$

$$\therefore \quad (x + 2)(x - 1)(x - 3) = 0$$

$$(x + 2)(x^2 - 3x - x + 3) = 0$$

$$(x + 2)(x^2 - 4x + 3) = 0$$

$$x^3 - 4x^2 + 3x + 2x^2 - 8x + 6 = 0$$

$$x^3 - 2x^2 - 5x + 6 = 0$$

Notation for Indices

We use a shorthand called '**index notation**' to indicate repeated multiplication.

For example, we write $2 \times 2 \times 2 \times 2 \times 2$ as 2^5.

This is read as '2 to the power of 5'.

> 2 is the **base**.
>
> 5 is the **index** or **power**.

The power or index simply tells you how many times a number is multiplied by itself.

Rules of Indices

1. $a^m . a^n = a^{m+n}$ Example: $2^4 . 2^3 = 2^{4+3} = 2^7$

   Multiplying powers of the same number: **add** the indices.

2. $\dfrac{a^m}{a^n} = a^{m-n}$ Example: $\dfrac{3^9}{3^5} = 3^{9-5} = 3^4$

   Dividing powers of the same number: **subtract** the index on the bottom from the index on top.

3. $(a^m)^n = a^{mn}$ Example: $(4^5)^3 = 4^{5 \times 3} = 4^{15}$

   Raising the power of a number to a power, **multiply** the indices.

4. $(ab)^m = a^m b^m$ Example: $(2 \times 3)^5 = 2^5 \times 3^5$

   Raising a product to a power, **every** factor is raised to the power.

5. $\left(\dfrac{a}{b}\right)^m = \dfrac{a^m}{b^m}$ Example: $\left(\dfrac{2}{5}\right)^3 = \dfrac{2^3}{5^3}$

   Raising a fraction to a power, **both** top and bottom are raised to the power.

6. $a^0 = 1$ Example: $4^0 = 1$

   Any number to the power of zero is 1.

7. $a^{-m} = \dfrac{1}{a^m}$ Example: $5^{-2} = \dfrac{1}{5^2}$

   A number with a negative index is equal to its **reciprocal** with a positive index.

   Note: If a term is brought from the top to the bottom of a fraction (or vice versa), the sign of its index is changed.

8. $a^{m/n} = (a^{1/n})^m$ Example: $32^{3/5} = (32^{1/5})^3$

   Take the root first and then raise to the power (or vice versa).

$8^{1/3}$ means, the number that multiplied by itself three times will equal 8.

Thus, $8^{1/3} = 2$, as $2 \times 2 \times 2 = 8$

Similarly, $25^{1/2} = 5$, as $5 \times 5 = 25$ and $81^{1/4} = 3$, as $3 \times 3 \times 3 \times 3 = 81$.

Note: $\sqrt{a} = a^{1/2}$, for example, $\sqrt{16} = 16^{1/2} = 4$.

Also, $\sqrt{a}\sqrt{a} = a^{1/2} . a^{1/2} = a^{1/2 + 1/2} = a^1 = a$

Alternative notation: $a^{1/n} = \sqrt[n]{a}$, example $8^{1/3} = \sqrt[3]{8}$

                        $a^{m/n} = \sqrt[n]{a^m}$, example $32^{2/5} = \sqrt[5]{32^2}$

When dealing with fractional indices, the calculations are simpler if the root is taken first and the result is raised to the power.

For example, $16^{3/4} = (16^{1/4})^3 = (2)^3 = 8$

$\qquad\qquad\qquad\quad \uparrow \qquad\qquad\ \uparrow$

$\qquad\qquad$ (root first) $\quad$ (power next)

Using a calculator

A calculator can be used to evaluate an expression such as $32^{3/5}$.

$$\left(\boxed{\blacksquare}\ 32\ \boxed{y^x}\ 3\ \boxed{a\frac{b}{c}}\ 5\ \boxed{=} \right)$$

The calculator will give an answer 8.

However, there are problems when dealing with negative indices or raising a fraction to a power, as the calculator can give the answer as a decimal.

For example, $8^{-2\backslash 3} = \dfrac{1}{8^{2/3}} = \dfrac{1}{(8^{1/3})^2} = \dfrac{1}{(2)^2} = \dfrac{1}{4}$

Using a calculator,

$$\left(\boxed{\blacksquare}\ 8\ \boxed{y^x}\ \boxed{+/-}\ 2\ \boxed{a\frac{b}{c}}\ 3\ \boxed{=} \right) \quad \text{gives an answer 0.25}$$

Note: $\dfrac{1}{4} = 0.25$

Also, $\left(\dfrac{8}{27}\right)^{2/3} = \dfrac{8^{2/3}}{27^{2/3}} = \dfrac{(8^{1/3})^2}{(27^{1/3})^2} = \dfrac{(2)^2}{(3)^2} = \dfrac{4}{9}$

Using a calculator,

$$\left(\boxed{\blacksquare}\ \boxed{(}\ 8\ \boxed{a\frac{a}{b}}\ 27\ \boxed{)}\ \boxed{y^x}\ 2\ \boxed{a\frac{b}{c}}\ 3\ \boxed{=} \right) \quad \text{gives an answer 0.444444444...}$$

Note: $\dfrac{4}{9} = 0.444444444...$

So avoid using a calculator with negative indices or when raising a fraction to a power.

Example 1

Simplify each of the following:

(i) $32^{\frac{4}{5}}$ (ii) $27^{1\frac{2}{3}}$ (iii) $64^{-\frac{2}{3}}$ (iv) $27^{\frac{2}{3}}.16^{-\frac{3}{4}}$

Solution:

(i) $32^{\frac{4}{5}} = \left(32^{\frac{1}{5}}\right)^4 = (2)^4 = 16$

(ii) $27^{1\frac{2}{3}} = 27^{\frac{5}{3}} = \left(27^{\frac{1}{3}}\right)^5 = (3)^5 = 243$

(iii) $64^{-\frac{2}{3}} = \dfrac{1}{64^{\frac{2}{3}}} = \dfrac{1}{\left(64^{\frac{1}{3}}\right)^2} = \dfrac{1}{(4)^2} = \dfrac{1}{16}$

(iv) $27^{\frac{2}{3}}.16^{-\frac{3}{4}} = \dfrac{27^{\frac{2}{3}}}{16^{\frac{3}{4}}} = \dfrac{\left(27^{\frac{1}{3}}\right)^2}{\left(16^{\frac{1}{4}}\right)^3} = \dfrac{(3)^2}{(2)^3} = \dfrac{9}{8}$

Example 2

(i) Express $2^{\frac{5}{2}}$ in the form $a\sqrt{2}$.

(ii) Express b in terms of a and c where $\dfrac{8a-5b}{b} = c$.

(iii) Hence, or otherwise, evaluate b when $a = 2^{\frac{5}{2}}$ and $c = 3^3$.

Solution:

(i) $2^{\frac{5}{2}} = 2^{2\frac{1}{2}} = 2^{2+\frac{1}{2}} = 2^2 \times 2^{\frac{1}{2}} = 4\sqrt{2}$ $(2^2 = 4$ and $2^{\frac{1}{2}} = \sqrt{2})$

(ii)
$$\frac{8a - 5b}{b} = c$$

$$8a - 5b = bc$$

$$8a = bc + 5b$$

$$8a = b(c + 5)$$

$$\frac{8a}{c + 5} = b$$

(iii)
$$b = \frac{8a}{c + 5}$$

$$b = \frac{8(2^{\frac{5}{2}})}{3^3 + 5} \qquad \text{(put in } a = 2^{\frac{5}{2}} \text{ and } c = 3^3\text{)}$$

$$b = \frac{8 \times 4\sqrt{2}}{27 + 5} \qquad (2^{\frac{5}{2}} = 4\sqrt{2})$$

$$b = \frac{32\sqrt{2}}{32}$$

$$b = \sqrt{2}$$

Exponential Equations

Exponent is another name for power or index.

An equation involving the variable in the power is called an '**exponential equation**'.

For example, $3^{2x+3} = 9$ is an exponential equation.

Exponential equations are solved with the following steps:

> 1. Write all the numbers as powers of the same number (usually a prime number).
> 2. Write both sides as one power of the same number, using the laws of indices.
> 3. Equate these powers and solve this equation.

Example 1

(i) Evaluate $8^{\frac{1}{3}}$ **(ii)** Express $4^{\frac{1}{4}}$ in the form 2^k, where $k \in \mathbf{Q}$.

(iii) Solve for x the equation $2^{x-5} = \left(8^{\frac{1}{3}}\right)\left(4^{\frac{1}{4}}\right)$

Solution:

(i) $8^{\frac{1}{3}} = 2$ $\left[\begin{array}{c}\boxed{}\end{array} 8 \;\boxed{y^x}\; \boxed{(}\; 1 \;\boxed{\div}\; 3 \;\boxed{)}\; \boxed{=}\right]$

Alternatively $8^{\frac{1}{3}} = (2^3)^{\frac{1}{3}} = 2^{3 \times \frac{1}{3}} = 2^1 = 2$

(ii) $k \in \mathbf{Q}$ means k could be a fraction.

$$4^{\frac{1}{4}} = (2^2)^{\frac{1}{4}} = 2^{2 \times \frac{1}{4}} = 2^{\frac{1}{2}} \qquad (4 = 2^2)$$

(iii)

$$2^{x-5} = \left(8^{\frac{1}{3}}\right)\left(4^{\frac{1}{4}}\right)$$

$$2^{x-5} = \left(2^1\right) \times \left(2^{\frac{1}{2}}\right) \qquad \left(8^{\frac{1}{3}} = 2 = 2^1 \text{ and } 4^{\frac{1}{4}} = 2^{\frac{1}{2}}\right)$$

$$2^{x-5} = 2^1 \times 2^{\frac{1}{2}}$$

$$2^{x-5} = 2^{1+\frac{1}{2}} \qquad \text{(add the indices on the right-hand side)}$$

$$2^{x-5} = 2^{1\frac{1}{2}}$$

$$x - 5 = 1\tfrac{1}{2} \qquad \text{(equate the powers)}$$
$$2x - 10 = 3 \qquad \text{(multiply each term by 2)}$$
$$2x = 13$$
$$x = \frac{13}{2}$$

Example 2

(i) Write $\dfrac{81}{\sqrt{3}}$ in the form 3^n, when $n \in \mathbf{Q}$.

(ii) Solve the equation $3^{x-2} = \left(\dfrac{81}{\sqrt{3}}\right)^2$.

Solution:

(i) $n \in \mathbf{Q}$ means n could be a fraction

$$\frac{81}{\sqrt{3}} = \frac{3^4}{3^{\frac{1}{2}}} = 3^{4-\frac{1}{2}} = 3^{\frac{7}{2}}$$

(Subtract the index on the bottom from the index on top.)

(ii) $3^{x-2} = \left(\dfrac{81}{\sqrt{3}}\right)^2$

$$3^{x-2} = \left(3^{\frac{7}{2}}\right)^2 \qquad \left(\frac{81}{\sqrt{3}} = 3^{\frac{7}{2}}\right)$$

$$3^{x-2} = 3^{\frac{7}{2} \times 2} \qquad \text{(multiply the indices on the right-hand side)}$$

$$3^{x-2} = 3^7$$

$$x - 2 = 7 \qquad \text{(equate the powers)}$$

$$x = 9$$

Chapter 3. COMPLEX NUMBERS

Addition, Subtraction and Multiplication by a Real Number

Example

If $z_1 = 2 + 3i$, $z_2 = 1 - 4i$ and $z_3 = -2i$, express:

(i) $3z_1 - 2z_2$ (ii) $5z_2 - 4z_3$ in the form $a + bi$.

Solution:

(i) $3z_1 - 2z_2$

$= 3(2 + 3i) - 2(1 - 4i)$

$= 6 + 9i - 2 + 8i$

$= 4 + 17i$

(ii) $5z_2 - 4z_3$

$= 5(1 - 4i) - 4(-2i)$

$= 5 - 20i + 8i$

$= 5 - 12i$

Multiplication

Multiplication of complex numbers is performed using the usual algebraic method except, i^2 **is replaced with** -1.

Example 1

Simplify $2 + 3i(4 + 5i) - 6i$ and express your answer in the form $p + qi$, where $p, q \in \mathbf{R}$.

Solution:

$2 + 3i\,(4 + 5i) - 6i$

$= 2 + 12i + 15i^2 - 6i$ (remove the brackets)

$= 2 + 12i + 15(-1) - 6i$ (replace i^2 with -1)

$= 2 + 12i - 15 - 6i$

$= -13 + 6i$

Example 2

If $z_1 = 2 - 5i$ and $z_2 = -1 - i$, express in the form $x + yi$, where $x, y \in R$.

(i) $z_1 . z_2$ (ii) $z_1{}^2$ (iii) iz_1z_2

Solution:

(i) $z_1 \cdot z_2$

$= (2 - 5i)(-1 - i)$

$= -2 - 2i + 5i + 5i^2$

$= -2 - 2i + 5i + 5(-1)$

(replace i^2 with -1)

$= -2 - 2i + 5i - 5$

$= -7 + 3i$

(ii) $z_1{}^2$

$= (2 - 5i)(2 - 5i)$

$= 4 - 10i - 10i + 25i^2$

$= 4 - 10i - 10i + 25(-1)$

(replace i^2 with -1)

$= 4 - 10i - 10i - 25$

$= -21 - 20i$

(iii) iz_1z_2

$= i(2 - 5i)(-1 - i)$

First work out $i(2 - 5i)$ and then multiply your answer by $(-1 - i)$

$i(2 - 5i)$

$= 2i - 5i^2$

$= 2i - 5(-1)$

$= 2i + 5$

$= 5 + 2i$

$(5 + 2i)(-1 - i)$

$= -5 - 5i - 2i - 2i^2$

$= -5 - 5i - 2i - 2(-1)$

$= -5 - 5i - 2i + 2$

$= -3 - 7i$

Division

Multiply the top and bottom by the conjugate of the bottom

This will convert the complex number on the bottom into a real number. The division is then performed by dividing the real number on the bottom into **each part** on the top.

If $z = a + bi$ then $\bar{z} = a - bi$,

i.e. simply change the sign of the imaginary part.

For example, if $z_1 = -3 + 2i$ then $\bar{z}_1 = -3 - 2i$ and

$\qquad$ if $z_2 = -5 + 4i$ then $\bar{z}_2 = -5 - 4i$

Example 1

Express $\dfrac{1 + 7i}{4 + 3i}$ in the form $a + bi$, where $a, b \in N$.

Solution:

$$\frac{1 + 7i}{4 + 3i} = \frac{1 + 7i}{4 + 3i} \cdot \frac{4 - 3i}{4 - 3i} \qquad \text{[Multiply top and bottom by the conjugate of the bottom]}$$

Top by the Top	Bottom by the Bottom
$= (1 + 7i)(4 - 3i)$	$= (4 + 3i)(4 - 3i)$
$= 1(4 - 3i) + 7i(4 - 3i)$	$= 4(4 - 3i) + 3i(4 - 3i)$
$= 4 - 3i + 28i - 21i^2$	$= 16 - 12i + 12i - 9i^2$
$= 4 - 3i + 28i - 21(-1)$	$= 16 - 9(-1)$
$= 4 - 3i + 28i + 21$	$= 16 + 9$
$= 25 + 25i$	$= 25$

$$\therefore \frac{1 + 7i}{4 + 3i} = \frac{25 + 25i}{25} = \frac{25}{25} + \frac{25}{25}i = 1 + i$$

Example 2

If $\dfrac{2-i}{1-2i} = p + qi$, where $p, q \in \mathbf{Q}$ evaluate $p^2 + q^2$.

Solution:

$p, q \in \mathbf{Q}$ means 'p and q could be fractions'.

This is a division question in disguise.

$$\frac{2-i}{1-2i} = \frac{2-i}{1-2i} \cdot \frac{1+2i}{1+2i} \qquad \left(\begin{array}{l}\text{Multiply top and bottom by}\\ \text{the conjugate of the bottom}\end{array}\right)$$

Top by the Top	Bottom by the Bottom
$(2-i)(1+2i)$	$(1-2i)(1+2i)$
$= 2 + 4i - i - 2i^2$	$= 1 + 2i - 2i - 4i^2$
$= 2 + 4i - i - 2(-1)$	$= 1 + 2i - 2i - 4(-1)$
$= 2 + 4i - i + 2$	$= 1 + 2i - 2i + 4$
$= 4 + 3i$	$= 5$

$\therefore \dfrac{2-i}{1-2i} = \dfrac{4+3i}{5} = \dfrac{4}{5} + \dfrac{3}{5}i$

$\therefore \dfrac{4}{5} + \dfrac{3}{5}i = p + qi$

$\therefore p = \dfrac{4}{5}$ and $q = \dfrac{3}{5}$

$p^2 + q^2$

$= \left(\dfrac{4}{5}\right)^2 + \left(\dfrac{3}{5}\right)^2$

$= \dfrac{16}{25} + \dfrac{9}{25}$

$= \dfrac{25}{25}$

$= 1$

Argand Diagram

An Argand diagram is used to plot complex numbers. It is very similar to the x- and y-axes used in coordinate geometry, except that the **horizontal** axis is called the **real axis (Re)** and the **vertical** axis is called the imaginary axis (**Im**). It is also called the **complex plane**.

Each complex number must be written in the form $a + bi$ and then plot the point (a,b). For example, the complex number $5 - 4i$ is represented by the point $(5, -4)$.

Example

$z = 2 + 3i.$ Plot z, $z - 3$, $i\,z$, $-i\,\bar{z}$ and $\dfrac{13}{z}$ on an Argand diagram.

Solution:

First write each complex number in the form $a + bi$.

$z = 2 + 3i = (2, 3)$

$z - 3 = 2 + 3i - 3 = -1 + 3i$ $(-1, 3)$

$iz = i(2 + 3i) = 2i + 3i^2 = 2i + 3(-1) = 2i - 3 = -3 + 2i = (-3, 2)$

$-i\,\bar{z} = -i(2 - 3i) = -2i + 3i^2 = -2i + 3(-1) = -2i - 3 = -3 - 2i = (-3, -2)$

$\dfrac{13}{z} = \dfrac{13}{2 + 3i} = \dfrac{13}{2 + 3i} \cdot \dfrac{2 - 3i}{2 - 3i} = \dfrac{26 - 39i}{4 - 6i + 6i - 9i^2} = \dfrac{26 - 39i}{13} = 2 - 3i = (2, -3)$

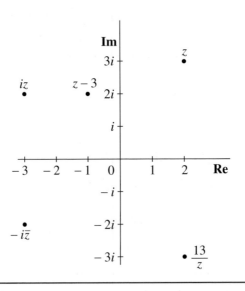

58

Modulus

The **modulus** of a complex number is the distance from the origin to the point representing the complex number on the Argand diagram.

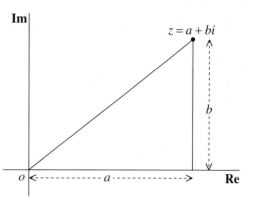

If $z = a + bi$, then the modulus of z is written $|z|$ or $|a + bi|$.

The point z represents the complex number $a + bi$.

The modulus of z is the distance from the origin, o, to the complex number $a + bi$.

Using the theorem of Pythagoras, $|z| = \sqrt{a^2 + b^2}$.

$$\text{If } z = a + bi, \text{ then}$$
$$|z| = |a + bi| = \sqrt{a^2 + b^2}$$

Example 1

Find   **(i)** $|4 + 3i|$ **(ii)** $|5 - i|$ **(iii)** $|2i|$

Solution:

(i) $|4 + 3i|$

$= \sqrt{4^2 + 3^2}$

$= \sqrt{16 + 9}$

$= \sqrt{25} = 5$

(ii) $|5 - i|$

$= \sqrt{5^2 + 1^2}$

$= \sqrt{25 + 1}$

$= \sqrt{26}$

(iii) $|2i| = |0 + 2i|$

$= \sqrt{0^2 + 2^2}$

$= \sqrt{0 + 4}$

$= \sqrt{4} = 2$

Example 2

Let $u = 3 - 6i$ where $i^2 = -1$.   Calculate $|u + 2i|$.

Solution:

$u = 3 - 6i$

$u + 2i = 3 - 6i + 2i$

$u + 2i = 3 - 4i$

$|u + 2i|$

$= |3 - 4i|$

$= \sqrt{3^2 + 4^2}$

$= \sqrt{9 + 16} = \sqrt{25} + 5$

Example 3

Let $z_1 = 2 + 3i$ and $z_2 = 5 - i$.

Investigate whether $|z_1 + z_2| > |z_1 - z_2|$.

Solution:

$$z_1 = 2 + 3i \qquad \text{and} \qquad z_2 = 5 - i$$

$z_1 + z_2$

$= (2 + 3i) + (5 - i)$

$= 2 + 3i + 5 - i$

$= 7 + 2i$

$\therefore \ |z_1 + z_2|$

$= |7 + 2i| = \sqrt{7^2 + 2^2} = \sqrt{49 + 4} = \sqrt{53}$

$\left(\boxed{} \ \sqrt{53} = 7.280109899 \right)$

$z_1 - z_2$

$= (2 + 3i) - (5 - i)$

$= 2 + 3i - 5 + i$

$= -3 + 4i$

$\therefore \ |z_1 - z_2|$

$= |-3 + 4i| = \sqrt{3^2 + 4^2} = \sqrt{9 + 16} = \sqrt{25} = 5$

$$\sqrt{53} > 5$$

$$\therefore \ |z_1 + z_2| > |z_1 - z_2|$$

Example 4

If $z_1 = 1 + 7i$ and $z_2 = 1 - 3i$, show that:

(i) $\ |z_1 . z_2| = |z_1|.|z_2|$

(ii) $\ \dfrac{|z_1|}{|z_2|} = \left| \dfrac{z_1}{z_2} \right|$

Solution:

(i)

$|z_1| = |1 + 7i| = \sqrt{1^2 + 7^2} = \sqrt{1 + 49} \ = \sqrt{50}$

$|z_2| = |1 - 3i| = \sqrt{1^2 + 3^2} = \sqrt{1 + 9} \ = \sqrt{10}$

$\therefore \qquad |z_1|.|z_2| = \sqrt{50} . \sqrt{10} = \sqrt{50 . 10} = \sqrt{500}$

$|z_1 . z_2|$

First write $z_1 . z_2$ in the form $a + bi$.

$$z_1 . z_2 = (1 + 7i)(1 - 3i) = 1 - 3i + 7i - 21i^2 = 22 + 4i$$

$$\therefore \ |z_1 . z_2| = |22 + 4i| = \sqrt{22^2 + 4^2} = \sqrt{484 + 16} = \sqrt{500}$$

$$\therefore \ |z_1 . z_2| = |z_1| . |z_2|$$

(ii) $\dfrac{|z_1|}{|z_2|} = \dfrac{\sqrt{50}}{\sqrt{10}} = \sqrt{\dfrac{50}{10}} = \sqrt{5}$ $\left(\dfrac{\sqrt{a}}{\sqrt{b}} = \sqrt{\dfrac{a}{b}} \right)$

$\left| \dfrac{z_1}{z_2} \right|$

First write $\dfrac{z_1}{z_2}$ in the form $a + bi$.

$$\dfrac{z_1}{z_2} = \dfrac{1 + 7i}{1 - 3i} = \dfrac{1 + 7i}{1 - 3i} \bullet \dfrac{1 + 3i}{1 + 3i} = \dfrac{1 + 3i + 7i + 21i^2}{1 + 3i - 3i - 9i^2}$$

$$= \dfrac{1 + 3i + 7i - 21}{1 + 9} = \dfrac{-20 + 10i}{10} = -2 + i$$

$$\therefore \left| \dfrac{z_1}{z_2} \right| = |-2 + i| = \sqrt{2^2 + 1^2} = \sqrt{4 + 1} = \sqrt{5}$$

$$\therefore \dfrac{|z_1|}{|z_2|} = \left| \dfrac{z_1}{z_2} \right|$$

Example 5

For what values of k is $|11 + ki| = |10 - 5i|$, where $k \in \mathbf{Z}$.

Solution:

Given: $\qquad |11 + ki| = |10 - 5i|$

$\therefore \qquad \sqrt{11^2 + k^2} = \sqrt{10^2 + 5^2}$

$\qquad\qquad \sqrt{121 + k^2} = \sqrt{100 + 25}$

$\qquad\qquad \sqrt{121 + k^2} = \sqrt{125}$

$\qquad\qquad 121 + k^2 = 125 \qquad\qquad$ (square both sides)

$\qquad\qquad\qquad k^2 = 4$

$\qquad\qquad\qquad k = \pm\sqrt{4}$

$\qquad\qquad\qquad k = \pm 2$

Example 6

Let $z_1 = 2 - 3i$ and $z_2 = 5 + 12i$.

Find the value of the real number k such that $k|z_1| = |z_2|$.

Solution:

$$|z_1| = |2 - 3i| = |2^2 + 3^2| = \sqrt{4 + 9} = \sqrt{13}$$
$$|z_2| = |5 + 12i| = \sqrt{5^2 + 12^2} = \sqrt{25 + 144} = \sqrt{169} = 13$$

Given:
$$k|z_1| = |z_2|$$
$$k\sqrt{13} = 13$$
$$\sqrt{13}k = 13$$
$$k = \frac{13}{\sqrt{13}} \qquad \left(\text{divide both sides by } \sqrt{13}\right)$$
$$k = \sqrt{13}$$

Note: $\dfrac{13}{\sqrt{13}} = \dfrac{13}{\sqrt{13}} \times \dfrac{\sqrt{13}}{\sqrt{13}} = \dfrac{13\sqrt{13}}{13} = \sqrt{13}$

Equality of Complex Numbers

If two complex numbers are equal then:
their real parts are equal and their imaginary parts are also equal.

For example, if $a + bi = c + di$,

then $a = c$ and $b = d$.

This definition is very useful when dealing with equations involving complex numbers.

Equations involving complex numbers are usually solved with the following steps:

1. Remove the brackets.
2. Put an **R** under the real parts and an **I** under the imaginary parts to identify them.
3. Let the real parts equal the real parts and the imaginary parts equal the imaginary parts.
4. Solve these resultant equations (usually simultaneous equations).

Note: If one side of the equation does not contain a real part or an imaginary part it should be replaced with 0 or $0i$, respectively.

Example 1

Solve for real s and real t

$$s(2-i) + ti(4+2i) = 1 + s + ti.$$

Solution:

$$s(2-i) + ti(4+2i) = 1 + s + ti$$

$$2s - si + 4ti + 2ti^2 = 1 + s + ti \qquad \text{(remove the brackets)}$$

$$2s - si + 4ti + 2t(-1) = 1 + s + ti \qquad \text{(replace } i^2 \text{ with } -1)$$

$$2s - si + 4ti - 2t = 1 + s + ti$$

$$\mathbf{R} \quad \mathbf{I} \quad \mathbf{I} \quad \mathbf{R} \quad \mathbf{R} \quad \mathbf{R} \quad \mathbf{I} \qquad \text{(identify real and imaginary parts)}$$

Real parts = Real parts	Imag. parts = Imag. parts
$2s - 2t = 1 + s$	$-s + 4t = t$
$s - 2t = 1 \qquad$ ①	$-s + 3t = 0 \qquad$ ②

Now solve the simultaneous equations ① and ② :

$$s - 2t = 1 \qquad ①$$

$$\underline{-s + 3t = 0 \qquad ②}$$

$$t = 1 \text{ (add)}$$

put $t = 1$ into ① or ②

$$-s + 3t = 0 \qquad ②$$

$$-s + 3(1) = 0$$

$$-s + 3 = 0$$

$$-s = -3$$

$$s = 3$$

Thus, $s = 3$, $t = 1$.

Example 2

(i) Express $\dfrac{3-2i}{1-4i}$ in the form $x+yi$.

(ii) Hence, or otherwise, find the values of the real numbers p and q such that

$$p + 2qi = \frac{17(3-2i)}{1-4i}.$$

Solution:

(i) $\dfrac{3-2i}{1-4i}$

$= \dfrac{3-2i}{1-4i} \bullet \dfrac{1+4i}{1+4i}$

$= \dfrac{3+12i-2i-8i^2}{1+4i-4i-16i^2}$

$= \dfrac{3+12i-2i+8}{1+4i-4i+16}$

$= \dfrac{11+10i}{17}$

(ii) $p + 2qi = \dfrac{17(3-2i)}{1-4i}$

$p + 2qi = 17\left(\dfrac{3-2i}{1-4i}\right)$

$p + 2qi = 17\left(\dfrac{11+10i}{17}\right)$

$p + 2qi = 11 + 10i$

$\quad$ **R** $\quad$ **I** $\quad$ **R** $\quad$ **I**

$\quad p = 11 \qquad\qquad 2q = 10$

$\quad p = 11 \qquad\qquad q = 5$

Example 3

(i) Let $w = 1 + i$.   Express $\dfrac{6}{w}$ in the form $x + yi$, where x . $y \in \mathbf{Z}$.

(ii) a and b are real numbers such that

$$a\left(\frac{6}{w}\right) - b(w + 1) = 3(w + i).$$

Find the value of a and the value of b.

Solution:

(i) $\dfrac{6}{w} = \dfrac{6}{1+i}$ (multiply top and bottom by the conjugate of the bottom)

$$= \frac{6}{1+i} \bullet \frac{1-i}{1-i} = \frac{6-6i}{1-i+i-i^2} = \frac{6-6i}{1+1} = \frac{6-6i}{2} = 3 - 3i$$

(ii) $\quad a\left(\dfrac{6}{w}\right) - b(w + 1) = 3(w + i)$

$a(3 - 3i) - b(1 + i + 1) = 3(1 + i + i)$ $\qquad$ (put in $\dfrac{6}{w} = 3 - 3i$ and $w = 1 + i$)

$\quad a(3 - 3i) - b(2 + i) = 3(1 + 2i)$

$\quad 3a - 3ai - 2b - bi = 3 + 6i$

$\qquad \mathbf{R} \quad \mathbf{I} \quad \mathbf{R} \quad \mathbf{I} \quad \mathbf{R} \quad \mathbf{I}$ $\qquad$ (identify real and imaginary parts)

Real parts $\;=\;$ Real parts $\qquad\qquad$ Imaginary parts $=$ Imaginary parts

$3a - 2b \quad = \quad 3 \quad$ ① $\qquad\qquad\qquad -3a - b = 6$

Now solve the simultaneous equations ① and ②:

$3a - 2b = 3 \quad$ ①	Put in $b = -3$ into ① or ②.
$\underline{-3a - b = 6 \quad ②}$	$3a - 2b = 3 \quad$ ①
$-3b = 9 \quad$ (add)	$\downarrow$
$3b = -9$	$3a - 2(-3) = 3$
$b = -3$	$3a + 6 = 3$
	$3a = -3$
	$a = -1$

Thus, $a = -1$ and $b = -3$

Example 4

Let $z = 3 - 2i$, solve for real s and real t

$$\frac{s + ti}{1 + 2i} = \bar{z}$$

Solution:

$$\frac{s + ti}{1 + 2i} = \bar{z}$$

$$\frac{s + ti}{1 + 2i} = 3 + 2i \qquad \text{[replace } \bar{z} \text{ with } (3 + 2i)]$$

$$s + ti = (1 + 2i)(3 + 2i) \qquad \text{[multiply both sides by } (1 + 2i)]$$

$$s + ti = 3 + 2i + 6i + 4i^2 \qquad \text{[remove brackets]}$$

$$s + ti = 3 + 2i + 6i + 4(-1) \qquad \text{[replace } i^2 \text{ with } -1]$$

$$s + ti = 3 + 2i + 6i - 4$$

$$s + ti = -1 + 8i$$

$$\textbf{R} \quad \textbf{I} \qquad \textbf{R} \quad \textbf{I} \qquad \text{[identify real and imaginary parts]}$$

Thus, $s = -1$ and $t = 8$. $\qquad \text{[\textbf{R}'s = \textbf{R}'s and \textbf{I}'s = \textbf{I}'s]}$

Quadratic Equations with Complex Roots

When a quadratic equation cannot be solved by factorisation the following formula can be used:

> The equation $ax^2 + bx + c = 0$ has roots given by:
>
> $$x = \frac{-b \pm \sqrt{b^2 - 4ac}}{2a}$$

Note: The whole of the top of the right-hand side, including $-b$, is divided by $2a$. It is often called the '**quadratic**' or $-$'**b**' formula.

If $b^2 - 4ac < 0$, then the number under the square root sign will be negative, and so the solutions will be complex numbers.

Example 1

Solve the equation   **(i)** $z^2 + 4z + 5 = 0$ **(ii)** $z^2 - 6z + 13 = 0$.

Write your answers in the form $x + yi$ where $x, y \in \mathbf{R}$.

Solution:

(i) $z^2 + 4z + 5 = 0$

$az^2 + bz + c = 0$

$a = 1, \quad b = 4, \quad c = 5$

$z = \dfrac{-b \pm \sqrt{b^2 - 4ac}}{2a}$

$z = \dfrac{-4 \pm \sqrt{(4)^2 - 4(1)(5)}}{2(1)}$

$z = \dfrac{-4 \pm \sqrt{16 - 20}}{2}$

$z = \dfrac{-4 \pm \sqrt{-4}}{2}$

$z = \dfrac{-4 \pm 2i}{2}$

$z = -2 \pm i$

(ii) $z^2 - 6z + 13 = 0$

$az^2 + bz + c = 0$

$a = 1, \quad b = -6, \quad c = 13$

$z = \dfrac{-b \pm \sqrt{b^2 - 4ac}}{2a}$

$z = \dfrac{6 \pm \sqrt{(-6)^2 - 4(1)(13)}}{2(1)}$

$z = \dfrac{6 \pm \sqrt{36 - 52}}{2}$

$z = \dfrac{6 \pm \sqrt{-16}}{2}$

$z = \dfrac{6 \pm 4i}{2}$

$z = 3 \pm 2i$

Note: Notice in both solutions the roots occur in conjugate pairs. If one root of a quadratic equation, with real coefficients, is a complex number, then the other root must also be complex and the conjugate of the first.

i.e. if $3 - 4i$ is a root, then $3 + 4i$ is also a root;

if $-2 - 5i$ is a root, then $-2 + 5i$ is also a root;

if $a + bi$ is a root, then $a - bi$ is also a root.

Example 2

Verify that $-2 + 5i$ is a root of the equation $z^2 + 4z + 29 = 0$ and find the other root.

Solution:

Method 1:

If $-2 + 5i$ is a root, then when z is replaced by $-2 + 5i$ in the equation, the equation will be satisfied, i.e.

$$(-2 + 5i)^2 + 4(-2 + 5i) + 29 = 0$$

Check:

$(-2 + 5i)^2 + 4(-2 + 5i) + 29$

$= (-2 + 5i)(-2 + 5i) + 4(-2 + 5i) + 29$

$= 4 - 10i - 10i - 25 - 8 + 20i + 29$

$= 33 - 33 + 20i - 20i$

$= 0$

∴ $-2 + 5i$ is a root and

$-2 - 5i$ is the other root

(the conjugate of $-2 + 5i$)

Method 2:

$z^2 + 4z + 29 = 0$

$a = 1, b = 4, c = 29$

$$z = \frac{-b \pm \sqrt{b^2 - 4ac}}{2a}$$

$$z = \frac{-4 \pm \sqrt{(4)^2 - 4(1)(29)}}{2(1)}$$

$$z = \frac{-4 \pm \sqrt{16 - 116}}{2}$$

$$z = \frac{-4 \pm \sqrt{-100}}{2}$$

$$z = \frac{-4 \pm 10i}{2}$$

$z = -2 \pm 5i$

∴ $-2 + 5i$ is a root and

$-2 - 5i$ is the other root

Sometimes we have to find unknown coefficients.

Example 3

Let $z = 3 - 4i$ be one root of the equation $z^2 + pz + q = 0$, $p, q \in \mathbf{R}$.
Find the value of p and the value of q.

Solution:

If $3 - 4i$ is a root, then $3 + 4i$ is also a root (roots occur in conjugate pairs).

Method: Form a quadratic equation with roots $3 - 4i$ and $3 + 4i$.

$$\text{Let } z = 3 - 4i \quad \text{and} \quad z = 3 + 4i$$

$$\therefore \qquad z - 3 + 4i = 0 \qquad \text{and} \qquad z - 3 - 4i = 0$$

and
$$(z - 3 + 4i)(z - 3 - 4i) = 0 \qquad (0 \times 0 = 0)$$

$$z(z - 3 - 4i) - 3(z - 3 - 4i) + 4i(z - 3i - 4i) = 0$$

$$z^2 - 3z - 4\!\!\!/i - 3z + 9 + 12\!\!\!/i + 4\!\!\!/i - 12\!\!\!/i - 16i^2 = 0$$

$$z^2 - 6z + 9 - 16(-1) = 0 \qquad (i^2 = -1)$$

$$z^2 - 6z + 25 = 0$$

By comparing $z^2 - 6z + 25 = 0$ to $z^2 + pz + q = 0$

$$p = -6 \quad \text{and} \quad q = 25$$

Higher Powers of i

Every integer power of i is a member of the set $\{1, -1, i, -i\}$.

$i = \sqrt{-1}$

$i^2 = -1$

$i^3 = i^2 \cdot i = (-1)i = -i$

$i^4 = i^2 \cdot i^2 = (-1)(-1) = 1$

$i = \sqrt{-1}$

$i^2 = -1$

$i^3 = -i$

$i^4 = 1$

Example

Simplify   **(i)** i^8 **(ii)** i^7 **(iii)** $-i(i^4 + i^5 + i^6)$

Solution:

(i) $i^8 = i^4 \times i^4 \qquad = 1 \times 1 = 1$

(ii) $i^7 = i^4 \times i^3 \qquad = 1 \times -i = -i$

(iii) $-i(i^4 + i^5 + i^6)$

$= -i(1 + i - 1)$

$= -i(i)$

$= -i^2 = -(-1) = 1$

$i^4 = 1$

$i^5 = i^4 \times i^1 = 1 \times i = i$

$i^6 = i^4 \times i^2 = 1 \times -1 = -1$

Chapter 4. SEQUENCES AND SERIES

A sequence is a list of numbers, e.g. 2, 5, 8, 11, 14, ...
A series is a sequence 'added up', e.g. $2 + 5 + 8 + 11 + 14 + ...$
T_n is the nth term.
S_n is the sum of the first n terms.

Arithmetic Sequences and Series

$$a, a + d, a + 2d, a + 3d, ...$$

a = first term $\qquad\qquad$ d = common difference

1. $T_n = a + (n - 1)d$

2. $T_n - T_{n-1} = $ constant = common difference = d

   (e.g. $T_3 - T_2 = T_2 - T_1 = d$)

3. $S_n = \dfrac{n}{2}[2a + (n - 1)d]$

Geometric Sequences and Series

$$a, ar, ar^2, ar^3, ...$$

a = first term $\qquad\qquad$ r = common ratio

1. $T_n = ar^{n-1}$

2. $\dfrac{T_n}{T_{n-1}} = $ constant = common ratio = r

   (e.g. $\dfrac{T_3}{T_2} = \dfrac{T_2}{T_1} = r$)

3. (a) $S_n = \dfrac{a(r^n - 1)}{r - 1}$ $\qquad$ ($r > 1$ or $r < -1$)

   (b) $S_n = \dfrac{a(1 - r^n)}{1 - r}$ $\qquad$ ($-1 < r < 1$)

For all Series

$$T_n = S_n - S_{n-1}$$ and $$T_1 = S_1$$

(e.g. $T_2 = S_2 - S_1$ $T_8 = S_8 - S_7$ etc.)

We use this when given S_n of a series in terms of n and are asked to find a, d, r or T_n (or any term).

General Term, T_n

Example 1

The nth term of a sequence is given by $T_n = n^2 + 1$.

(i)   Write down the first three terms of the sequence.

(ii)   Show that $T_1 + T_2 + T_3 = T_4$.

(iii)   Show that $\dfrac{T_7}{T_3} = T_2$

Solution:

$T_n = n^2 + 1$

(i) $T_1 = (1)^2 + 1 = 1 + 1 = 2$ (put in 1 for n)

$T_2 = (2)^2 + 1 = 4 + 1 = 5$ (put in 2 for n)

$T_3 = (3)^2 + 1 = 9 + 1 = 10$ (put in 3 for n)

Thus, the first three terms are 2, 5, 10.

(ii) $T_4 = (4)^2 + 1 = 16 + 1 = 17$

$T_1 + T_2 + T_3 = 2 + 5 + 10 = 17$

$\therefore\ T_1 + T_2 + T_3 = T_4$

i.e. $17 = 17$

(iii) $T_7 = (7)^2 + 1 = 49 + 1 = 50$

$\dfrac{T_7}{T_3} = \dfrac{50}{10} = 5 = T_2$

$\therefore\ \dfrac{T_7}{T_3} = T_2$ $(5 = 5)$

Example 2

The nth term of a sequence is given by $T_n = \dfrac{n}{n+1}$.

(i) Find T_2, the second term.   **(ii)** Show that $T_2 + T_3 > 1$.

Solution:

(i) $T_n = \dfrac{n}{n+1}$

$T_2 = \dfrac{2}{2+1} = \dfrac{2}{3}$

(ii) $T_3 = \dfrac{3}{3+1} = \dfrac{3}{4}$

$T_2 + T_3 = \dfrac{2}{3} + \dfrac{3}{4} = \dfrac{17}{12} > 1$

$\therefore \ T_2 + T_3 > 1$

Arithmetic Sequences and Series

Example 1

The first term of an arithmetic sequence is 17 and the common difference is -8.
(i) Find, in terms of n, an expression for T_n, the nth term.
(ii) Find, T_5, the fifth term.

Solution:

(i) $a = 17, d = -8$

$T_n = a + (n-1)d$

$= 17 + (n-1)(-8)$

$= 17 - 8n + 8$

$= 25 - 8n$

(ii) $T_n = 25 - 8n$

$T_5 = 25 - 8(5)$

$= 25 - 40$

$= -15$

Example 2

The nth term of an arithmetic series is given by $T_n = 5n + 1$

(i) The first term is a and the common differences is d.
Find the value of a and the value of d.

(ii) Find the value of n for which $T_n = 156$.

(iii) Find S_{12}, the sum of the first 12 terms.

Solution:

$$T_n = 5n + 1$$

(i) $a = T_1 = 5(1) + 1 = 5 + 1 = 6$ $\qquad$ $d = T_2 - T_1$

$\qquad T_2 = 5(2) + 1 = 10 + 1 = 11$ $\qquad\qquad = 11 - 6 = 5$

$$\text{Thus, } a = 6 \text{ and } d = 5$$

(ii) Given: $\qquad\qquad T_n = 156$ $\qquad$ **(iii)** $S_n = \dfrac{n}{2}[2a + (n-1)d]$

$\qquad \therefore \qquad a + (n-1)d = 156$

$\qquad\qquad 6 + (n-1)5 = 156$ $\qquad\qquad S_{12} = \dfrac{12}{2}[2(6) + (12-1)(5)]$

$\qquad$ (put in $a = 6$ and $d = 5$)

$\qquad\qquad\qquad$ (put in $n = 12$, $a = 6$ and $d = 5$)

$\qquad\qquad 6 + 5n - 5 = 156$ $\qquad\qquad\qquad = 6[12 + 11(5)]$

$\qquad\qquad\qquad 5n + 1 = 156$ $\qquad\qquad\qquad\qquad = 6[12 + 55]$

$\qquad\qquad\qquad\quad 5n = 155$ $\qquad\qquad\qquad\qquad = 6[67]$

$\qquad\qquad\qquad\qquad n = 31$ $\qquad\qquad\qquad\qquad = 402$

Example 3

In an arithmetic sequence, the fifth term, T_4, is 15 and the eighth term, T_7, is 27. Find the first term, a, and the common difference, d.

Solution:

We are given two equations in disguise and we use these to find a and d.

$$T_n = a + (n-1)d$$

Given: $\qquad T_4 = 15$ $\qquad\qquad$ Given: $\qquad T_7 = 27$

$\therefore \qquad a + 3d = 15 \qquad$ ① $\qquad\qquad \therefore \qquad a + 6d = 27 \qquad$ ②

Now solve the simultaneous equations ① and ② to find the value of a and the value of d.

$$-a - 3d = -15 \quad ① \times -1$$

$$a + 6d = 27 \quad ②$$

$$\overline{}$$

$$3d = 12 \quad \text{(add)}$$

$$d = 4$$

Put $d = 4$ into ① or ②

$$a + 3d = 15 \quad ①$$

$$a + 3(4) = 15$$

$$a + 12 = 15$$

$$a = 3$$

Thus, $a = 3$ and $d = 4$.

Example 4

The first three terms in an arithmetic sequence are $k + 6$, $2k + 1$, $k + 18$.
Calculate the value of k and write down the first three terms.

Solution:

We use the fact that in an arithmetic sequence the difference between any two consecutive terms is always the same. We are given the first three terms.

$\therefore$
$$T_3 - T_2 = T_2 - T_1 \qquad \text{(common difference)}$$

$$(k + 18) - (2k + 1) = (2k + 1) - (k + 6) \qquad \text{(put in given values)}$$

$$k + 18 - 2k - 1 = 2k + 1 - k - 6$$

$$-k + 17 = k - 5 \qquad \text{(simplify both sides)}$$

$$-k - k = -5 - 17$$

$$-2k = -22$$

$$2k = 22 \qquad \text{(multiply both sides by} -1\text{)}$$

$$k = 11$$

$T_1 = k + 6 = 11 + 6 = 17$

$T_2 = 2k + 1 = 2(11) + 1 = 22 + 1 = 23$

$T_3 = k + 18 = 11 + 18 = 29$

Thus, the first three terms are 17, 23, 29.

Example 5

The general term, T_n, of an arithmetic sequence is given by $T_n = 2n + 5$. Find the first term, a, and the common difference, d. For what value of n is $S_n = 160$?

Solution:

$T_n = 2n + 5$

$T_1 = 2(1) + 5 = 2 + 5 = 7 = a$

$T_2 = 2(2) + 5 = 4 + 5 = 9$

$d = T_2 - T_1$

$= 9 - 7$

$= 2$

Thus, $a = 7$ and $d = 2$

Equation given in disguise:

$$S_n = 160$$

$$\frac{n}{2}[2a + (n-1)d] = 160 \qquad \text{(we know } a \text{ and } d, \text{ find } n)$$

$$\frac{n}{2}[2(7) + (n-1)2] = 160 \qquad \text{(put in } a = 7 \text{ and } d = 2)$$

$$\frac{n}{2}(14 + 2n - 2) = 160$$

$$\frac{n}{2}(2n + 12) = 160$$

$$n(n + 6) = 160 \qquad \left(\frac{1}{2}(2n + 12) = n + 6\right)$$

$$n^2 + 6n = 160$$

$$n^2 + 6n - 160 = 0$$

$$(n - 10)(n + 16) = 0$$

$$n - 10 = 0 \quad \text{or} \quad n + 16 = 0$$

$$n = 10 \quad \text{or} \quad n = -16$$

(reject $n = -16$)

Thus, $n = 10$

Note: If n is a fraction, or a negative number, reject it.

Example 6

In an arithmetic series, the tenth term, T_{10}, is 19 and the sum to ten terms, S_{10}, is 55. Find the first term, a, and the common difference, d.

Show that

$$2S_n = 3n^2 - 19n.$$

Solution:

We are given two equations in disguise and we use them to find a and d.

$T_n = a + (n-1)d$	$S_n = \dfrac{n}{2}[2a + (n-1)d]$
$T_{10} = 19$ (given)	$S_{10} = 55$ (given)
$\therefore \quad a + 9d = 19$ ①	$\therefore \quad \dfrac{10}{2}(2a + 9d) = 55$
	$5(2a + 9d) = 55$
	$2a + 9d = 11$ ②

We now solve between the simultaneous equations ① and ②:

$a + 9d = 19$ ①	$a + 9d = 19$ ①
$-2a - 9d = -11$ ② × -1	$-8 + 9d = 19$
$\quad -a = 8$ (add)	$9d = 27$
$\quad a = -8$	$d = 3$
Put $a = -8$ into ① or ②	

Thus, the first term, a, is -8 and the common difference, d, is 3.

$$S_n = \frac{n}{2}\,[2a + (n-1)d]$$

$$S_n = \frac{n}{2}\,[2(-8) + (n-1)3] \qquad \text{(put in } a = -8 \text{ and } d = 3)$$

$$S_n = \frac{n}{2}\,[-16 + 3n - 3]$$

$$S_n = \frac{n}{2}\,(3n - 19)$$

$$2S_n = n\,(3n - 19) \qquad \text{(multiply both sides by 2)}$$

$$2S_n = 3n^2 - 19n \qquad \text{(remove the brackets)}$$

Example 7

The first three terms in an arithmetic series are $1 + 3 + 5 + \ldots$

(i)   Show that: (a) $T_n = 2n - 1$ (b) $S_n = n^2$.

(ii) Hence, or otherwise, evaluate: (a) T_{20} (b) S_{20}.

(iii) Show that $T_{10} = S_{10} - S_9$.

Solution:

Note: Even though each term is separated by a plus sign rather than a comma, we still write $T_1 = 1$, $T_2 = 3$, $T_3 = 5$, etc.

$$a = T_1 = 1 \qquad d = T_2 - T_1 = 3 - 1 = 2$$

(i)   (a) $T_n = a + (n - 1)d$

$\qquad = 1 + (n - 1)(2)$

$\qquad = 1 + 2n - 2$

$\qquad = 2n - 1$

(b) $S_n = \dfrac{n}{2}[2a + (n - 1)d]$

$\qquad = \dfrac{n}{2}[2(1) + (n - 1)(2)]$

$\qquad = \dfrac{n}{2}[2 + 2n - 2]$

$\qquad = \dfrac{n}{2}(2n)$

$\qquad = n^2$

(ii)   **Using hence**

(a) $T_n \quad = 2n - 1$

$\quad T_{20} \ = 2(20) - 1 = 40 - 1 = 39$

(b) $S_n = n^2$

$\quad S_{20} = (20)^2 = 400$

(iii) $T_n = 2n - 1$

$\quad T_{10} = 2(10) - 1 = 20 - 1 = 19$

$\quad S_{10} - S_9 = 100 - 81 = 19 = T_{10}$

Thus, $T_{10} = S_{10} - S_9$

$S_n = n^2$

$S_{10} = (10)^2 = 100 \qquad S_9 = (9)^2 = 81$

To verify that a sequence is arithmetic we must show the following:

$$\boxed{T_n - T_{n-1} = \text{constant}}$$

To show that a sequence is **not arithmetic**, it is only necessary to show that the difference between any two consecutive terms is not the same. In practice, this usually involves showing that $T_3 - T_2 \neq T_2 - T_1$ or similar.

Example 8

(i) T_n of a sequence is $5n + 3$. Verify that the sequence is arithmetic.

(ii) T_n of a sequence is $n^2 + 3n + 2$. Verify that the sequence is not arithmetic.

Solution:

(i) $T_n = 5n + 3$

$$T_{n-1} = 5(n-1) + 3 \qquad \text{[replace } n \text{ with } (n-1)]$$
$$= 5n - 5 + 3$$
$$= 5n - 2$$

$$T_n - T_{n-1}$$
$$= (5n + 3) - (5n - 2)$$
$$= 5n + 3 - 5n + 2$$
$$= 5 \qquad \text{(a constant, i.e. does not contain } n)$$

$$T_n - T_{n-1} = \text{a constant}$$

Thus, the sequence is arithmetic.

(ii) $T_n = n^2 + 3n + 2$

$T_1 = (1)^2 + 3(1) + 2$	$T_2 = (2)^2 + 3(2) + 2$	$T_3 = (3)^2 + 3(3) + 2$
$= 1 + 3 + 2$	$= 4 + 6 + 2$	$= 9 + 9 + 2$
$= 6$	$= 12$	$= 20$
$T_3 - T_2 = 20 - 12 = 8$		$T_2 - T_1 = 12 - 6 = 6$

$$T_3 - T_2 \neq T_2 - T_1$$

Thus, the sequence is not arithmetic.

Note: We could also have shown $T_n - T_{n-1} \neq$ a constant to show that the sequence is not arithmetic.

Given S_n of an arithmetic series in terms of n

In many problems we are given an expression for S_n in terms of n and we need to find a and d. In this type of problem we use the fact that for all types of series:

$$\boxed{T_n = S_n - S_{n-1}} \qquad \text{and} \qquad \boxed{T_1 = S_1}$$

(e.g. $T_2 = S_2 - S_1$ $T_3 = S_3 - S_2$ $T_{11} = S_{11} - S_{10}$ etc.)

Example 9

In an arithmetic series, $S_n = 2n^2 - 3n$.
Find the first term, a, and the common difference, d.

Solution:

$$S_n = 2n^2 - 3n$$

$$S_1 = 2(1)^2 - 3(1) \qquad\qquad S_2 = 2(2)^2 - 3(2)$$
$$= 2 - 3 \qquad\qquad\qquad = 2(4) - 3(2)$$
$$= -1 \qquad\qquad\qquad\quad = 8 - 6$$
$$\qquad\qquad\qquad\qquad = 2$$

$$a = T_1 = S_1 = -1 \qquad\qquad T_2 = S_2 - S_1 = 2 - (-1) = 2 + 1 = 3$$

$$d = T_2 - T_1 = 3 - (-1) = 3 + 1 = 4$$

$$\text{Thus, } a = -1 \text{ and } d = 4$$

Geometric Sequences and Series

Example 1

The first term of a geometric sequence is 4 and the common ratio is 1.5. Write down the next three terms of the sequence.

Solution:

$$a = T_1 = 4 \qquad\qquad\qquad r = 1.5$$

$$T_n = ar^{n-1}$$

$$T_2 = 4(1.5)^{2-1} = 4(1.5)^1 = 4(1.5) = 6$$

$$T_3 = 4(1.5)^{3-1} = 4(1.5)^2 = 4(2.25) = 9$$

$$T_4 = 4(1.5)^{4-1} = 4(1.5)^3 = 4(3.375) = 13.5$$

Thus, the next three terms are, 6, 9 and 13.5.

Example 2

The first three terms of a geometric sequence are 5, 15, 45.

(i) Find the first term, a, and the common ratio, r.

(ii) Write down an expression for T_n and, hence, calculate T_9.

(iii) Calculate S_6, the sum to six terms.

(iv) Which term of the sequence is equal to 10,935?

Solution:

(i) $a = 5$ (given) $r = \dfrac{T_2}{T_1} = \dfrac{15}{5} = 3$

Thus, $a = 5$ and $r = 3$

(ii) $T_n = ar^{n-1} = 5(3)^{n-1}$

$T_9 = 5(3)^{9-1} = 5(3)^8 = 5(6{,}561) = 32{,}805$

(iii) $S_n = \dfrac{a(r^n - 1)}{r - 1}$

$\therefore \quad S_6 = \dfrac{5(3^6 - 1)}{3 - 1} = \dfrac{5(729 - 1)}{2} = \dfrac{5(728)}{2} = \dfrac{3{,}640}{2} = 1{,}820$

(iv) Equation give in disguise:

$T_n = 10{,}935$

$ar^{n-1} = 10{,}935$ (we know a and r, find n)

$5(3)^{n-1} = 10{,}935$ (put in $a = 5$ and $r = 3$)

$3^{n-1} = 2{,}187$ (divide both sides by 5)

$3^{n-1} = 3^7$ (both as powers of 3; $2{,}187 = 3^7$)

$n - 1 = 7$ (equate the powers)

$n = 8$ (add 1 to both sides)

Thus the 8th term of the sequence is 10,935.

Example 3

The first two terms of a geometric series are $32 + 16 + \ldots$

Find:

(i) r, the common ratio

(ii) T_n, the nth term

(iii) S_n, the sum of n terms

(iv)   the value of $S_6 + T_8$.

Solution:

(i) $r = \dfrac{T_2}{T_1} = \dfrac{16}{32} = \dfrac{1}{2}$ (multiply top and bottom by 2)

(ii) $T_n = ar^{n-1} = 32\left(\dfrac{1}{2}\right)^{n-1}$

(iii) $S_n = \dfrac{a(1 - r^n)}{1 - r} = \dfrac{32\left[1 - \left(\frac{1}{2}\right)^n\right]}{1 - \frac{1}{2}} = \dfrac{32\left[1 - \left(\frac{1}{2}\right)^n\right]}{\frac{1}{2}} = 64\left[1 - \left(\dfrac{1}{2}\right)^n\right]$

(iv) $S_n = 64\left[1 - \left(\dfrac{1}{2}\right)^n\right]$

$\therefore\quad S_6 = 64\left[1 - \left(\dfrac{1}{2}\right)^6\right]$

$\qquad = 64\left(1 - \dfrac{1}{64}\right)$

$\qquad = 64 - 1$

$\qquad = 63$

$T_n = 32\left(\dfrac{1}{2}\right)^{n-1}$

$\therefore\quad T_8 = 32\left(\dfrac{1}{2}\right)^7$

$\qquad = 32\left(\dfrac{1}{128}\right)$

$\qquad = \dfrac{32}{128}$

$\qquad = \dfrac{1}{4}$

$$\therefore\ S_6 + T_8 = 63 + \tfrac{1}{4} = 63\tfrac{1}{4}$$

Example 4

The first three terms of a geometric sequence are $3k - 5$, $k - 1$, $k - 2$.

Find the values of k, where k is a real number.

Solution:

We use the fact that in a geometric sequence, any term divided by the previous term is always a constant.

$\therefore \qquad \dfrac{T_3}{T_2} = \dfrac{T_2}{T_1}$ (common ratio)

$\dfrac{k - 2}{k - 1} = \dfrac{k - 1}{3k - 5}$ (put in given values)

$(k - 2)(3k - 5) = (k - 1)(k - 1)$ (multiply both sides by $(k - 1)(3k - 5)$)

$3k^2 - 11k + 10 = k^2 - 2k + 1$ (remove brackets)

$2k^2 - 9k + 9 = 0$ (every term of the left-hand side)

$(2k - 3)(k - 3) = 0$ (factorise)

$2k - 3 = 0 \quad$ or $\quad k - 3 = 0$ (let each factor $= 0$)

$2k = 3 \quad$ or $\quad k = 3$

$k = \dfrac{3}{2} \quad$ or $\quad k = 3$

Thus, the values of k are $\dfrac{3}{2}$ or 3.

Example 5

The nth term of a geometric series is $T_n = 4\left(\frac{1}{2}\right)^n$.

(i) Find a, the first term.

(ii) Find r, the common ratio.

(iii) Write $4 - S_{10}$ in the form $\frac{1}{2^k}$, $k \in \mathbf{N}$, where S_{10} is the sum of the first ten terms.

Solution:

(i) $T_n = 4\left(\frac{1}{2}\right)^n$

$a = T_1 = 4\left(\frac{1}{2}\right)^1 = 4\left(\frac{1}{2}\right) = 2$

(ii) $T_2 = 4\left(\frac{1}{2}\right)^2$

$= 4\left(\frac{1}{4}\right) = 1$

$r = \dfrac{T_2}{T_1} = \dfrac{1}{2}$

Thus, $a = 2$ and $r = \dfrac{1}{2}$

(iii) $S_n = \dfrac{a(1 - r^n)}{1 - r}$ (multiply top and bottom by 2)

$$S_{10} = \frac{2\left[1 - \left(\frac{1}{2}\right)^{10}\right]}{1 - \frac{1}{2}} = \frac{2\left[1 - \left(\frac{1}{2}\right)^{10}\right]}{\frac{1}{2}} = \frac{4\left[1 - \left(\frac{1}{2}\right)^{10}\right]}{1} = 4\left[1 - \left(\frac{1}{2}\right)^{10}\right]$$

$\therefore \quad 4 - S_{10} = 4 - 4\left[1 - \left(\frac{1}{2}\right)^{10}\right]$

$= 4 - 4 + 4\left(\frac{1}{2}\right)^{10} = 4\left(\frac{1}{2}\right)^{10}$

$4 = 2^2$ and $\left(\frac{1}{2}\right)^{10} = \frac{1}{2^{10}} = 2^{-10}$

Thus, $4\left(\frac{1}{2}\right)^{10} = 2^2 \times 2^{-10} = 2^{2-10} = 2^{-8} = \dfrac{1}{2^8}$.

Example 6

The first three terms of a geometric series are $1 + 2 + 4 + \ldots$

(i) Write down the values of a and r.

(ii) How many terms of the series must be added together to get a total of 2,047?

(iii) Show that $S_{33} < 2^{33}$.

Solution:

(i) $a = 1$ (given) $\qquad\qquad\qquad\qquad r = \dfrac{T_2}{T_1} = \dfrac{2}{1} = 2$

(ii) Equation given in disguise:

$$S_n = 2{,}047$$

$$\therefore \frac{a(r^n - 1)}{r - 1} = 2{,}047 \qquad\qquad \text{(we know } a \text{ and } r \text{, find } n\text{)}$$

$$\frac{1(2^n - 1)}{2 - 1} = 2{,}047 \qquad\qquad \text{(put in } a = 1 \text{ and } r = 2\text{)}$$

$$\frac{2^n - 1}{1} = 2{,}047$$

$$2^n - 1 = 2{,}047$$

$$2^n = 2{,}048 \qquad\qquad \text{(add 1 to both sides)}$$

$$2^n = 2^{11} \qquad\qquad \text{(both as power 2; } 2{,}048 = 2^{11}\text{)}$$

$$n = 11 \qquad\qquad \text{(equate the powers)}$$

Thus, the sum of the first 11 items will give 2,048.

(iii) $\qquad\qquad S_n = \dfrac{a(r^n - 1)}{r - 1}$

$$\therefore \qquad S_{33} = \frac{1(2^{33} - 1)}{2 - 1} \qquad\qquad \text{(put in } n = 33, a = 1 \text{ and } r = 2\text{)}$$

$$= \frac{2^{33} - 1}{1}$$

$$= 2^{33} - 1$$

$$2^{33} - 1 < 2^{33}$$

$$\therefore \qquad\qquad S_{33} < 2^{33}$$

Example 7

T_n of a sequence is $3(5)^n$. Verify that the sequence is geometric.

Solution:

To verify that a sequence is geometric we must show the following:

$$\frac{T_n}{T_{n-1}} = \text{constant}$$

$T_n = 3(5)^n$ $\qquad\qquad\qquad\qquad$ $T_{n-1} = 3(5)^{n-1}$ $\qquad$ [replace n with $(n-1)$]

$$\frac{T_n}{T_{n-1}} = \frac{3(5)^n}{3(5)^{n-1}}$$

$\qquad\qquad = \dfrac{5^n}{5^{n-1}}$ $\qquad\qquad$ (divide top and bottom by 3)

$\qquad\qquad = 5^{n-(n-1)}$ $\qquad\quad$ (subtract index on the bottom from the index on top)

$\qquad\qquad = 5^{n-n+1}$

$\qquad\qquad = 5^1 = 5$ $\qquad\qquad$ (a constant, i.e. does not contain n)

$\dfrac{T_n}{T_{n-1}}$ is a constant, thus the sequence is geometric.

Note: To show that a sequence is **geometric**, it is necessary to show that $T_n \div T_{n-1}$ is a constant. To show that a sequence is **not geometric**, it is only necessary to show that the ratio of any two consecutive terms is not the same. In practice, this usually involves showing that $T_3 \div T_2 \neq T_2 \div T_1$ or similar.

Example 8

In a geometric sequence $T_2 = -6$ and $T_5 = 48$.

Find, the first term, a, the common ratio, r, T_n and T_{10}.

Solution:

$$T_n = ar^{n-1}$$

Given: $\quad T_2 = -6$ $\qquad\qquad\qquad$ Given: $\quad T_5 = 48$

$\therefore \qquad ar = -6 \quad$ ① $\qquad\qquad\qquad \therefore \qquad ar^4 = 48 \quad$ ②

We now divide ② by ① to eliminate a and find r.

$$\frac{②}{①}$$

$$\frac{ar^4}{ar} = \frac{48}{-6}$$

Now put $r = -2$ into ① or ②:

$$ar = -6 \text{ ①}$$

$$r^3 = -8$$

$$a(-2) = -6$$

$$r = -2$$

$$-2a = -6$$

$$2a = 6$$

$$a = 3$$

Thus, $a = 3$, $r = -2$

$$T_n = ar^{n-1} = 3(-2)^{n-1}$$

$$T_{10} = 3(-2)^9 = 3(-512) - 1{,}536$$

Note: If the index of r is even, we get two values for r, positive and negative.

Chapter 5. FUNCTIONS

Terminology and Notation

A function is a rule that changes one number (input) into another number (output). Functions are often represented by the letters f, g, h or k. We can think of a function, f, as a number machine which changes an input, x, into an output, $f(x)$.

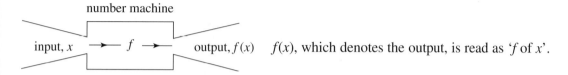

number machine

input, x → f → output, $f(x)$ $f(x)$, which denotes the output, is read as 'f of x'.

For example, let's represent the function 'double input and then add 5' by the letter f.

This can be written as:

$$f: x \rightarrow 2x + 5 \quad \text{or} \quad f(x) = 2x + 5 \quad \text{or} \quad y = 2x + 5$$

$$(\text{input, output}) = (x, f(x)) = (x, \ 2x + 5) = (x, \ y)$$

Note: A **function** is also called a '**mapping**' or simply a '**map**'.

One number is mapped onto another number.
In the above example, x is mapped onto $2x + 5$, usually written $f: x \rightarrow 2x + 5$.

Input number

If $f: x \rightarrow 2x + 5$, then $f(3)$ means 'input 3 into the function',
i.e. it is the result of applying the function f to the number 3.

$$f(3) = 2(3) + 5 = 6 + 5 = 11 \qquad (\text{input} = 3, \text{output} = 11)$$

$$(\text{input, output}) = (3, f(3)) = (3, \ 11)$$

> A function does exactly the same to each input number, and produces only one output number for each input number.

The set of numbers that are put into a function is called the '**domain**'.
The set of numbers that comes out of a function is called the '**range**'.
A function connects **every** input in the domain to an input in the range.
A function is another way of writing an algebraic formula that links input to output.

Example 1

(i) Let $f(x) = 5x - 2$ for $x \in \mathbf{R}$.   Evaluate $f(4)$.

(ii) Let $g(x) = \frac{1}{3}(x - 8)$ for $x \in \mathbf{R}$.   Evaluate $g(5)$.

Solution:

(i) $f(x) = 5x - 2$

$f(4) = 5(4) - 2$

(put in $x = 4$)

$= 20 - 2$

$= 18$

(ii) $g(x) = \frac{1}{3}(x - 8)$

$g(5) = \frac{1}{3}(5 - 8)$

(put in $x = 5$)

$= \frac{1}{3}(-3)$

$= -1$

Example 2

Let $g(x) = \dfrac{1}{x^2 + 1}$ for $x \in \mathbf{R}$.   Evaluate, as decimals,   **(i)** $g(2)$ **(ii)** $g(3)$.

Express $g(2) + g(3)$ in the form $\dfrac{a}{b}$, where $a,\ b \in \mathbf{N}$.

Solution:

$$g(x) = \frac{1}{x^2 + 1}$$

(i) $g(2) = \dfrac{1}{2^2 + 1}$

$= \dfrac{1}{4 + 1} = \dfrac{1}{5} = 0.2$

(ii) $g(3) = \dfrac{1}{3^2 + 1}$

$= \dfrac{1}{9 + 1} = \dfrac{1}{10} = 0.1$

$$g(2) + g(3) = \frac{1}{5} + \frac{1}{10} = \frac{3}{10}$$

Example 3

(i)   If $f(x) = 5x - 8$ and $g(x) = 13 - 2x$, find the value of x for which $f(x) = g(x)$.

(ii) Let $f(x) = 2(3x - 1)$, $x \in \mathbf{R}$. Find the value of x for which $f(x) = 0$.

Solution:

(i)   Given: $f(x) = g(x)$

$$\therefore \qquad 5x - 8 = 13 - 2x$$
$$5x + 2x = 13 + 8$$
$$7x = 21$$
$$x = 3$$

(ii) Given: $f(x) = 0$

$$\therefore \qquad 2(3x - 1) = 0$$
$$6x - 2 = 0$$
$$6x = 2$$
$$x = \frac{2}{6} = \frac{1}{3}$$

Example 4

The function f is defined by $f : x \rightarrow 7 - 3x$.

Find $f(-2)$ and find a number k such that $kf(-2) = f(24)$.

Solution:

$$f(-2) = 7 - 3(-2) = 7 + 6 = 13$$
$$f(24) = 7 - 3(24) = 7 - 72 = -65$$

Given: $kf(-2) = f(24)$
$$\qquad\qquad \downarrow \qquad \downarrow$$

$\therefore$ $k(13) = -65$

$$13k = -65$$
$$k = -5$$

Example 5

$f : x \rightarrow x^2 - 1$ and $g : x \rightarrow 1 - 2x$.

Find the values of x for which $3f(x) = 5g(x)$.

Solution:

Given: $\qquad 3f(x) = 5g(x)$

$\therefore \qquad 3(x^2 - 1) = 5(1 - 2x)$

$\qquad 3x^2 - 3 = 5 - 10x$

$3x^2 - 3 - 5 + 10x = 0$

$\qquad 3x^2 + 10x - 8 = 0$

$\qquad (3x - 2)(x + 4) = 0$

$\qquad 3x - 2 = 0 \qquad$ or $\qquad x + 4 = 0$

$\qquad\qquad 3x = 2 \qquad$ or $\qquad x = -4$

$\qquad\qquad x = \dfrac{2}{3} \qquad$ or $\qquad x = -4$

Example 6

Let $h(x) = x^2 + 2x - 1$, $x \in \mathbf{R}$.

(i) Simplify $h(x - 5)$.   **(ii)** Find the value of x for which $\quad h(x - 5) = h(x) - 5$.

Solution:

(i) $\quad h(x) = x^2 + 2x - 1$

$h(x - 5) = (x - 5)^2 + 2(x - 5) - 1 \qquad\qquad$ (put in $(x - 5)$ for x)

$\qquad\qquad = (x^2 - 10x + 25) + 2(x - 5) - 1$

$\qquad\qquad = x^2 - 10x + 25 + 2x - 10 - 1$

$\qquad\qquad = x^2 - 8x + 14$

$$\begin{aligned}
(x - 5)^2 &= (x - 5)(x - 5) \\
&= x(x - 5) - 5(x - 5) \\
&= x^2 - 5x - 5x + 25 \\
&= x^2 - 10x + 25
\end{aligned}$$

90

(ii) Given: $h(x-5) = h(x) - 5$

$$\therefore \quad (x^2 - 8x + 14) = (x^2 + 2x - 1) - 5$$
$$x^2 - 8x + 14 = x^2 + 2x - 1 - 5$$
$$x^2 - 8x + 14 = x^2 + 2x - 6$$
$$-8x + 14 = 2x - 6 \qquad \text{(subtract } x^2 \text{ from both sides)}$$
$$-8x - 2x = -6 - 14$$
$$-10x = -20$$
$$10x = 20 \qquad \text{(multiply both sides by } -1)$$
$$x = 2 \qquad \text{(divide both sides by 10)}$$

Example 7

The graph of the quadratic function

$$f : x \to x^2 + 2x - 15, \qquad x \in \mathbf{R},$$

cuts the axes at p, q and r as shown.

Find the coordinates of each of the points p, q and r.

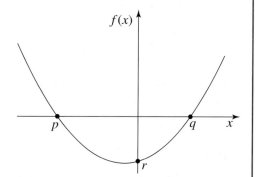

Solution:

For the graph, $y = x^2 + 2x - 15$.

To solve this problem we use the following facts:

1. On the x-axis, $y = 0$	**2.** On the y-axis, $x = 0$

The graph cuts the x-axis at the points p and q. On the x-axis, $y = 0$.

Thus, to find the coordinates of p and q we let $y = 0$ and solve.

$$\therefore \quad x^2 + 2x - 15 = 0$$
$$(x + 5)(x - 3) = 0$$
$$x + 5 = 0 \quad \text{or} \quad x - 3 = 0$$
$$x = -5 \quad \text{or} \quad x = 3$$

$\boxed{\begin{aligned} y &= x^2 + 2x - 15 \\ \text{Let } y &= 0 \\ \therefore \quad x^2 &+ 2x - 15 = 0 \end{aligned}}$

$\therefore$ the curve cuts the x-axis at -5 and 3.

Thus, the coordinates of p are $(-5, 0)$ and the coordinates of q are $(3, 0)$.

The graph cuts the y-axis at the point r. On the y-axis, $x = 0$.

Thus, to find the coordinates of r we let $x = 0$ and solve.

$$y = x^2 + 2x - 15$$
$$y = (0)^2 + 2(0) - 15$$
$$y = 0 + 0 - 15$$
$$y = -15$$

$\therefore$ the curve cuts the y-axis at -15.

Thus, the coordinates of r are $(0, -15)$.

Functions with Missing Coefficients

In some questions, coefficients of the functions are missing and we are asked to find them. In this type of question we are given equations in disguise, and by solving these equations we can calculate the missing coefficients.

Notation

$f(x) = y$
$f(2) = 3$ means when $x = 2$, $y = 3$, or the point $(2, 3)$ is on the graph of the function.
$f(-1) = 0$ means when $x = -1$, $y = 0$, or the point $(-1, 0)$ is on the graph of the function.

Example 1

$f : x \rightarrow 5x + k$ and $g : x \rightarrow x^2 + hx - 4$ are two functions defined on **R**.

(i) If $f(1) = -2$, find the value of k. (ii) If $g(-2) = -6$, find the value of h.

Solution:

(i) $f(x) = 5x + k$

Given: $f(1) = -2$

$\therefore$ $5(1) + k = -2$

$5 + k = -2$

$k = -2 - 5$

$k = -7$

(ii) $g(x) = x^2 + hx - 4$

Given: $g(-2) = -6$

$\therefore$ $(-2)^2 + h(-2) - 4 = -6$

$4 - 2h - 4 = -6$

$-2h = -6$

$2h = 6$

$h = 3$

Example 2

Let $f(x) = 2x^3 + ax^2 + bx + 14$.

If $f(-1) = 0$ and $f(3) = -4$, find the value of a and the value of b.

Solution:

$$f(x) = 2x^3 + ax^2 + bx + 14$$

Given: $\qquad\qquad\qquad f(-1) = 0$

$\therefore\ 2(-1)^3 + a(-1)^2 + b(-1) + 14 = 0$

$\qquad 2(-1) + a(1) + b(-1) + 14 = 0$

$\qquad\qquad\qquad -2 + a - b + 14 = 0$

$\qquad\qquad\qquad\qquad a - b + 12 = 0$

$\qquad\qquad\qquad\qquad\quad a - b = -12 \quad ①$

Given: $\qquad\qquad\qquad f(3) = -4$

$\therefore\ 2(3)^3 + a(3)^2 + b(3) + 14 = -4$

$\qquad 2(27) + a(9) + b(3) + 14 = -4$

$\qquad\qquad 54 + 9a + 3b + 14 = -4$

$\qquad\qquad\qquad 9a + 3b + 68 = -4$

$\qquad\qquad\qquad\qquad 9a + 3b = -72$

$\qquad\qquad\qquad\qquad 3a + b = -24 \quad ②$

We now solve the simultaneous equations ① and ②:

$$\begin{aligned} a - b &= -12 \quad ① \\ 3a + b &= -24 \quad ② \\ \hline 4a &= -36 \quad \text{(add)} \\ a &= -9 \end{aligned}$$

Put $a = -9$ into ① or ②

$$\begin{aligned} a - b &= -12 \qquad ① \\ -9 - b &= -12 \\ -b &= -12 + 9 \\ -b &= -3 \\ b &= 3 \end{aligned}$$

Thus, $a = -9$ and $b = 3$

Example 3

The graph of the quadratic function

$f : x \rightarrow x^2 + px + q, \qquad x \in \mathbf{R}$, is shown.

Find the value of p and the value of q.

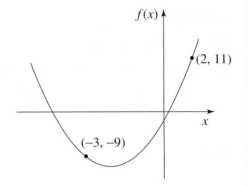

Solution:

$$f(x) = x^2 + px + q$$

The graph goes through the point $(-3, -9)$	The graph goes through the point $(2, 11)$
$\therefore$ Given: $\quad f(-3) = -9$	$\therefore$ Given: $\qquad f(2) = 11$
$\therefore$ $(-3)^2 + p(-3) + q = -9$	$\therefore$ $\qquad (2)^2 + p(2) + q = 11$
$9 - 3p + q = -9$	$4 + 2p + q = 11$
$-3p + q = -18$	$2p + q = 7$ ②
$3p - q = 18$ ①	

We now solve the simultaneous equations ① and ②:

$$3p - q = 18 \quad ①$$
$$\underline{2p + q = 7 \quad ②}$$
$$5p = 25 \quad \text{(add)}$$
$$p = 5$$

Put $p = 5$ into ① or ②

$$2p + q = 7 \quad ②$$
$$2(5) + q = 7$$
$$10 + q = 7$$
$$q = -3$$

$$\text{Thus, } p = 5 \quad \text{and} \quad q = -3$$

Alternatively, let $y = f(x)$, i.e. $y = x^2 + px + q$.

$(-3, -9)$ is on the graph of the curve	$(2, 11)$ is on the graph of the curve
$\therefore \quad -9 = (-3)^2 + p(-3) + q$	$\therefore \quad 11 = (2)^2 + p(2) + 1$
(put in $x = -3$, $y = -9$)	(put in $x = 2$, $y = 11$)
$-9 = 9 - 3p + q$	$11 = 4 + 2p + q$
$-18 = -3p + q$	$7 = 2p + q$ ②
$18 = 3p - q$ ①	

Then solve the simultaneous equations ① and ② before, to get $p = 5$ and $q = -3$.

Example 4

Let $f(x) = x^2 + ax + t, \quad a, t \in \mathbf{R}$.

(i)   Express $f(5)$ and $f(-1)$ in terms of a and t.

(ii)   Find the value of a, given that $f(5) = f(-1)$.

(iii) If $f(2) = -16$, find the value of t.

Solution:

$$f(x) = x^2 + ax + t$$

(i) $f(5) = (5)^2 + a(5) + t$ $f(-1) = (-1)^2 + a(-1) + t$

      $f(5) = 25 + 5a + t$ $f(-1) = 1 - a + t$

(ii)   Given: $f(5) = f(-1)$ (iii) $f(x) = x^2 + ax + t$

      $\therefore \quad 25 + 5a + t = 1 - a + t$ $\therefore \quad f(x) = x^2 - 4x + t \quad (a = -4)$

             $25 + 5a = 1 - a$ Given: $f(2) = -16$

      (subtract t from both sides) $\therefore \quad (2)^2 - 4(2) + t = -16$

                 $6a = -24$ $4 - 8 + t = -16$

                   $a = -4$ $-4 + t = -16$

                                                $t = -12$

Periodic Functions

A function whose graph repeats itself at regular intervals is called '**periodic**'.
For example, the graph below is a graph of a periodic function, $y = f(x)$.

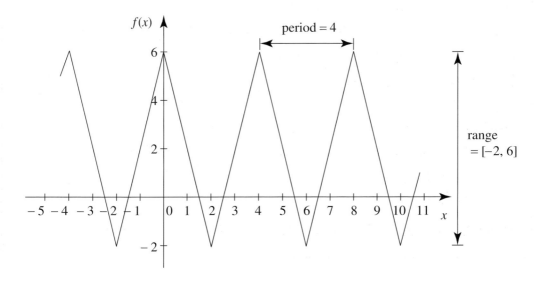

The 'period' is the horizontal width it takes for a graph to repeat itself.
In this case the period = 4 (graph repeats itself after a distance of 4).
The 'range' is the interval from the least value of y to the greatest value of y.
In this case the range = [− 2, 6] (lower value is written first).
A feature of the graphs of periodic functions is that we can add, or subtract, the period, or integer multiples of the period, to the value of $f(x)$ and the value of the function is unchanged.
For example, using the graph above:

$f(-4) = f(0) = f(4) = f(8) = 6$ $[f(-4) = f(-4+4) = f(-4+8) = f(-4+12)...]$

$f(10) = f(6) = f(2) = f(-2) = -2$ $[f(10) = f(10-4) = f(10-8) = f(10-12)...]$

On our course we will be given the graph of a periodic function on scaled and labelled axes. The period will be a positive whole number and the range will be a closed interval [a, b], where a and b are whole numbers, positive or negative.

Example 1

$f : x \rightarrow f(x)$ is a periodic function defined for $x \in \mathbf{R}$.
The period is as indicated in the diagram.

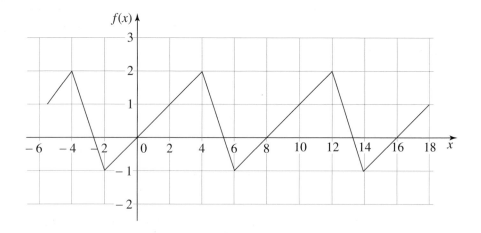

(i) Write down the period and the range of the function.

(ii) Find $f(44)$.

Solution:

(i)

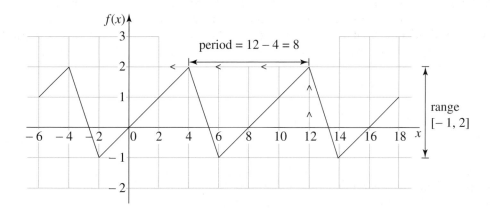

Period = 8   and   range = $[-1, 2]$

(ii) To find $f(44)$ we **repeatedly subtract the period 8** until we reach the domain of the portion of the graph that we are given.

$f(44) = f(36) = f(28) = f(20) = f(12) = 2$ (from the graph)

Example 2

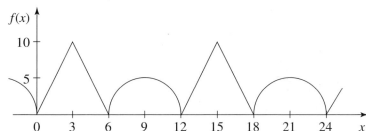

The graph shows portion of a periodic function $f : x \to f(x)$ which is defined for $x \in \mathbf{R}$.

(i) Write down the period and the range of $f(x)$.

(ii) Complete the following table:

x	3	12	21	30	39
$f(x)$					

Solution:

(i)

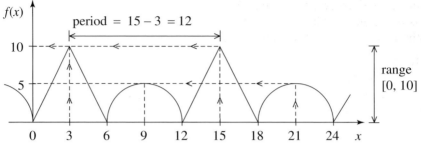

Period = 12 and range = [0, 10]

(ii)

From the graph, $f(3) = 10$, $f(12) = 0$ and $f(21) = 5$.

To find $f(30)$ and $f(39)$ we **repeatedly subtract the period 12** until we reach the domain of the portion of the graph that we are given.

$f(30) = f(18) = 0$ (from the graph)

$f(39) = f(27) = f(15) = 10$ (from the graph)

Completed table:

x	3	12	21	30	39
$f(x)$	10	0	5	0	10

Graphing and Using Functions

The notation $y = f(x)$ means 'the value of the output y depends on the value of the input x, according to some rule called f'. Hence, y and $f(x)$ are interchangeable, and the y-axis can also be called the $f(x)$-axis.

Once we have drawn the graph, we are usually asked to use it to answer some questions. Below are examples of the general types of problem where graphs are used.

Notes:

1. In general, if given x find y, and vice versa.

2. It is very important not to draw a graph outside the given value of x.

3. All graphs are read 'from left to right'.

Examples of the main types of problem, once the graph is drawn:

1. **Find the values of x for which $f(x) = 0$.**
   This question is asking:
   'Where does the curve meet the x-axis?'

   Solution:
   Write down the values of x where the graph meets the x-axis.
   From the graph: $x = -1$ or $x = 1$ or $x = 3$

   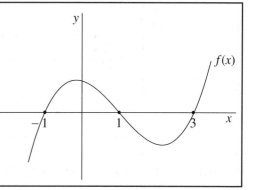

2. **Find the values of x for which $f(x) = 6$.**
   This question is asking:
   'When $y = 6$, what are the values of x?'

   Solution:
   Draw the line $y = 6$. Where this line meets the curve draw broken perpendicular lines onto the x-axis.
   Write down the values of x where these broken lines meet the x-axis.
   From the graph:
   When $y = 6$, $x = -1.1$ or $x = 1.3$ or $x = 2.9$

   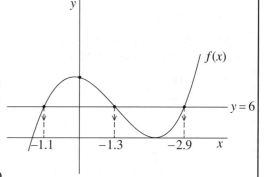

3. **Find the value of $f(-1.6)$.**
   This question is asking:
   'When $x = -1.6$, what is the value of y?'

   Solution:
   From $x = -1.6$, on the x-axis draw a broken perpendicular line to meet the curve. From this draw a broken horizontal line to meet the y-axis. Write down the value of y where this line meets the y-axis.
   From the graph:
   $f(-1.6) = -7$

   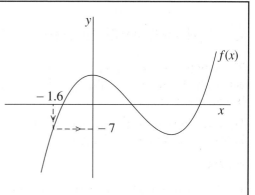

4. Local maximum and minimum points or the local maximum and minimum values

Often we are asked to find the local maximum and minimum points or the local maximum and minimum values. Consider the graph on the right. The local maximum and minimum points are where the graph turns, $(1, 4)$ and $(4, -2)$, respectively. The local maximum and minimum values are found by drawing a line from the turning points to the y-axis and reading the values where these lines meet the y-axis. The maximum and minimum values are 4 and -2, respectively.

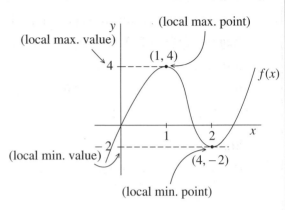

5. Increasing and decreasing

Graphs are read from left to right.

Increasing: $f(x)$ is increasing where the graph is **rising** as we go from left to right.

Decreasing: $f(x)$ is decreasing where the graph is **falling** as we go from left to right.

Find the values of x for which:

(i) $f(x)$ **is increasing**

(ii) $f(x)$ **is decreasing,**

   in the domain $-4 \leqslant x \leqslant 3$.

Solution:

(i) $f(x)$ increasing, graph rising from left to right.
   The values of x are:
   $-4 \leqslant x < -2$ and $1 < x \leqslant 3$

(ii) $f(x)$ decreasing, graph falling from left to right.
   The values of x are: $-2 < x < 1$

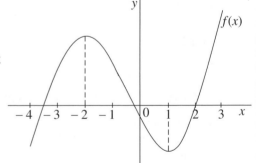

Note: At $x = -2$ and $x = 1$, the graph is neither increasing nor decreasing.

6. Positive and negative

Positive, $f(x) > 0$: Where the graph is **above** the x-axis.

Negative, $f(x) < 0$: Where the graph is **below** the x-axis.

Find the values of x for which:

(i) $f(x) > 0$ (ii) $f(x) < 0$,

    in the domain $-2 \leqslant x \leqslant 4$.

Solution:

(i) $f(x) > 0$, curve **above** the x-axis.
    The values of x are:
    $-1 < x < 1$ and $3 < x \leqslant 4$

(ii) $f(x) > 0$, curve **below** the x-axis.
    The values of x are:
    $-2 \leqslant x < -1$ and $1 < x < 3$

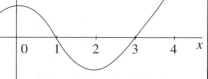

Note: If the question used $f(x) \geqslant 0$ or $f(x) \leqslant 0$, then the values of x where the graph meets the x-axis must also be included.

---

7. Two functions graphed on the same axes and scales

The diagram shows the graph of two functions: $f(x)$, a curve, and $g(x)$, a line.

Find the values of x for which:

(i) $f(x) = g(x)$ (ii) $f(x) \leqslant g(x)$ (iii) $f(x) \geqslant g(x)$

Solution:

(i) $f(x) = g(x)$
    (curve = line)
    The values of x are: 0.4, 1.4 and 3.1

(ii) $f(x) \leqslant g(x)$
    (curve equal to and below the line)
    The values of x are:
    $-1 \leqslant x \leqslant 0.4$ and $1.4 \leqslant x \leqslant 3.1$

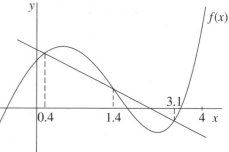

(iii) $f(x) \geqslant g(x)$
    (curve equal to and above the line)
    The values of x are:
    $0.4 \leqslant x \leqslant 1.4$ and $3.1 \leqslant x \leqslant 4$

Note: If the question uses $f(x) < g(x)$ or $f(x) > g(x)$, then the values of x where the graphs meet (0.4, 1.4 and 3.1) are **not** included in the solution.

8. Graph above or below a constant value (an inequality)

Find the values of x for which: (i) $f(x) \geqslant 2$ (ii) $f(x) \leqslant 2$,

in the domain $-2 \leqslant x \leqslant 4$.

These questions are asking:
'What are the values of x for which the curve, $f(x)$, is:
(i) 2 or above   (ii) 2 or below?'

Solution:

Draw the line $y = 2$.

Write down the values of x for
which the curve is:

(i)   on or above the line $y = 2$
(ii)   on or below the line $y = 2$.

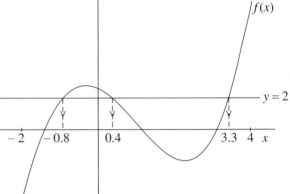

(i) $f(x) \geqslant 2$, curve on or above
     the line $y = 2$.
The values of x are: $-0.8 \leqslant x \leqslant 0.4$
and $3.3 \leqslant x \leqslant 4$

(ii) $f(x) \leqslant 2$, curve on or below the line $y = 2$.
The values of x are: $-2 \leqslant x \leqslant -0.8$ and $0.4 \leqslant x \leqslant 3.3$

Note: If the question uses $f(x) > 2$ or $f(x) < 2$, then the values of x where the curve
         meets the line $y = 2$ (-0.8, 0.4 and 3.3) are **not** included in the solution.

---

9. Using two graphs to estimate square roots and cube roots
The diagram shows graphs of the functions:

$f : x \rightarrow x^3 - 3x + 4$ and $g : x \rightarrow 6 - 3x$, in the domain $-2 \leqslant x \leqslant 3$.

Show how the graphs may be used to estimate the value of $\sqrt[3]{2}$.

Solution:

The values of x where two graphs meet is the
most common way to use graphs to estimate
square roots and cube roots.

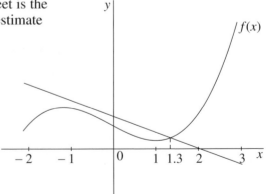

$\quad$ Let $f(x) = g(x) \qquad$ [curve = line]

$\qquad x^3 - 3x + 4 = 6 - 3x$

$\qquad\qquad x^3 + 4 = 6$

$\qquad\qquad\quad x^3 = 2$

$\qquad\qquad\quad x = \sqrt[3]{2}$

Hence, where the two graphs meet can be used to estimate the value of $\sqrt[3]{2}$.
Where the two graphs intersect, draw a broken line to meet the x-axis.
This line meets the x-axis at 1.3.
Thus, using the graphs, we estimate the value of $\sqrt[3]{2}$ to be 1.3.

Note: A calculator gives $\sqrt[3]{2} = 1.25992104989$

10. Number of times a graph meets the x-axis

The number of times a graph meets the x-axis gives the number of roots of its equation. Often we need to find a range of values of a constant, which shifts a graph up or down, giving a graph a certain number of roots, e.g.:

For what values of k does the equation $f(x) = k$ have three roots?

Solution:

The equation $f(x) = k$ will have three roots if the line $y = k$ cuts the graph three times. So we have to draw lines parallel to the x-axis that cut the graph three times.

The range of values of k will be in between the lowest and highest values on the y-axis, so that the line $y = k$ cuts the graph three times.

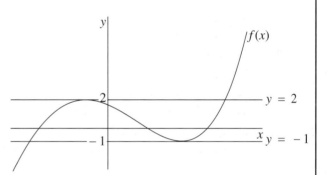

Question: Find the range of values of k for which $f(x) = k$ has three roots.

Solution:

The range of values of k is found by finding the range of the equations of the lines, parallel to the x-axis, which cut the graph three times.

Any lines drawn parallel to the y-axis between $y = -1$ and $y = 2$, will cut the graph three times.

$\therefore$ k will lie between -1 and 2

$\therefore$ $f(x) = k$ will have three roots for $-1 < k < 2$.

Example 1

(i) On the same axes and scales, graph the functions:

$f:x \to x^3 - 2x^2 - 6x + 4$ and $g:x \to 2x - 5$, in the domain $-2 \leqslant x \leqslant 4$, $x \in \mathbf{R}$.

Use your graphs to estimate the values of x for which:

(ii) $f(x) = 0$ **(iii)** $f(-0.4)$ **(iv)** $g(x) > f(x)$ **(v)** $x < 0$ and $f(x) > 0$

Solution:

(i) **On the same axes and scales, graph the functions:**

$f:x \to x^3 - 2x^2 - 6x + 4$ **and** $g:x \to 2x - 5$, **in the domain** $-2 \leqslant x \leqslant 4$, $x \in \mathbf{R}$.

Let $y = f(x)$, $\therefore \ y = x^3 - 2x^2 - 6x + 4$

x	$x^3 - 2x^2 - 6x + 4$	y
-2	$-8 - 8 \quad + 12 + 4$	0
-1	$-1 - 2 \quad + 6 + 4$	7
0	$0 - 0 \quad + 0 + 4$	4
1	$1 - 2 \quad - 6 + 4$	-3
2	$8 - 8 \quad - 12 + 4$	-8
3	$27 - 18 \quad - 18 + 4$	-5
4	$64 - 32 \quad - 24 + 4$	12

Let $y = g(x)$, $\therefore \quad y = 2x - 5$

x	$2x - 5$	y
-2	$-4 \ - 5$	-9
4	$8 \ - 5$	3

$f(x)$ is a curve and $g(x)$ is a line.

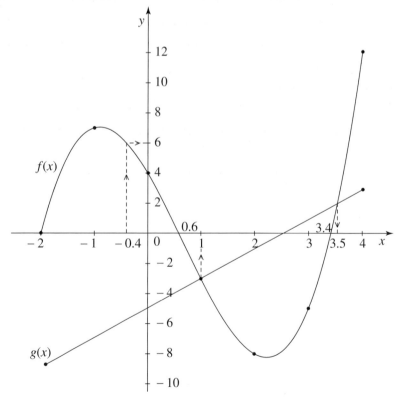

(ii) **Estimate the values of x for which $f(x) = 0$.**

This question is asking, 'Where does the curve meet the x-axis?'
The curve meets the x-axis at -2, 0.6 and 3.4.
Therefore, the values of x for which $f(x) = 0$, are -2, 0.6 and 3.4.

Note: 'Find the values of x for which $x^3 - 2x^2 - 6x + 4 = 0$' is another way of asking the same question.

(iii) **Estimate the value of $f(-0.4)$.**

This question is asking, 'When $x = -0.4$, what is the value of y?'
From $x = -0.4$ on the x-axis draw a broken perpendicular line to meet the curve.
From this draw a broken horizontal line to meet the y-axis.
This line meets the y-axis at 6.
Therefore $f(-0.4) = 6$.

(iv) **Estimate the values of x for which $g(x) > f(x)$.**

$f(x)$ is the curve, $g(x)$ is the line.
This question is asking, 'What are the values of x where the line is **above** the curve?'
First work out the values of x where the curve and line intersect.
Where the curve and line meet, draw broken perpendicular lines to meet the x-axis.
These lines meet the x-axis at 1 and 3.5.
Therefore, the values of x for which $f(x) = g(x)$ are 1 and 3.5.
From the graphs, the line is above the curve between 1 and 3.5.
Therefore, the values of x for which $g(x) > f(x)$ are $1 < x < 3.5$.

Note: $x = 1$ and $x = 3.5$ are **not** included because at $x = 1$ and $x = 3.5$.
$f(x) = g(x)$ and we are given $g(x) > f(x)$ not $g(x) \geqslant f(x)$.

(v) **Estimate the values of x for which $x > 0$ and $f(x) < 0$.**

$x < 0$ means 'we only consider the part of the graph where x is negative (left of the y-axis)'.
$f(x) > 0$ means 'we only consider the part of the curve **above** the x-axis'.
The graph of $f(x)$ is **above** the x-axis and $x < 0$ when x is between -2 and 0.
$\therefore$ the values of x for which $x < 0$ and $f(x) > 0$ is $-2 < x < 0$.

Note: $x = -2$ and $x = 0$ are **not** included because at $x = -2$ and $x = 0$,
$f(x) = 0$ and we are given $f(x) > 0$ (not $f(x) \geqslant 0$).

Example 2

$g(x) = \dfrac{1}{x-2}$ and $h(x) = x + 2$.

(i)   Find $g(1.5)$ and $g(2.5)$.

(ii) For what real value of x is $g(x)$ not defined.

(iii) On the same axes and scales, graph the functions:

$g(x) = \dfrac{1}{x-2}$ in the domain $-1 \leqslant x \leqslant 5$

$h(x) = x + 2$ in the domain $-1 \leqslant x \leqslant 3$

(iv) Draw the vertical asymptote to $g(x)$ with a broken line.

(v)   Show how your graphs may be used to estimate the value of $\sqrt{5}$.

Solution:

(i)   Find $g(1.5)$ and $g(2.5)$.

$$g(x) = \dfrac{1}{x-2}$$

$g(1.5) = \dfrac{1}{0.5-2} = \dfrac{1}{-0.5} = -2$ $\Big|$ $g(2.5) = \dfrac{1}{2.5-2} = \dfrac{1}{0.5} = 2$

(ii) For what real value of x is $g(x)$ not defined?

$g(x) = \dfrac{1}{x-2}$

Division by zero is undefined (for example $\dfrac{1}{0}$ is undefined).

$\therefore$ $\dfrac{1}{x-2}$ is undefined when $x - 2 = 0$ or $x = 2$

Thus $g(x) = \dfrac{1}{x-2}$ is undefined for $x = 2$.

(iii) On the same axes and scales, graph the functions:

$g(x) = \dfrac{1}{x-2}$ in the domain $-1 \leqslant x \leqslant 5$

$h(x) = x + 2$ in the domain $-1 \leqslant x \leqslant 3$

Let $y = g(x)$,　　$\therefore$　　$y = \dfrac{1}{x-2}$

x	$\dfrac{1}{x-2}$	y
-1	$\dfrac{1}{-1-2}$	$-\dfrac{1}{3}$
0	$\dfrac{1}{0-2}$	$-\dfrac{1}{2}$
1	$\dfrac{1}{1-2}$	-1
2	$\dfrac{1}{2-2}$	$\dfrac{1}{0}$
3	$\dfrac{1}{3-2}$	1
4	$\dfrac{1}{4-2}$	$\dfrac{1}{2}$
5	$\dfrac{1}{5-2}$	$\dfrac{1}{3}$

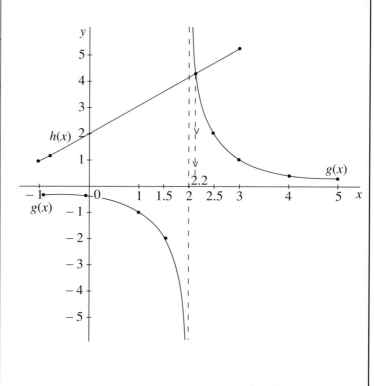

$g(1.5) = -2$ and $g(2.5) = 2$

Let $y = h(x)$,　　$\therefore$　　$y = x + 2$

x	$x + 2$	y
-1	$-1 + 2$	1
3	$3 + 2$	5

(iv) Draw the vertical asymptote to $g(x)$ with a broken line.

The vertical asymptote is indicated on the graph with a vertical broken line
through $x = 2$ on the x-axis ($x = 2$ is the value of x for which $g(x)$ is undefined).

(v) **Show how your graphs may be used to estimate the value of $\sqrt{5}$.**

Consider the equation:

$g(x) = h(x)$	(curve = line)
$\dfrac{1}{x-2} = x + 2$	
$1 = (x-2)(x+2)$	(multiply both sides by $x-2$)
$1 = x^2 + 2x - 2x - 4$	(remove brackets)
$1 = x^2 - 4$	(simplify the right-hand side)
$5 = x^2$	(add 4 to both sides)
$x^2 = 5$	(swop sides)
$x = \pm\sqrt{5}$	(take the square root of both sides)

Thus, the point of intersection of the graphs of the curve $g(x)$, and the line $h(x)$, can be used to estimate $\sqrt{5}$.

Consider the value of x where the curve and the line meet.
Where the curves meet draw a broken vertical line to meet the x-axis. This line meets the x-axis at 2.2, close to the calculator estimate of $\sqrt{5}$.

Note: Using a calculator $\sqrt{5} = 2.236067977$

Example 3

The temperature, C, in degrees Celsius, of a liquid in an insulated container is related to time t, in hours, by

$$C = 86 - 6t.$$

(i) Draw the straight line graph of this relation, putting t on the horizontal axis, for $0 \leqslant t \leqslant 8$.

(ii) Use your graph to estimate the temperature when $t = 5.5$ hours.

(iii) Use your graph to estimate the time it takes for the temperature to fall from 80 degrees to 60 degrees.

Solution:

(i) **Draw the straight line graph of this relation, putting t on the horizontal axis, for $0 \leqslant t \leqslant 8$.**

The graph of $C = 86 - 6t$ is a straight line.

Hence, two points are all that are needed to graph it.

Choose two suitable values of t (usually the two extreme values) and find the corresponding values of C.

t	$86 - 6t$	C
0	$86 - 0$	86
8	$86 - 48$	38

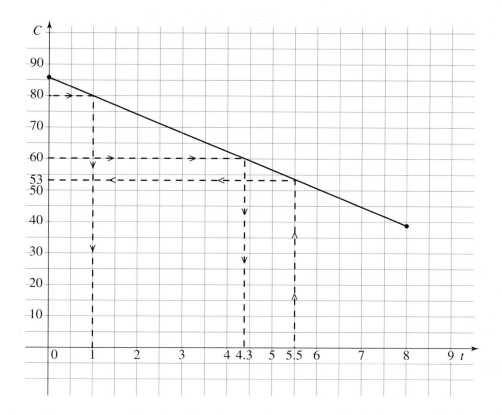

(ii) Use your graph to estimate the temperature when $t = 5.5$ hours.

From 5.5 on the time axis, draw a broken vertical line to meet the line.

Where this broken line meets the line, draw a broken horizontal line to the temperature axis.

This broken line meets the temperature axis at 53.

Thus, we estimate the temperature after 5.5 hours to be 53 degrees Celsius.

(iii) Use your graph to estimate the time it takes for the temperature to fall from 80 degrees to 60 degrees.

From 80 and 60 on the temperature axis draw two broken horizontal lines.

Where these broken lines meet the line draw two vertical broken lines to meet the time axis.

These broken lines meet the time axis at 1 and 4.3, respectively.

Thus, we estimate that the time it takes for the temperature to fall from 80 degrees to 60 degrees = 4.3 − 1 = 3.3 hours.

Chapter 6. DIFFERENTIATION

Notation

Differentiation, or differential calculus, is the branch of mathematics measuring rates of change.

$$y = f(x)$$
$$\frac{dy}{dx} = f'(x)$$

If $y = f(x)$, then $\dfrac{dy}{dx}$ or $f'(x)$, gives the '**rate of change of y with respect to x**'.

$\dfrac{dy}{dx}$ or $f'(x)$ is called the: '**differential coeffcient**' or '**first derivative of y with respect to x**'.

Differentiation from First Principles

Differentiation from first principles involves four steps:

Find:

1. $f(x+h)$

2. $f(x+h) - f(x)$

3. $\dfrac{f(x+h) - f(x)}{h}$

4. $\lim\limits_{h \to 0} \dfrac{f(x+h) - f(x)}{h}$

Example

Differentiate $3x^2 - x$ from first principles with respect to x.

Solution:

$$f(x) = 3x^2 - x$$

1. $\quad f(x+h) = 3(x+h)^2 - (x+h)$ [replace x with $(x+h)$]

$\qquad f(x+h) = 3(x^2 + 2hx + h^2) - (x+h)$ [$(x+h)^2 = x^2 + 2hx + h^2$]

$\qquad f(x+h) = 3x^2 + 6hx + 3h^2 - x - h$

2. $\quad f(x+h) - f(x) = 3x^2 + 6hx + 3h^2 - x - h - 3x^2 + x$

$\qquad f(x+h) - f(x) = 6hx + 3h^2 - h$

3. $\quad \dfrac{f(x+h) - f(x)}{h} = 6x + 3h - 1$ [divide both sides by h]

4. $\quad \displaystyle\lim_{h \to 0} \dfrac{f(x+h) - f(x)}{h} = 6x + 3(0) - 1 = 6x - 1$ [take the limit]

The Four Rules

1. General Rule

$$y = x^n \quad \text{then} \quad \frac{dy}{dx} = nx^{n-1}$$

$$y = ax^n \quad \text{then} \quad \frac{dy}{dx} = nax^{n-1}$$

In words: Multiply by the power and reduce the power by 1.

2. Product Rule

Suppose u and v are functions of x.

If $y = uv$,

then $\dfrac{dy}{dx} = u\dfrac{dv}{dx} + v\dfrac{du}{dx}$

In words: First by the derivative of the second + second by the derivative of the first.

Note: The word '**product**' refers to quantities being multiplied.

3. Quotient Rule

Suppose u and v are functions of x.

If $y = \dfrac{u}{v}$,

then $\dfrac{dy}{dx} = \dfrac{v\dfrac{du}{dx} - u\dfrac{dv}{dx}}{v^2}$.

In words: $\dfrac{\text{Bottom by the derivative of the top} - \text{Top by the derivative of the bottom}}{(\text{Bottom})^2}$

Note: Quotient is another name for a fraction. The quotient rule refers to one quantity divided by another.

4. Chain Rule

The chain rule is used when the given function is raised to a power, e.g. $y = (x^2 - 3x + 4)^4$.

To differentiate using the chain rule, do the following in *one* step:

(a) Treat what is inside the bracket as a single variable and differentiate this (multiply by the power and reduce the power by one).

(b) Multiply this result by the derivative of what is inside the bracket.

If $y = (\text{function})^n$,

then $\dfrac{dy}{dx} = n\,(\text{function})^{n-1}\,(\text{derivative of the function})$.

Example 1

Differentiate each of the following with respect to x:

(i) $5x^3 - 4x^2 - 3x + 2$ (ii) $(x^3 - 4)(5x^2 - 2)$ (iii) $(2x^2 - 1)^7$

(iv) $\dfrac{x^3 - 4x}{x^2 - 1}$

Solution:

(i) $y = 5x^3 - 4x^2 - 3x + 2$

$$\frac{dy}{dx} = 15x^2 - 8x - 3$$

(ii) $y = (x^3 - 4)(5x^2 - 2)$ (product rule)

$$\frac{dy}{dx} = u\frac{dv}{dx} + v\frac{du}{dx}$$

$$= (x^3 - 4)(10x) + (5x^2 - 2)(3x^2)$$

$$= 10x^4 - 40x + 15x^4 - 6x^2$$

$$= 25x^4 - 6x^2 - 40x$$

$$u = x^3 - 4 \qquad v = 5x^2 - 2$$
$$\frac{du}{dx} = 3x^2 \qquad \frac{dv}{dx} = 10x$$

(iii) $y = (2x^2 - 1)^7$ (chain rule)

$$\frac{dy}{dx} = 7(2x^2 - 1)^6(4x) = 28x(2x^2 - 1)^6$$

(iv) $y = \dfrac{x^3 - 4x}{x^2 - 1}$ (quotient rule)

$$\frac{dy}{dx} = \frac{v\frac{du}{dx} - u\frac{dv}{dx}}{v^2}$$

$$= \frac{(x^2 - 1)(3x^2 - 4) - (x^3 - 4x)(2x)}{(x^2 - 1)^2}$$

$$= \frac{3x^4 - 4x^2 - 3x^2 + 4 - 2x^4 + 8x^2}{(x^2 - 1)^2}$$

$$= \frac{x^4 + x^2 + 4}{(x^2 - 1)^2}$$

$$u = x^3 - 4x \qquad v = x^2 - 1$$
$$\frac{du}{dx} = 3x^2 - 4 \qquad \frac{dv}{dx} = 2x$$

Note: It is usual practice to multiply out and simplify the top but **not** the bottom.

Example 2

Let $f(x) = x^5 - 17 + \dfrac{1}{x^5}$, for all $x \in \mathbf{R}$.

Find $f'(x)$.

Solution:

$$f(x) = x^5 - 17 + \frac{1}{x^3}$$
$$f(x) = x^5 - 17 + x^{-5}$$
$$f'(x) = 5x^4 - 0 - 5x^{-6}$$
$$f'(x) = 5x^4 - 5x^{-6}$$

or

$$f'(x) = 5x^4 - \frac{5}{x^6}$$

$$\left(\frac{1}{x^5} = x^{-5}\right)$$

$$(-5 - 1 = -6)$$

$$\left(-5x^{-6} = -5 \times \frac{1}{x^6} = -\frac{5}{x^6}\right)$$

Evaluating Derivatives

Often we may be asked to find the value of the derivative for a particular value of the function.

Example

(i) Find the value of $\dfrac{dy}{dx}$ at $x = 2$ when $y = (1 - x^2)^3$.

(ii) If $h = 20t - 5t^2$, find $\dfrac{dh}{dt}$ when $t = 4$

(iii) Find the value of $\dfrac{dy}{dx}$ at $x = -1$ when $y = \dfrac{2x^2 + 3}{2x - 1}$

Solution:

(i) $y = (1 - x^2)^3$ (use chain rule)

$$\frac{dy}{dx} = 3(1 - x^2)^2(-2x)$$

$$\left.\frac{dy}{dx}\right|_{x=2} = 3(1 - 2^2)^2[-2(2)]$$
$$= 3(1 - 4)^2(-4)$$
$$= 3(-3)^2(-4)$$
$$= 3(9)(-4)$$
$$= -108$$

(ii) $h = 20t - 5t^2$

$$\frac{dh}{dt} = 20 - 10t$$

$$\left.\frac{dh}{dt}\right|_{t=4} = 20 - 10(4)$$
$$= 20 - 40$$
$$= -20$$

(iii) $y = \dfrac{2x^2 + 3}{2x - 1}$ (use quotient rule)

$$\dfrac{dy}{dx} = \dfrac{(2x - 1)(4x) - (2x^2 + 3)(2)}{(2x - 1)^2}$$

$$\left[\dfrac{v\dfrac{du}{dx} - u\dfrac{dv}{dx}}{v^2}\right]$$

$$\left.\dfrac{dy}{dx}\right|_{x = -1} = \dfrac{(-2 - 1)(-4) - (2 + 3)(2)}{(-2 - 1)^2}$$

$$= \dfrac{(-3)(-4) - (5)(2)}{(-3)^2}$$

$$= \dfrac{12 - 10}{9}$$

$$= \dfrac{2}{9}$$

Finding the Slope and Equation of a Tangent to a Curve at a Point on the Curve

$\dfrac{dy}{dx}$ = the slope of a tangent to a curve at any point on the curve.

To find the slope and equation of a tangent to a curve at a given point (x_1, y_1), on the curve, do the following:

Step 1:   Find $\dfrac{dy}{dx}$.

Step 2:   Evaluate $\left.\dfrac{dy}{dx}\right|_{x = x_1}$ (this gives the slope of the tangent, m)

Step 3:   Use m (from step 2) and the given point (x_1, y_1) in the equation:

$$(y - y_1) = m(x - x_1)$$

Note: Sometimes only the value of x is given. When this happens, substitute the value of x into the original function to find y for step 3.

Example

Find the equation of the tangent to the curve $f(x) = \dfrac{x-1}{x+2}$ at the point $(-1, -2)$.

Solution:

For the curve, $y = f(x)$.

1.
$$y = \frac{x-1}{x+2}$$

(use quotient rule)

$$\frac{dy}{dx} = \frac{(x+2)(1) - (x-1)(1)}{(x+2)^2}$$

2. At the point $(-1, -2)$, $x = -1$

$$\left.\frac{dy}{dx}\right|_{x=-1} = \frac{(-1+2)(1) - (-1-1)(1)}{(-1+2)^2}$$

$$= \frac{(1)(1) - (-2)(1)}{(1)^2}$$

$$= \frac{1+2}{1} = \frac{3}{1} = 3$$

3. $m = 3, \quad x_1 = -1, \quad y_1 = -2$

$$(y - y_1) = m(x - x_1)$$

$$(y + 2) = 3(x + 1)$$

$$y + 2 = 3x + 3$$

$$-3x + y + 2 - 3 = 0$$

$$-3x + y - 1 = 0$$

$$3x - y + 1 = 0$$

Given $\dfrac{dy}{dx}$, to Find the Coordinates of the Corresponding Points on a Curve

Sometimes the value of $\dfrac{dy}{dx}$ (slope of the curve at any point on it) is given and we need to find the coordinates of the point, or points, corresponding to this slope.

When this happens do the following:

Step 1: Find $\dfrac{dy}{dx}$.

Step 2: Let $\dfrac{dy}{dx}$ equal the given value of the slope and solve this equation for x.

Step 3: Substitute the x values obtained in step 2 into the original function to get the corresponding values of y.

Example 1

Let $f(x) = 2x^3 - 3x^2 - 13x + 2, \quad x \in \mathbf{R}$.
Find the derivative of $f(x)$.

Find the coordinates of the points on the curve $f(x)$ at which the tangents to the curve are parallel to the line $y = 5 - x$. Find the equations of the tangents at these points.

Solution:

For the graph, $y = f(x)$.

Curve: $y = 2x^3 - 3x^2 - 13x + 2$ $\qquad\qquad$ Line: $y = 5 - x$

$\dfrac{dy}{dx} = 6x^2 - 6x - 13$ $\qquad\qquad\qquad\qquad$ $\dfrac{dy}{dx} = -1$

Given: $\qquad\qquad$ Slope of curve = Slope of line

$$6x^2 - 6x - 13 = -1$$
$$6x^2 - 6x - 12 = 0$$
$$x^2 - x - 2 = 0$$
$$(x - 2)(x + 1) = 0$$
$$x - 2 = 0 \quad \text{or} \quad x + 1 = 0$$
$$x = 2 \quad \text{or} \quad x = -1$$

We have the x coordinates on the curve, now we need the y coordinates.

$$y = 2x^3 - 3x^2 - 13x + 2$$

$x = 2$	$x = -1$
$y = 2(2)^3 - 3(2)^2 - 13(2) + 2$	$y = 2(-1)^3 - 3(-1)^2 - 13(-1) + 2$
$= 2(8) - 3(4) - 13(2) + 2$	$= 2(-1) - 3(1) - 13(-1) + 2$
$= 16 - 12 - 26 + 2$	$= -2 - 3 + 13 + 2$
$= 18 - 38$	$= 15 - 5$
$= -20$	$= 10$
$\therefore x = 2, y = -20$	$\therefore x = -1, y = 10$

Thus, $(2, -20)$ and $(-1, 10)$ are the required points.

At both of these points the slope of the tangents are equal to -1.

$m = -1, \quad x_1 = 2, \quad y = -20$	$m = -1, \quad x_1 = -1, \quad y_1 = 10$
$(y - y_1) = m(x - x_1)$	$(y - y_1) = m(x - x_1)$
$(y + 20) = -1(x - 2)$	$(y - 10) = -1(x + 1)$
$y + 20 = -x + 2$	$y - 10 = -x - 1$
$x + y + 20 - 2 = 0$	$x + y - 10 + 1 = 0$
$x + y + 18 = 0$	$x + y - 9 = 0$

Thus, the equations of the tangents are $x + y + 18 = 0$ and $x + y - 9 = 0$

Example 2

Let $y = x^2 - 5x + 6$, $x \in \mathbf{R}$.

Find the slopes of the tangents to the graph of y at the points $(2, 0)$ and $(3, 0)$, and investigate if these two tangents are at right angles to each other.

Solution:

$$y = x^2 - 5x + 6$$

$$\frac{dy}{dx} = 2x - 5 \qquad \text{(Slope at any point)}$$

at $(2, 0)$, $x = 2$

$$\left.\frac{dy}{dx}\right|_{x=2} = 2(2) - 5$$
$$= 4 - 5$$
$$= -1$$

$\therefore$ Slope at $x = 2$ is -1

at $(3, 0)$, $x = 3$

$$\left.\frac{dy}{dx}\right|_{x=3} = 2(3) - 5$$
$$= 6 - 5$$
$$= 1$$

$\therefore$ Slope at $x = 3$ is 1

(Slope at $x = 2$)(Slope at $x = 3$) $= (-1)(1) = -1$

$\therefore$ the tangents are at right angles to each other.

Example 3

Let $f(x) = \dfrac{1}{x+1}$ for $x \in \mathbf{R}$.

(i) Find $f'(x)$.

(ii) Find the coordinates of the point s on the curve of $f(x)$ at which the tangent has slope of $-\dfrac{1}{4}$.

Solution:

(i)
$$f(x) = \frac{1}{x+1}$$

$$f'(x) = \frac{(x+1)(0) - (1)(1)}{(x+1)^2}$$

$$f'(x) = \frac{-1}{(x+1)^2}$$

[use quotient rule]

$$\left[\frac{v\dfrac{du}{dx} - u\dfrac{dv}{dx}}{v^2} \right]$$

118

(ii) $f'(x)$ is the slope of a tangent to a curve at any point on the curve.

Equation given in disguise:

$$\text{Slope} = -\frac{1}{4}$$

$$\therefore \qquad f'(x) = -\frac{1}{4} \qquad\qquad (f'(x) = \text{slope of tangent})$$

$$\therefore \qquad \frac{-1}{(x+1)^2} = -\frac{1}{4}$$

$$\frac{1}{(x+1)^2} = \frac{1}{4} \qquad\qquad \text{(multiply both sides by } -1)$$

$$4 = (x+1)^2 \qquad\qquad \text{(multiply both sides by } 4(x+1)^2)$$

$$(x+1)^2 = 4 \qquad\qquad \text{(swop sides)}$$

$$x^2 + 2x + 1 = 4 \qquad\qquad ((x+1)^2 = x^2 + 2x + 1)$$

$$x^2 + 2x - 3 = 0$$

$$(x+3)(x-1) = 0$$

$$x + 3 = 0 \qquad \text{or} \qquad x - 1 = 0$$

$$x = -3 \qquad \text{or} \qquad x = 1$$

We have the x coordinates, now we need to find the y coordinates.

$$f(x) = \frac{1}{(x+1)}$$

$$f(-3) = \frac{1}{-3+1} = \frac{1}{-2} = -\frac{1}{2} \qquad\qquad \therefore \text{ one point is } \left(-3, -\frac{1}{2}\right)$$

$$f(1) = \frac{1}{1+1} = \frac{1}{2} \qquad\qquad \therefore \text{ another point is } \left(1, \frac{1}{2}\right)$$

Thus, $\left(-3, -\frac{1}{2}\right)$ and $\left(1, \frac{1}{2}\right)$ are the required points.

Sometimes we have to find unknown coefficients.

Example 4

Let $f(x) = x^3 - ax + 7$ for all $x \in \mathbf{R}$ and for $a \in \mathbf{R}$.

(i) Find $f'(x)$, the derivative of $f(x)$.

(ii) The slope of the tangent to the curve $y = f(x)$ at $x = 1$ is -9.
Find the value of a.

Solution:

(i) $f(x) = x^3 - ax + 7$

$f'(x) = 3x^2 - a$

(ii) Equation given in disguise:

$$\text{Slope of the tangent} = -9 \qquad \text{(when } x = 1)$$
$$\therefore \qquad f'(x) = -9 \qquad \text{(when } x = 1)$$
$$\therefore \qquad 3x^2 - a = -9 \qquad \text{(when } x = 1)$$
$$3(1)^2 - a = -9 \qquad \text{(put in } x = 1)$$
$$3 - a = -9$$
$$-a = -12$$
$$a = 12$$

Maximum and Minimum Points

At a maximum or minimum point, $\dfrac{dy}{dx} = 0$.

To find the maximum or minimum points on a curve, do the following:

Step 1: Find $\dfrac{dy}{dx}$.

Step 2: Let $\dfrac{dy}{dx} = 0$ and solve this equation for x.

Step 3: Substitute x values obtained in step 2 into the original function to get the corresponding values of y.

Step 4: By comparing the y values we can determine which point is the local maximum or minimum point. The point with the greater y value is the local maximum point and vice versa.

Example

Find, using calculus, the coordinates of the local maximum and minimum points of the curve $y = 5 + 18x + 6x^2 - 2x^3$.

Solution:

1. $$y = 5 + 18x + 6x^2 - 2x^3$$

    $$\frac{dy}{dx} = 18 + 12x - 6x^2$$

2. Let $\frac{dy}{dx} = 0$ and solve for x.

    $$18 + 12x - 6x^2 = 0$$
    $$-6x^2 + 12x + 18 = 0$$
    $$6x^2 - 12x - 18 = 0$$
    $$x^2 - 2x - 3 = 0$$
    $$(x - 3)(x + 1) = 0$$
    $$x - 3 = 0 \quad \text{or} \quad x + 1 = 0$$
    $$x = 3 \quad \text{or} \quad x = -1$$

3. Now find the y values:

$y = 5 + 18x + 6x^2 - 2x^3$	$y = 5 + 18x + 6x^2 - 2x^3$
$x = 3$	$x = -1$
$y = 5 + 18(3) + 6(3)^2 - 2(3)^3$	$y = 5 + 18(-1) + 6(-1)^2 - 2(-1)^3$
$= 5 + 18(3) + 6(9) - 2(27)$	$= 5 + 18(-1) + 6(1) - 2(-1)$
$= 5 + 54 + 54 - 54$	$= 5 - 18 + 6 + 2$
$= 59$	$= -5$
point $(3, 59)$	point $(-1, -5)$

4. $$59 > -5$$

Thus, the local maximum point is $(3, 59)$ and the local minimum point is $(-1, -5)$.

Sometimes we have to find an unknown coefficient.

Example

Let $f(x) = x^2 + px + 10$, $x \in \mathbf{R}$, where $p \in \mathbf{Z}$.

(i) Find $f'(x)$, the derivative of $f(x)$.

(ii) The minimum value of $f(x)$ is at $x = 3$. Find the value of p.

Solution:

(i) $f(x) = x^2 + px + 10$

$\quad f'(x) = 2x + p$

(ii) Minimum value of $f(x)$ at $x = 3$ means:

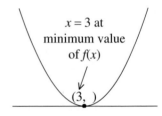

Slope of the tangent $= 0$	(when $x = 3$)
$\therefore$ $\quad f'(x) = 0$	(when $x = 3$)
$\therefore$ $\quad 2x + p = 0$	(when $x = 3$)
$2(3) + p = 0$	(put in $x = 3$)
$6 + p = 0$	
$p = -6$	

$x = 3$ at minimum value of $f(x)$

(3,)

Slope of the tangent $= 0$ when $x = 3$

$\therefore \quad \dfrac{dy}{dx} = 0$ when $x = 3$

Increasing and Decreasing

$\frac{dy}{dx}$, being the slope of a tangent to a curve at any point on the curve, can be used to

determine if, and where, a curve is increasing or decreasing.

Note: Graphs are read from left to right.

Where a curve is increasing, the tangent to the curve will have a positive slope.

Therefore, where a curve is increasing, $\frac{dy}{dx}$ will be positive.

Where a curve is decreasing, the tangent to the curve will have a negative slope.

Therefore, where a curve is decreasing, $\frac{dy}{dx}$ will be negative.

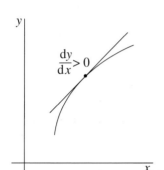

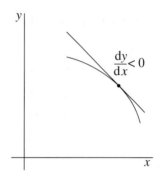

Example 1

Let $y = 6x^2 - 12x + 7$, $x \in \mathbf{R}$.

Find the range of values of x for which the graph of y is increasing.

Solution:

$$y = 6x^2 - 12x + 7$$

$$\frac{dy}{dx} = 12x - 12$$

Increasing: $\frac{dy}{dx} > 0$

$\therefore \quad 12x - 12 > 0$

$12x > 12$

$x > 1$

Thus, the graph of y is increasing for all $x > 1$

Example 2

If $y = \dfrac{4x+1}{x-3}$, $x \in \mathbf{R}$, show that $\dfrac{dy}{dx} < 0$ for all $x \neq 3$.

Solution:

$$y = \frac{4x+1}{x-3}$$

(quotient, $\therefore$ use quotient rule)

$$\frac{dy}{dx} = \frac{(x-3)(4) - (4x+1)(1)}{(x-3)^2}$$

$$\left[\frac{v\dfrac{du}{dx} - u\dfrac{dv}{dx}}{v^2} \right]$$

$$= \frac{4x - 12 - 4x - 1}{(x-3)^2}$$

$$= \frac{-13}{(x-13)^2}$$

$$\frac{dy}{dx} = \frac{-13}{(x-3)^2}$$

Top: -13 is always negative   Bottom: $(x-3)^2$ is always positive, for $x \neq 3$.

i.e. the top is always negative and the bottom is always positive

$\qquad \therefore$ this fraction is always negative

i.e. $\dfrac{-13}{(x-3)^2} < 0$, for all $x \neq 3$

$\qquad \therefore \qquad \dfrac{dy}{dx} < 0$, for all $x \neq 3$

Note: (any real number)^2 will always be a positive number unless the number is zero.
$\therefore$ $(x-3)^2$ must always be positive, unless $x = 3$ which gives $0^2 = 0$.
However, we are given $x \neq 3$.

Rates of Change

The derivative $\dfrac{dy}{dx}$ is called the 'rate of change of y with respect to x'.

It shows how changes in y are related to changes in x.

The derivative $\dfrac{dh}{dt}$ is called the 'rate of change of h with respect to t'.

The derivative $\dfrac{dR}{dV}$ is called the 'rate of change of R with respect to V'.

If s denotes the displacement (position) of a particle, from a fixed point p at time t, then:

> **1.** Velocity $= v = \dfrac{ds}{dt}$,
>
> the rate of change of position with respect to time.
>
> **2.** Acceleration $= a = \dfrac{dv}{dt} = \dfrac{d^2s}{dt^2}$,
>
> the rate of change of velocity with respect to time.

To find $\dfrac{d^2s}{dt^2}$, simply find $\dfrac{ds}{dt}$ and differentiate this.

In other words, differentiate twice.

Note: 'Speed' is often used instead of 'velocity'. However, speed can never be negative, whereas velocity can be negative.

Example 1

A car begins to slow down at p in order to stop at a red traffic light at q.

p q

The distance of the car from p, after t seconds, is given by $s = 12t - \dfrac{3}{2}t^2$, when s in metres.

(i) Find the speed of the car as it passes p.

(ii) Find the time taken to stop.

(iii) The car stops exactly at q. Find the distance from p to q.

(iv) Find the acceleration of the car.

Solution:

(i) Find the speed of the car as it passes *p*.

$$s = 12t - \frac{3}{2}t^2$$

$$\text{Speed} = \frac{ds}{dt} = 12 - 2\left(\frac{3}{2}\right)t$$

$$= 12 - 3t \quad \text{(speed at time } t\text{)}$$

At *p*, $t = 0$ (clock is set)

$$\text{Speed} = 12 - 3t$$

When $t = 0$,

$$\text{Speed} = 12 - 3(0) = 12$$

∴ Speed at $p = 12$ m/s

(ii) Find the time taken to stop.

The car is stopped when its speed $= 0$

$$\therefore \quad \frac{ds}{dt} = 0$$

$$\therefore \quad 12 - 3t = 0$$

$$-3t = -12$$

$$3t = 12$$

$$t = 4$$

∴ the car reaches *q* after 4 seconds (time taken to stop)

(iii) The car stops exactly at q. Find the distance from *p* to *q*.

It takes 4 seconds to go from *p* to *q*.

$$s = 12t - \frac{3}{2}t^2 \qquad \text{(distance in terms of time } t\text{)}$$

$$s = 12(4) - \frac{3}{2}(4)^2 \qquad \text{(put in } t = 4\text{)}$$

$$s = 48 - 24$$

$$s = 24$$

∴ the distance from *p* to *q* is 24 m.

(iv) Acceleration of the car

$$\text{Speed} = \frac{ds}{dt} = 12 - 3t$$

$$\text{Acceleration} = \frac{d^2s}{dt^2} = -3$$

∴ the acceleration of the car $= -3$ m/s^2 (minus means 'slowing down').

Example 2

A missile is fired straight up in the air. The height, h metres, of the missile above the firing position is given by $h = t(200 - 5t)$

where t is the time in seconds from the instant the missile was fired.

(i)   Find the speed and acceleration of the missile in terms of t.
(ii) Find the height of the missile after 8 seconds.
(iii) Find the speed of the missile after 10 seconds.
(iv) One second before reaching its greatest possible height, the missile strikes a target. Find the height of the target.

Solution:

(i)   **Find the speed and acceleration of the missile in terms of t.**

$$h = t(200 - 5t)$$
$$h = 200t - 5t^2 \qquad \text{(remove brackets)}$$
$$\textbf{Speed} = \frac{dh}{dt} = (200 - 10t) \text{ m/s} \qquad \text{(speed at any time } t\text{)}$$
$$\textbf{Acceleration} = \frac{d^2h}{dt^2} = -10 \text{ m/s}^2 \qquad \text{(acceleration at any time } t\text{)}$$

(ii) **Height after 8 seconds**

$$h = 200t - 5t^2$$
When $t = 8$,
$$h = 200(8) - 5(8)^2$$
$$h = 1{,}600 - 320$$
$$h = 1{,}280$$
$\therefore$ Height after 8 seconds $= 1{,}280$ m

(iii) **Speed after 10 seconds**

$$\text{Speed} = \frac{dh}{dt} = 200 - 10t$$
When $t = 10$,
$$\text{Speed} = 200 - 10(10)$$
$$= 200 - 100$$
$$= 100$$
$\therefore$ Speed after 10 seconds $= 100$ m/s

(iv) **One second before reaching its greatest possible height, the missile strikes a target. Find the height of the target.**

The way to approach this problem is to first calculate the time to reach the greatest possible height of the missile if it did not hit a target.

The missile reaches its greatest possible height when its speed $= 0$.

Speed $= 0$

$$\frac{dh}{dt} = 0$$

$$200 - 10t = 0$$

$$-10t = -200$$

$$10t = 200$$

$$t = 20$$

Greatest possible height
Speed $= 0$

$\therefore$ the missile reaches its greatest possible height after 20 seconds.

Thus, the missile strikes the target after 19 seconds (one second before reaching the greatest possible height).

When the missile strikes the target, the missile and the target have the same height. Thus, we need to find the height reached by the missile after 19 seconds.

$$h = 200t - 5t^2 \qquad \text{(height of missile at any time } t\text{)}$$

$$h = 200(19) - 5(19)^2 \qquad \text{(put in } t = 19\text{)}$$

$$h = 3,800 - 1,805$$

$$h = 1,995$$

Thus, the height of the target was 1,995 m.

Chapter 7. PERIMETER, AREA AND VOLUME

Perimeter and Area

Formulas required:

1. Rectangle  Area $= lb$ Perimeter $= 2l + 2b = 2(l + b)$	**2. Square** Area $= l^2$ Perimeter $= 4l$
3. Triangle 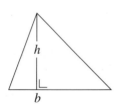 Area $= \dfrac{1}{2}bh$	**4. Parallelogram** 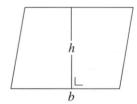 Area $= bh$
5. Circle (Disc) 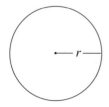 Area $= \pi r^2$ Circumference $= 2\pi r$	**6. Sector of a circle** 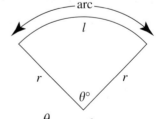 Area $= \dfrac{\theta}{360} \times \pi r^2$ Length of arc $= \dfrac{\theta}{360} \times 2\pi r$ $\left(\text{Similar to circle with } \dfrac{\theta}{360} \text{ in front of formulas}\right)$

Notes: 1. When using $\pi = \dfrac{22}{7}$, it is good practice to write the radius as a fraction.

For example, $21 = \dfrac{21}{1}$ or $4.5 = \dfrac{9}{2}$

2. If a question says 'give your answer in terms of π', then leave π in the answer: do **not** use 3.14 or $\dfrac{22}{7}$ for π.

3. If not given an approximate value for π then you must use the value given by the calculator.

Example 1

The figure on the right is made up of a semi-circle, a rectangle and a triangle.

Find the area of the figure.

All dimensions in cm.

$\left(\text{assume } \pi = \dfrac{22}{7}\right)$

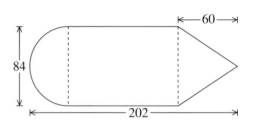

Solution:

Split the figure up into regular shapes, for which we have formulas to calculate the area. Find the area of each shape separately and add these results together.

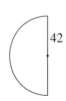

Radius $= \dfrac{84}{2} = 42$	Length $= 202 - 42 - 60 = 100$	Base $= 84$ and Height $= 60$
Area of semi-circle	Area of rectangle	Area of triangle
$= \dfrac{1}{2}\,\pi r^2 = \dfrac{1}{2} \times \dfrac{22}{7} \times 42 \times 42$	$= lb = 100 \times 84$	$= \dfrac{1}{2}\,bh = \dfrac{1}{2} \times 84 \times 60$
$= 2{,}772 \text{ cm}^2$	$= 8{,}400 \text{ cm}^2$	$= 2{,}520 \text{ cm}^2$

$\therefore$ Area of the figure $= 2{,}772 + 8{,}400 + 2{,}520 = 13{,}692 \text{ cm}^2$.

Example 2

The diagram shows a rectangle of length 42 cm.
The area of the rectangle is 966 cm^2.

(i) Find the height of the rectangle.

(ii) Find the area of the shaded triangle.

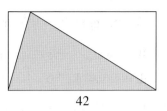

42

Solution:

(i) Equation given in disguise:

Area of rectangle = 966 cm^2

∴ $lh = 966$

$42\,h = 966$ (given $l = 42$)

$h = 23$ cm

(ii) Area of shaded triangle

$= \dfrac{1}{2}$ (area of rectangle)

$= \dfrac{1}{2} \times 42 \times 23$

$= 483$ cm^2

Example 3

The diagram represents a sector of a circle of radius
20 cm. $|\angle poq| = 144°$.
Find:

(i) the area of the sector *opq*, in terms of π

(ii) the perimeter of the sector; assume $\pi = 3.14$.

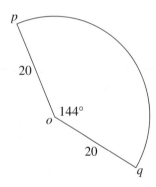

p

20

144°

o

20

q

Solution:

(i) Area of sector

$= \dfrac{\theta}{360} \times \pi r^2$

$= \dfrac{144}{360} \times \pi \times 20 \times 20$

$= \dfrac{2}{5} \times \pi \times 20 \times 20$

$= 160\,\pi$ cm^2

(ii) Length of arc *pq*

$= \dfrac{\theta}{360} \times 2\pi r$

$= \dfrac{144}{360} \times 2 \times 3.14 \times 20$

$= \dfrac{2}{5} \times 2 \times 3.14 \times 20$

$= 50.24$ cm

Perimeter $= 20 + 20 + 50.24 = 90.24$ cm

Example 4

The area of a circle is 81π cm^2. Its length is $k\pi$ cm. Calculate k.

Solution:

Equation given in disguise:

$$\text{Area} = 81\pi \text{ cm}^2$$

$$\therefore \qquad \pi r^2 = 81\pi$$

$$r^2 = 81$$

$$r = 9 \text{ cm}$$

length of a circle

$$= 2\pi r$$

$$= 2\pi(9) \quad (\text{put in } r = 9)$$

$$= 18\pi \text{ cm}$$

Comparing: $\quad k\pi = 18\pi$

$$\therefore \qquad\quad k = 18$$

Example 5

A piece of wire of length 154 cm is in the shape of a semi-circle.

Find the radius length of the semi-circle.

$$\left(\text{assume } \pi = \frac{22}{7}\right)$$

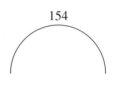

154

Solution:

Equation given in disguise:

Length of the semi-circle = 154 cm

$$\therefore \qquad \frac{1}{2} \times 2\pi r = 154$$

$$\pi r = 154$$

$$r = \frac{154}{\pi}$$

$$r = \frac{154}{\frac{22}{7}}$$

$$r = 49 \text{ cm}$$

(length of a circle $= 2\pi r$)

$$\left(\frac{1}{2} \times 2 = 1\right)$$

(divide both sides by π)

$$\left(\text{put in } \pi = \frac{22}{7}\right)$$

$$\left(\boxed{}\ 154\ \boxed{\div}\ 22\ \boxed{a\frac{b}{c}}\ 7\ \boxed{=}\right)$$

Simpson's Rule

Simpson's rule gives a concise formula to enable us to make a very good approximation of the area of an irregular shape.

Consider the diagram below:

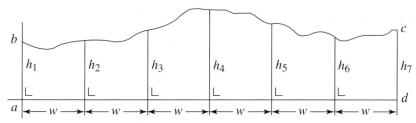

To find the area of the figure *abcd* do the following:

1. Divide the figure into an **even** number of strips of **equal** width, *w*.

2. Number and measure each height, *h*. There will be an **odd** number of heights.

3. Use the following formula:

$$\text{Area} = \frac{w}{3}[(h_1 + h_7) + 4(h_2 + h_4 + h_6) + 2(h_3 + h_5)]$$

$$\text{Area} = \frac{\text{width}}{3}[(\text{First} + \text{Last}) + 4(\text{Evens}) + 2(\text{Odds})]$$

Example 1

Archaeologists excavating a rectangular plot *abcd* measuring 72 m by 50 m divided the plot into twelve equal rectangular sections as shown on the diagram. At the end of the first phase of the work the shaded area had been excavated. To estimate the area excavated, perpendicular measurements were made to the edge of the excavated area, as shown.

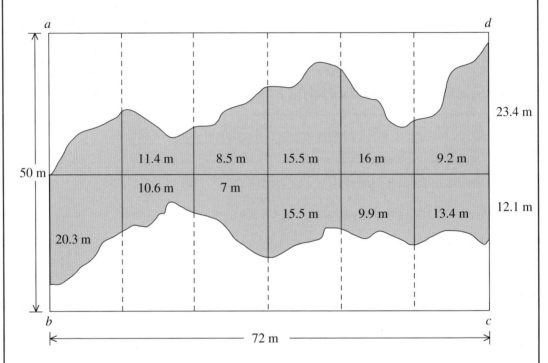

(i) Use Simpson's Rule to estimate the area excavated.

(ii) Express the excavated area as a percentage of the rectangular plot.

Solution:

(i) The length of the rectangular area is 72 m. It is divided up into six equal strips.

$\therefore$ the width of one strip $= \dfrac{72}{6} = 12$ m.

$$A = \frac{\text{width}}{3} \ [(\text{First} + \text{Last}) + 4(\text{Evens}) + 2(\text{Odds})]$$

$$= \frac{w}{3} \ [(h_1 + h_7) + 4(h_2 + h_4 + h_6) + 2(h_3 + h_5)]$$

$$= \frac{12}{3} \ [(20.3 + 35.5) + 4(22 + 31 + 22.6) + 2(15.5 + 25.9)]$$

$$= 4 \ [55.8 + 4(75.6) + 2(41.4)]$$

$$= 4 \ [55.8 + 302.4 + 82.8]$$

$$= 4 \ (441)$$

$$= 1{,}764 \ \text{m}^2$$

$w = 12$
$h_1 = 20.3$ (first)
$h_2 = 22$ (even)
$h_3 = 15.5$ (odd)
$h_4 = 31$ (even)
$h_5 = 25.9$ (odd)
$h_6 = 22.6$ (even)
$h_7 = 35.5$ (last)

(ii)   Area of rectangular plot $= 72 \times 50 = 3{,}600 \ \text{m}^2$.

Excavated area as a percentage of the rectangular plot

$$= \frac{\text{area of excavated region}}{\text{area of rectangular plot}} \times 100\%$$

$$= \frac{1{,}764}{3{,}600} \times 100\%$$

$$= 49\%$$

Sometimes we are given an equation in disguise.

Example 2

Surveyors make the following sketch in estimating the area of a building site, where k is the length shown. Using Simpson's Rule, they estimate the area of the site to be 100 square units. Find k.

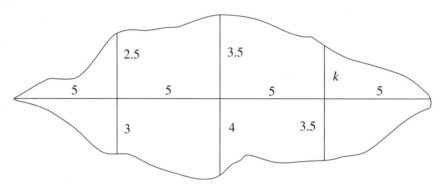

Solution:

Equation given in disguise:

$$\text{Area} = 100$$

$$\therefore \quad \frac{w}{3}[(F+L) + 4(E) + 2(R)] = 100$$

$$\frac{w}{3}[(h_1 + h_5) + 4(h_2 + h_4) + 2(h_3)] = 100$$

$$\frac{5}{3}[(0+0) + 4(5.5 + k + 3.5) + 2(7.5)] = 100$$

Given values	
$w = 5$	
$h_1 = 0$	(first)
$h_2 = 5.5$	(even)
$h_3 = 7.5$	(odd)
$h_4 = (k + 3.5)$	(even)
$h_5 = 0$	(last)

$$\frac{5}{3}(22 + 4k + 14 + 15) = 100 \qquad \text{(remove internal brackets)}$$

$$\frac{5}{3}(4k + 51) = 100$$

$$5(4k + 51) = 300 \qquad \text{(multiply both sides by 3)}$$

$$20k + 255 = 300 \qquad \text{(remove brackets)}$$

$$20k = 45 \qquad \text{(subtract 255 from both sides)}$$

$$k = 2.25 \qquad \text{(divide both sides by 20)}$$

Rectangular Solids

Formulas required:

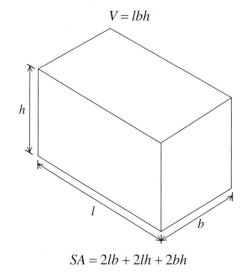

1. **Rectangular solid (cuboid)**

$$V = lbh$$

$$SA = 2lb + 2lh + 2bh$$

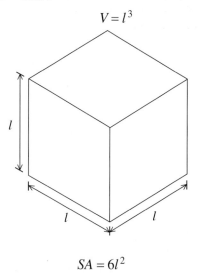

2. **Cube**

$$V = l^3$$

$$SA = 6l^2$$

Example 1

An open rectangular tank (no top) is full of water.
The volume of water in the tank is 2.4 litres.
If its length is 20 cm and its breadth is 15 cm, find
(i) its height, and **(ii)** its surface area.

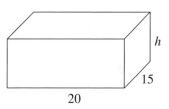

Solution:

1 litre = 1,000 cm^3, $\therefore$ 2.4 litres = 2.4(1,000) = 2,400 cm^3

(i) Equation given in disguise:

Volume = 2,400 cm^3

$\therefore$ $l \times b \times h = 2,400$

$(20)(15)\, h = 2,400$

$300\, h = 2,400$

$h = 8$ cm

(ii) Surface area

$= lb + 2lh + 2bh$ (no top)

$= (20)(15) + 2(20)(8) + 2(15)(8)$

$= 300 + 320 + 240$

$= 860$ cm^2

Example 2

The surface area of a cube is 54 cm^2.

Calculate its volume.

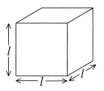

Solution:

Let the length of one side of the cube be l cm.

Equation given in disguise:

Surface area $= 54$ cm^2

$\therefore \quad 6\,l^2 = 54$

$\qquad l^2 = 9$

$\qquad l = 3$ cm

Volume $= l^3$

$\qquad = 3^3$

$\qquad = 27$ cm^3

Thus, the volume of the cube is 27 cm^3

Example 3

The surface area of a solid rectangular block is 258 cm^2. If its breadth is 6 cm and height is 5 cm, calculate its **(i)** length and **(ii)** volume.

Solution:

(i) Equation given in disguise:

$\qquad$ Surface area $= 258$

$\therefore \qquad 2lb + 2lh + 2bh = 258$

$\qquad 2l(6) + 2l(5) + 2(6)(5) = 258$

$\qquad 12l + 10l + 60 = 258$

$\qquad 22l + 60 = 258$

$\qquad 22l = 258 - 60$

$\qquad 22l = 198$

$\qquad l = \dfrac{198}{22} = 9$ cm

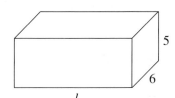

(ii) $\qquad$ Volume $= lbh$

$\qquad = (9)(6)(5)$

$\qquad = 270$

$\therefore \quad$ Volume $= 270$ cm^3

Uniform Cross-section

Many solid objects have the same cross-section throughout their length.

Here are some examples:

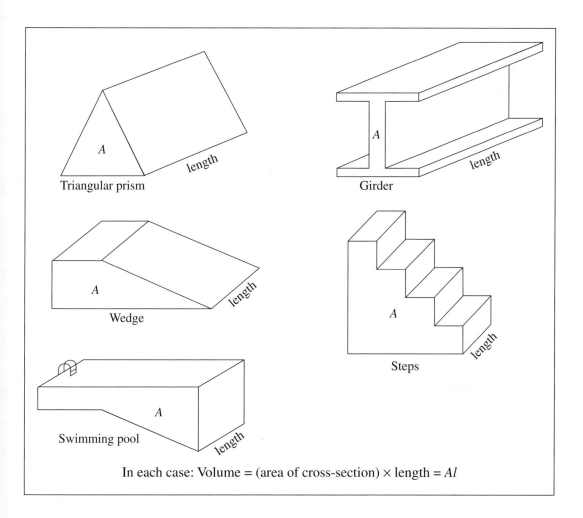

Triangular prism

Girder

Wedge

Steps

Swimming pool

In each case: Volume = (area of cross-section) × length = Al

The above objects are called prisms. A prism is a solid object which has the same cross-section throughout its length, and its sides are parallelograms.
A solid cylinder has a uniform cross-section, but it is not a prism.
So to find the volume of a solid object with uniform cross-section, find the area of the cross-section and multiply this by its length.

Example

Five rectangular shaped concrete steps are constructed as shown.

Each step measures 1.2 m by 0.4 m and the total height is 1.0 m with each step having the same height of 0.2 m.

Calculate the volume of the solid concrete construction.

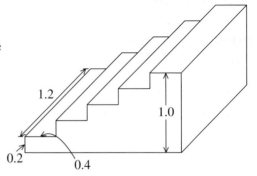

Solution:

The cross-section of the steps is made up of 5 rectangles, each of width 0.4 m.

The smallest rectangle has a height of 0.2 and the height of each rectangle after this increases by 0.2 m.

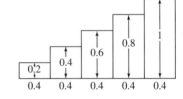

Area of cross-section

= Area of 5 rectangles

= (0.4)(0.2) + (0.4)(0.4) + (0.4)(0.6) +
   (0.4)(0.8) + (0.4)(1)

= 0.08 + 0.16 + 0.24 + 0.32 + 0.4

= 1.2 m^2

Volume = (Area of cross-section) × length

       = 1.2 × 1.2

       = 1.44 m^3

Thus, the volume of concrete used in the construction of the steps is 1.44 m^3

Cylinder, Sphere, Hemisphere and Cone

Formulas required:

Cylinder:

Volume, $\quad\quad\quad\quad\quad\quad\quad V = \pi r^2 h$

Curved Surface Area, $\quad CSA = 2\pi rh$

Total Surface Area, $\quad\quad TSA = 2\pi rh + 2\pi r^2$

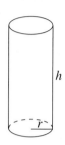 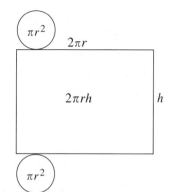

Sphere:

Volume, $\quad\quad\quad\quad\quad\quad\quad V = \frac{4}{3}\pi r^3$

Curved Surface Area, $\quad\quad CSA = 4\pi r^2$

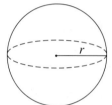

Hemisphere:

Volume, $\quad\quad\quad\quad\quad\quad\quad V = \frac{2}{3}\pi r^3$

Curved Surface Area, $\quad\quad CSA = 2\pi r^2$

Total Surface Area, $\quad\quad\quad TSA = 2\pi r^2 + \pi r^2 = 3\pi r^2$

Cone:

Volume, $\quad\quad\quad\quad\quad\quad\quad V = \frac{1}{3}\pi r^2 h$

Curved Surface Area, $\quad\quad CSA = \pi rl$

Total Surface Area, $\quad\quad\quad TSA = \pi rl + \pi r^2$

Pythagoras's Theorem: $\quad\quad l^2 = r^2 + h^2$

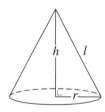

Compound Volumes

Many of the objects of which we need to find the volume will be made up of different shapes.

When this happens do the following:

> **1.** Split the solid up into regular shapes, for which we have formulas to calculate the volume or surface area.
>
> **2.** Add these results together.

Example

A solid object consists of 3 parts: a hemisphere, a cylinder and a cone, as shown, each having a diameter of 18 cm. If the height of the cone is 12 cm and the total height is 35 cm, calculate:

(i) The height of the cylinder.

(ii) The volume of the object in terms of π.

Solution:

(i) Height of the cylinder

$= 35 -$ height of the cone $-$ radius of the hemisphere

$= 35 - 12 - 9 = 14$ cm

(ii) Volume of cone $= \frac{1}{3}\pi r^2 h$

$= \frac{1}{3}\pi \times 9 \times 9 \times 12$

$= 324\pi$ cm^3

Volume of cylinder $= \pi r^2 h$

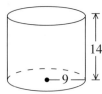

$= \pi \times 9 \times 9 \times 14$

$= 1{,}134\pi$ cm^3

Volume of hemisphere $= \frac{2}{3}\pi r^3$

$= \frac{2}{3}\pi \times 9 \times 9 \times 9$

$= 486\pi$ cm^3

Total volume = Volume of cone + Volume of cylinder + Volume of hemisphere
$= (324\pi + 1{,}134\pi + 486\pi)$ cm$^3 = 1{,}944\pi$ cm^3

Given the Volume or Surface Area

In some questions we are given the volume or surface area and asked to find a missing dimension. As before, write down the '**equation given in disguise**', and solve this equation to find the missing dimension.

Example 1

(i) A cylinder has a volume of 288π cm^3. If its radius is 6 cm, calculate its height.

(ii) The volume of a sphere is 121.5π cm^3. Calculate its radius.

Solution:

(i) Equation given in disguise:

$$\text{Volume of cylinder} = 288\pi \text{ cm}^3$$

$\therefore$

$$\pi r^2 h = 288\pi$$

$$r^2 h = 288 \qquad \text{(divide both sides by } \pi\text{)}$$

$$36\, h = 288 \qquad \text{(put in } r = 6,\ r^2 = 6^2 = 36\text{)}$$

$$h = 8 \text{ cm} \qquad \text{(divide both sides by 36)}$$

(ii) Equation given in disguise:

$$\text{Volume of sphere} = 121.5\pi \text{ cm}^3$$

$\therefore$

$$\frac{4}{3}\pi r^3 = 121.5\pi$$

$$4\pi r^3 = 364.5\pi \qquad \text{(multiply both sides by 3)}$$

$$4r^3 = 364.5 \qquad \text{(divide both sides by } \pi\text{)}$$

$$r^3 = 91.125 \qquad \text{(divide both sides by 4)}$$

$$r = 4.5 \text{ cm} \qquad \text{(take the cube root of both sides)}$$

 $91.125 \boxed{y^x} \boxed{(} 1 \boxed{\div} 3 \boxed{)} \boxed{=}$

Example 2

A solid block, as shown, has a height of 12 cm and a base measuring 30 cm by 15.7 cm.

A solid cylinder is cut out of the block from top to bottom, as in the diagram. If the volume of the cylinder is $\frac{1}{6}$ of the volume of the block, calculate the radius of the cylinder.

(assume $\pi = 3.14$)

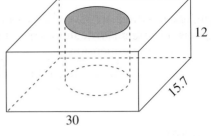

Solution:

Equation given in disguise:

Volume of cylinder $= \frac{1}{6}$ (Volume of block)

$\therefore \qquad \pi r^2 h = \frac{1}{6} lbh$ (we know π, h, l and b, find r)

$(3.14)r^2(12) = \frac{1}{6}(30)(15.7)(12)$ (put in $\pi = 3.14$, $h = 12$, $l = 30$, $b = 15.7$)

$37.68\ r^2 = 942$

$r^2 = 25$ (divide both sides by 37.68)

$r = 5$

Thus, the radius of the cylinder is 5 cm

Recasting

Many of the questions we meet require us to solve a recasting problem. What happens is that a certain solid object is melted down and its shape is changed. We use the following fact:

> The volume remains the same after it is melted down

Example

A sphere of radius 15 cm is made of lead. The sphere is melted down. Some of the lead is used to form a solid cone of radius 10 cm and height 27 cm. The rest of the lead is used to form a cylinder of base radius 12 cm. Calculate the height of the cylinder.

Solution:

Equation given in disguise:

Volume of cylinder $\quad+\quad$ Volume of cone $\quad=\quad$ Volume of sphere

(diagram of the situation)

$$\therefore \qquad \pi r^2 h \quad+\quad \tfrac{1}{3}\pi r^2 h \quad=\quad \tfrac{4}{3}\pi r^3$$

$$r^2 h \quad+\quad \tfrac{1}{3}r^2 h \quad=\quad \tfrac{4}{3}r^3 \qquad \text{(divide each part by } \pi\text{)}$$

$$(12)(12)(h) \quad+\quad \tfrac{1}{3}(10)(10)(27) \quad=\quad \tfrac{4}{3}(15)(15)(15) \qquad \text{(put in given values)}$$

$$144h \quad+\quad 900 \quad=\quad 4{,}500$$

$$144h \;=\; 4{,}500 - 900$$

$$144h \;=\; 3{,}600$$

$$h \;=\; 25$$

Thus, the height of the cylinder is 25 cm.

Displaced Liquid

In many questions we have to deal with situations where liquid is displaced by immersing, or removing, a solid object. In all cases the following principle helps us to solve these problems:

> Volume of displaced liquid = Volume of immersed solid object

Example

(i)   Find, in terms of π, the volume of a solid metal sphere of radius 6 cm.

(ii) Four such identical spheres are completely submerged in a cylinder containing water.

  If the radius of the cylinder is 8 cm, by how much will the level of the water drop if the spheres are removed from the cylinder?

Solution:

(i)   Volume of sphere $= \frac{4}{3}\,\pi r^3 = \frac{4}{3}\,\pi(6)(6)(6) = 288\pi$ cm^3

(ii) Diagram: Old situation   New situation

 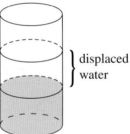

}displaced
water

  Equation given in disguise:

  Volume of displaced water = Volume of four spheres

Diagram: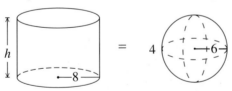

$\therefore$

$\pi r^2 h = 4(288\pi)$	(volume of sphere $= 288\pi$)
$\pi r^2 h = 1{,}152\pi$	($4 \times 288 = 1{,}152$)
$r^2 h = 1{,}152$	(divide both sides by π)
$64h = 1{,}152$	(put in $r = 8$, $r^2 = 8^2 = 64$)
$h = 18$	

Thus, the level of water in the cylinder would fall by 18 cm.

Moving Liquids

In many questions we have to deal with moving liquid from one container to another container of different dimensions or shape. Again to help us solve the problem we use the fact that:

> The volume of the moved liquid does not change

Example

The base of a right circular cone has a radius of length 5 cm. The height of the cone is 12 cm. Calculate the volume in terms of π.

The inverted cone is filled with water. The water then drips from the vertex at the rate $\dfrac{\pi}{5}$ cm^3/s.

Calculate the time in seconds until the cone is empty, assuming the volume of water to be the same as the volume of the cone.

If all the water dripped into a dry cylindrical can of diameter 10 cm in length, calculate the height of water in the can.

Solution:

$$\text{Volume of cone} = \tfrac{1}{3}\,\pi r^2 h$$

$$= \tfrac{1}{3}\,\pi(5)(5)(12)$$

$$= 100\pi \text{ cm}^3 \qquad \text{(multiply top and bottom by 5)}$$

$$\text{Time to empty cone} = \frac{\text{Volume of cone}}{\text{Rate of flow}} = \frac{100\pi}{\dfrac{\pi}{5}} = \frac{500\pi}{\pi} = 500 \text{ seconds}$$

Equation given in disguise:

Volume of cylinder = Volume of cone

$\therefore \qquad \pi r^2 h = 100\pi \qquad$ (volume of cone $= 100\pi$ cm^3)

$\qquad\quad r^2 h = 100 \qquad$ (divide both sides by π)

$\qquad\quad 25h = 100 \qquad$ (put in $r = 5$)

$\qquad\qquad h = 4$

Thus, the water will rise to a height of 4 cm in the cylinder.

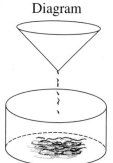

Diagram

147

Miscellaneous Questions

Example 1

A solid is in the shape of a hemisphere surmounted by a cone, as in the diagram.

(i) The volume of the hemisphere is 18π cm^3.
Find the radius, r, of the hemisphere.

(ii) The slant height of the cone is $3\sqrt{5}$ cm.
Find the height, h, of the cone.

(iii) Find the ratio:
Volume of the hemisphere : Volume of the cone

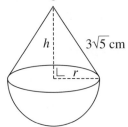

Solution:

(i) Equation given in disguise:

Volume of hemisphere $= 18\pi$ cm^3

$\therefore \quad \frac{2}{3}\pi r^3 = 18\pi$

$2\pi r^3 = 54\pi$ (multiply both sides by 3)

$2r^3 = 54$ (divide both sides by π)

$r^3 = 27$ (divide both sides by 2)

$r = 3$ cm   (take the cubed root of both sides)

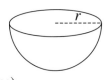

(ii) Using Pythagoras's Theorem:

$h^2 + r^2 = l^2$

$h^2 + (3)^2 = \left(3\sqrt{5}\right)^2$ $\left(r = 3,\, l = 3\sqrt{5}\right)$

$h^2 + 9 = 45$ $((3\sqrt{5})^2 = 45)$

$h^2 = 36$

$h = 6$ cm

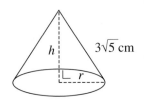

(iii) Volume of the hemisphere : Volume of the cone

$\frac{2}{3}\pi r^3 : \frac{1}{3}\pi r^2 h$

$2\pi r^3 : \pi r^2 h$ (multiply both sides by 3)

$2r^3 : r^2 h$ (divide both sides by π)

$2r : h$ (divide both sides by r^2)

$2(3) : 6$ $(r = 3,\, h = 6)$

$6 : 6$

$1 : 1$ (divide both sides by 6)

Example 2

A solid metal ornament consists of a hemisphere of radius length 4 cm surmounted by a solid cone.

The cone's volume is twice the hemisphere's.

Find, h, the height of the cone.

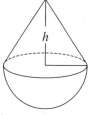

h

4 cm

Solution:

Equation given in disguise:

Volume of cone = twice the volume of the hemisphere

$\therefore$ $\qquad \frac{1}{3}\pi r^2 h = 2(\frac{2}{3}\pi r^3)$

$\qquad \frac{1}{3}\pi r^2 h = \frac{4}{3}\pi r^3$

$\qquad \pi r^2 h = 4\pi r^3$ $\qquad$ (multiply both sides by 3)

$\qquad r^2 h = 4r^3$ $\qquad$ (divide both sides by π)

$\qquad h = 4r$ $\qquad$ (divide both sides by r^2)

$\qquad h = 4(4)$ $\qquad$ (put in $r = 4$)

$\qquad h = 16$

Thus, the height of the cone is 16 cm.

Example 3

A small candle is in the shape of a cone which fits exactly on top of a cylinder as shown. The cylinder has a radius of length 2 cm. The slant length of the cone is 2.5 cm.

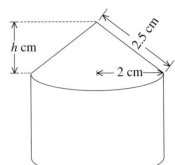

Calculate:

(i)   the height, h, of the cone

(ii)   the volume of the cone is terms of π.

The volume of the cylinder is 5 times the volume of the cone.

Calculate the total height and surface area of the candle, in terms of π.

Solution:

(i)   Using Pythagoras's theorem:

$$r^2 + h^2 = l^2 \qquad \text{(we know } r \text{ and } l\text{, find } h\text{)}$$

$$2^2 + h^2 = 2.5^2 \qquad \text{(put in } r = 2 \text{ and } l = 2.5\text{)}$$

$$4 + h^2 = 6.25$$

$$h^2 = 6.25 - 4$$

$$h^2 = 2.25$$

$$h = \sqrt{2.25}$$

$$h = 1.5 \text{ cm}$$

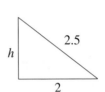

(ii)   Volume of cone $= \frac{1}{3}\pi r^2 h$

$$= \frac{1}{3}\pi\,(2)(2)(1.5)$$

$$= 2\pi \text{ cm}^3$$

Equation given in disguise:

Volume of cylinder $= 5$ (Volume of cone)

Diagram:

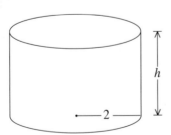 $= 5$ 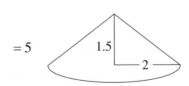

150

$$\therefore \qquad \pi r^2 h = 5(2\pi) \qquad \text{(volume of cone} = 2\pi)$$

$$\pi r^2 h = 10\pi \qquad \text{(we know } r\text{, find } h)$$

$$r^2 h = 10 \qquad \text{(divide both sides by } \pi)$$

$$4h = 10 \qquad \text{(put in } r = 2)$$

$$h = 2.5$$

height of the candle = height of cylinder + height of cone

$$= 2.5 + 1.5 = 4 \text{ cm}$$

Surface area = area of base of the candle + curved surface of cylinder
+ curved surface of area of cone.

$$= \pi r^2 + 2\pi rh + \pi rl$$

$$= \pi(2)^2 + 2\pi(2)(2.5) + \pi(2)(2.5)$$

$$= 4\pi + 10\pi + 5\pi$$

$$= 19\pi$$

Thus, the surface area of the candle is 19π cm^2

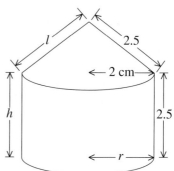

Example 4

The lower portion (A) of a test-tube is hemispherical and the upper portion (B) is cylindrical.

The length of the test-tube is 14.5 cm and the diameter is 3 cm.

Calculate:

(i) the length of B

(ii) the volume of the test-tube, in terms of π.

(iii) If water is poured into the test-tube find the depth, d, of the water when its volume is half the volume of the test-tube.

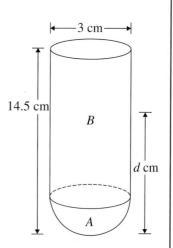

Solution:

(i) The radius of the hemisphere = 1.5 cm $\left(\frac{1}{2}\text{ the diameter of the cylinder}\right)$

$\therefore$ the length of the cylinder $B = 14.5 - 1.5 = 13$ cm

(ii) Volume of test-tube = Volume of cylinder B + Volume of hemisphere A

$$= \pi r^2 h + \frac{2}{3} \pi r^3$$

$$= \pi(1.5)(1.5)(13) + \frac{2}{3}\pi(1.5)(1.5)(1.5)$$

$$= 29.25\pi + 2.25\pi$$

$$= 31.5\pi \text{ cm}^3$$

Thus, the volume of the test-tube is 31.5π

(iii) The best way to approach this is to think of the test-tube turned upside down and imagine the water only going into the cylinder and find the height by which it would rise and subtract this from 14.5 to find d.

Equation given in disguise:

Volume of water in cylinder $= \frac{1}{2}$ (Volume of test-tube)

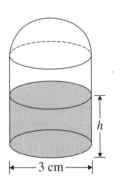

$\therefore$ $\pi r^2 h = \frac{1}{2}$ (31.5π)   (we know r, find h)

$\pi r^2 h = 15.75\pi$

$r^2 h = 15.75$ (divide both sides by π)

$(1.5)^2 h = 15.75$ (put in $r = 1.5$)

$2.25h = 15.75$

$h = 7$

Thus, the depth, d, the water would rise to in the test-tube $= 14.5 - 7 = 7.5$ cm

Example 5

An egg-timer consists of two identical cones of height 6 cm and base radius 4 cm. Sand occupies **half** the volume of one cone and flows from one to the other at a rate of $\frac{4\pi}{45}$ cm^3 per second.

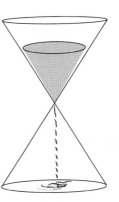

(i)   Calculate the volume of each cone in terms of π.

(ii) Calculate the length of time it takes for the sand to flow from one cone into the other.

Solution:

(i)   Volume of cone

$$= \tfrac{1}{3}\pi r^2 h$$

$$= \tfrac{1}{3}(\pi)(4)^2(6)$$

$$= 32\pi \text{ cm}^3$$

(ii) Volume of sand

$$= \tfrac{1}{2}\text{ (volume of cone)}$$

$$= \tfrac{1}{2}(32\pi \text{ cm}^3)$$

$$= 16\pi \text{ cm}^3$$

$\text{Time} = \dfrac{\text{Volume of sand}}{\text{Rate of flow}}$

$$= \dfrac{16\pi}{\dfrac{4}{45}\pi}$$

$$= \dfrac{16}{\dfrac{4}{45}} \quad \text{(divide top and bottom by } \pi)$$

$= 180$ ($\boxed{\Box}$ 16 $\div$ (4 $\div$ 45) $=$)

Thus, the length of time is 180 seconds or 3 minutes.

Chapter 8. COORDINATE GEOMETRY OF THE LINE

Formulas Required

In all cases (x_1, y_1) and (x_2, y_2) represent points.

1. **Distance between two points.**

$$\sqrt{(x_2 - x_1)^2 + (y_2 - y_1)^2}$$

2. **Midpoint of a line segment.**

$$\left(\frac{x_1 + x_2}{2}, \frac{y_1 + y_2}{2} \right)$$

3. **Slope of a line, m, given two points.**

$$m = \frac{y_2 - y_1}{x_2 - x_1}$$

4. **Parallel lines have equal slopes (and vice versa).**

$$\text{If } L_1 \parallel L_2, \text{ then } m_1 = m_2$$

5. **If two lines are perpendicular, when we multiply their slopes we always get -1 (and vice versa).**

$$\text{If } L_1 \perp L_2, \text{ then } m_1 . m_2 = -1$$

(In 4 and 5 above, m_1 = the slope of the line L_1 and m_2 = the slope of the line L_2.)

Note: If we know the slope of a line and we need to find the slope of a line perpendicular to it, simply do the following:

> Turn the known slope upside down and change its sign.

For example, if a line has a slope of $-\frac{3}{5}$, then the slope of a line perpendicular to it has a slope of $\frac{5}{3}$ (turn upside down and change its sign), because $-\frac{3}{5} \times \frac{5}{3} = -1$.

6. Equation of a line

> To find the equation of a line we need:
>
> 1. The slope of line, m 2. A point on the line, (x_1, y_1)
>
> Then use the formula: $(y - y_1) = m(x - x_1)$

In short: we need the **slope** and a **point** on the line.

7. Slope of a line when given its equation.

To find the slope of a line when given its equation, do the following:

Method 1:

> If the equation of the line is in the form $ax + by + c = 0$, then $-\dfrac{a}{b}$ is the slope.

In words: $\text{slope} = -\dfrac{\text{number in front of } x}{\text{number in front of } y}$

Note: When using this method, make sure every term is on the left-hand side in the given equation of the line.

Method 2:

> Get y on its own and the number in front of x is the slope.

Note: The number in front of x is called the **coefficient** of x.
In short, write the line in the form:

$y = mx + c$

$y = (\text{slope}) x + (\text{where the line cuts the } y\text{-axis})$

8. Proving lines are parallel or perpendicular.

To prove whether or not two lines are parallel, do the following:

> 1. Find the slope of each line.
>
> 2. (a) If the slopes are the same, the lines are parallel.
>
>   (b) If the slopes are different, the lines are **not** parallel.

To prove whether or not two lines are perpendicular, do the following:

1. Find the slope of each line.
2. Multiply both slopes.
3. (a) If the answer in step 2 is -1, the lines are perpendicular.

   (b) If the answer in step 2 is **not** -1, the lines are **not** perpendicular.

9. **Verify that a point belongs to a line.**

   Substitute the coordinates of the point into the equation of the line. If the coordinates satisfy the equation, then the point is on the line. Otherwise, the point is not on the line.

10. **Point of intersection of two lines.**

    Use the method of solving simultaneous equations to find the point of intersection of two lines.

11. **Area of a triangle.**

    [one point at $(0, 0)$]

    $$\frac{1}{2} \left| x_1 y_2 - x_2 y_1 \right|$$

Note: To find the area of a quadrilateral (four-sided figure), divide it into two triangles, find the area of each triangle separately and add the results.

12. **Graphing lines.**

    To draw a line only two points are needed. The easiest points to find are where lines cut the x- and y-axes. This is known as the **intercept method**.

    Note: On the x-axis, $y = 0$. On the y-axis, $x = 0$.

    To draw a line do the following:

    1. Let $y = 0$ and find x.
    2. Let $x = 0$ and find y.
    3. Plot these two points.
    4. Draw the line through these points.

    If the constant in the equation of a line is zero, e.g. $3x - 5y = 0$, or $4x = 3y$, then the line will pass through the origin, $(0, 0)$. In this case the **intercept method** will not work.

To draw a line that contains the origin, (0, 0), do the following:

> 1. Choose a suitable value for x and find the corresponding value for y (or vice versa).
>
> 2. Plot this point.
>
> 3. A line drawn through this point and the origin is the required line.

Note: A very suitable value is to let x equal the number in front of y and then find the corresponding value for y (or vice versa).

13. **Lines parallel to the axes.**

$x = 2$ is a line parallel to the y-axis through 2 on the x-axis.

$y = -1$ is a line parallel to the x-axis through -1 on the y-axis.

Note:
> $y = 0$ is the equation of the x-axis.
>
> $x = 0$ is the equation of the y-axis.

14. **Transformations of the plane.**

   (i) **Translation**

   A translation moves a point in a straight line.

   (ii) **Central symmetry**

   Central symmetry is a reflection in a point.

   (iii) **Axial symmetry**

   Axial symmetry is a reflection in a line.

   (iv) **Axial symmetry in the axes or central symmetry in the origin.**

> The following three patterns emerge and it is worth memorising them:
>
> 1. Axial symmetry in the x-axis → **change the sign of y.**
>
> 2. Axial symmetry in the y-axis → **change the sign of x.**
>
> 3. Central symmetry in the origin, (0, 0) → **change the sign of both x and y.**

Alternatively, plot the point on the coordinated plane and use your knowledge of axial symmetry and central symmetry to find the image.

Example 1

(i) Find the distance between the two points $(-5, 1)$ and $(7, -4)$.

(ii) $a(-2, 1)$ and $(-8, -3)$ are two points. Find $|ab|$.

Solution:

(i) $(-5, 1)$ and $(7, -4)$

$\quad (x_1, y_1) \qquad (x_2, y_2)$

$$d = \sqrt{(x_2 - x_1)^2 + (y_2 - y_1)^2}$$
$$= \sqrt{(7 + 5)^2 + (-4 - 1)^2}$$
$$= \sqrt{(12)^2 + (-5)^2}$$
$$= \sqrt{144 + 25}$$
$$= \sqrt{169} = 13$$

(ii) $a(-2, 1) \qquad$ and $\qquad b(-8, -3)$

$\qquad (x_1, y_1) \qquad\qquad\qquad (x_2, y_2)$

$$|ab| = \sqrt{(x_2 - x_1)^2 + (y_2 - y_1)^2}$$
$$= \sqrt{(-8 + 2)^2 + (-3 - 1)^2}$$
$$= \sqrt{(-6)^2 + (-4)^2}$$
$$= \sqrt{36 + 16}$$
$$= \sqrt{52}$$

Note: Always decide which point is (x_1, y_1) and which point is (x_2, y_2) before you use the formula.

The distance between the points a and b is written $|ab|$.

Example 2

$p(5, 8)$ and $q(11, -10)$ are two points. Find the midpoint of $[pq]$.

Solution:

$p(5, 8) \qquad\qquad\qquad q(11, -10) \qquad\qquad x_1 = 5 \qquad\qquad\qquad y_1 = 8$

$(x_1, y_1) \qquad\qquad\qquad (x_2, \quad y_2) \qquad\qquad x_2 = 11 \qquad\qquad\quad y_2 = -10$

$$\text{Midpoint} = \left(\frac{x_1 + x_2}{2}, \frac{y_1 + y_2}{2} \right) = \left(\frac{5 + 11}{2}, \frac{8 - 10}{2} \right) = \left(\frac{16}{2}, \frac{-2}{2} \right) = (8, -1)$$

In some questions we will be given the midpoint and one end point of a line segment and be asked to find the other end point.

To find the other end point use the following method:

1. Make a rough diagram.

2. Find the translation that maps (moves) the given end point to the midpoint.

3. Apply the same translation to the midpoint to find the other end point.

Example 3

If $m(7, -2)$ is the midpoint of $[pq]$, and $p = (5, 1)$, find the coordinates of q.

Solution:

1. Rough diagram.

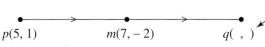

(missing coordinates)

$p(5, 1)$ $m(7, -2)$ $q(,)$

2. Translation from p to m, $\overrightarrow{pm}$. Rule: 'add 2 to x, take 3 from y'.

3. Apply this translation to m.

$m(7, -2) \rightarrow (7 + 2, -2 - 3) = (9, -5)$

$\therefore$ the coordinates of q are $(9, -5)$

Example 4

Find the equation of the following lines:

(i) containing the point $(-1, 4)$ with slope 2.

(ii) containing the point $(-3, -1)$ with slope $-\dfrac{3}{4}$.

Solution:

(i) containing $(-1, 4)$ with slope 2

$x_1 = -1, \quad y_1 = 4, \quad m = 2$

$(y - y_1) = m(x - x_1)$

$(y - 4) = 2(x + 1)$

$y - 4 = 2x + 2$

$-2x + y - 4 - 2 = 0$

$-2x + y - 6 = 0$

$2x - y + 6 = 0$

(ii) containing the point $(-3, -1)$ with slope $-\dfrac{3}{4}$

$x_1 = -3, \quad y_1 = -1, \quad m = -\dfrac{3}{4}$

$(y - y_1) = m(x - x_1)$

$(y + 1) = -\dfrac{3}{4}(x + 3)$

$4(y + 1) = -3(x + 3)$

(multiply both sides by 4)

$4y + 4 = -3x - 9$

$3x + 4y + 4 + 9 = 0$

$3x + 4y + 13 = 0$

Example 5

$a(-6, -1)$ and $b(-1, 2)$ are two points. Find the equation of the line ab.

Solution:

The slope is missing. We first find the slope and use **either** point to find the equation.

$(-6, -1) \qquad (-1, \; 2)$

$\;(x_1, \; y_1) \qquad\quad (x_2, y_2)$

$$m = \frac{y_2 - y_1}{x_2 - x_1}$$

$$m = \frac{2+1}{-1+6}$$

$$= \frac{3}{5}$$

$\therefore \quad$ slope of line ab is $\frac{3}{5}$

containing $(-6, -1)$ with slope $\frac{3}{5}$

$$x_1 = -6, \quad y_1 = -1, \quad m = -\frac{3}{5}$$

$$(y - y_1) = m(x - x_1)$$

$$(y + 1) = \frac{3}{5}(x + 6)$$

$$5(y + 1) = 3(x + 6)$$

(multiply both sides by 5)

$$5y + 5 = 3x + 18$$

$$-3x + 5y + 5 - 18 = 0$$

$$-3x + 5y - 13 = 0$$

$$3x - 5y + 13 = 0$$

Example 6

The equation of the line L is $2x - y + 1 = 0$. The line K contains the point $(1, 3)$.

If $K \perp L$, find the equation of K.

Solution:

We have a point $(1, 3)$. The slope is missing.

1. Find the slope of L

$2x - y + 1 = 0$

$$\text{Slope of } L = -\frac{\text{number in front of } x}{\text{number in front of } y}$$

$$= -\frac{2}{-1} = 2$$

2. Find the slope of K

$$\text{Slope of } L = 2 = \frac{2}{1}$$

$$L \perp K$$

$$\therefore \quad \text{slope of } K = -\frac{1}{2}$$

(turn upside down and change sign)

3. containing $(1, 3)$ with slope $-\frac{1}{2}$

$$x_1 = 1, \quad y_1 = 3, \quad m = -\frac{1}{2}$$

$$(y - y_1) = m(x - x_1)$$

$$(y - 3) = -\frac{1}{2}(x - 1)$$

$$2(y - 3) = -1(x - 1)$$

(multiply both sides by 2)

$$2y - 6 = -x + 1$$

$$x + 2y - 6 - 1 = 0$$

$$x + 2y - 7 = 0$$

Thus, the equation of the line K is $x + 2y - 7 = 0$

Example 7

(i) L is the line $x - 4y - 5 = 0$. Verify that the point $(1, -1)$ is on L.

(ii) K is the line $5x - 2y + 8 = 0$. The point $(2t, 3t)$ is on the line K. Find the value of t.

Solution:

(i) $L: x - 4y - 5 = 0$

Substitute $x = 1$ and $y = -1$

$(1, -1):$ $(1) - 4(-1) - 5$

$= 1 + 4 - 5$

$= 5 - 5$

$= 0$

$\therefore$ $(1, -1)$ is on the line L.

(ii) $K: 5x - 2y + 8 = 0$

Substitute $x = 2t$ and $y = 3t$

$(2t, 3t):$ $5(2t) - 2(3t) + 8 = 0$

$10t - 6t + 8 = 0$

$4t + 8 = 0$

$4t = -8$

$t = -2$

Example 8

(i) The point $(k, -2)$ is on the line $4x + 3y - 14 = 0$. Find the value of k.

(ii) The point $(1, 2)$ is on the line $3x + ty - 11 = 0$. Find the value of t.

Solution:

(i) $4x + 3y - 14 = 0$

Substitute $x = k$ and $y = -2$

$$(k, -2): \quad 4(k) + 3(-2) - 14 = 0$$

$$4k - 6 - 14 = 0$$

$$4k - 20 = 0$$

$$4k = 20$$

$$k = 5$$

(ii) $3x + ty - 11 = 0$

Substitute $x = 1$ and $y = 2$

$$(1, 2): \quad 3(1) + t(2) - 11 = 0$$

$$3 + 2t - 11 = 0$$

$$2t - 8 = 0$$

$$2t = 8$$

$$t = 4$$

Example 9

$a(2, 4)$, $b(7, 8)$, $c(2, 0)$, $d(7, 4)$ are four points. Show that $ab \parallel cd$.

Solution:

Let $m_1 =$ the slope of ab and $m_2 =$ the slope of cd.

$a(2, 4)$ $b(7, 8)$ $x_1 = 2$

(x_1, y_1) (x_2, y_2) $y_1 = 4$

$x_2 = 7$

$$m_1 = \frac{y_2 - y_1}{x_2 - x_1} \qquad y_2 = 8$$

$$= \frac{8 - 4}{7 - 2}$$

$$= \frac{4}{5}$$

$c(2, 0)$ $d(7, 4)$ $x_1 = 2$

(x_1, y_1) (x_2, y_2) $y_1 = 0$

$x_2 = 7$

$$m_2 = \frac{y_2 - y_1}{x_2 - x_1} \qquad y_2 = 4$$

$$= \frac{4 - 0}{7 - 2}$$

$$= \frac{4}{5}$$

$$m_1 = m_2$$

$$\therefore \quad ab \parallel cd$$

Example 10

$L: 5x + 2y - 10 = 0$ and $K: 2x - 5y + 20 = 0$ are two lines. Prove $L \perp K$.

Solution:

$$\text{Slope} = -\frac{\text{number in front of } x}{\text{number in front of } y}$$

Slope of L

$$= -\frac{5}{2}$$

Slope of K

$$= -\frac{2}{-5} = \frac{2}{5}$$

$$(\text{slope of } L) \times (\text{slope of } K) = -\frac{5}{2} \times \frac{2}{5} = -1$$

$$\therefore \quad L \perp K$$

Example 11

$L: 5x + 2y - 8 = 0$ and $K: x - 3y - 5 = 0$ are the equations of two lines.

Find the coordinates of q, the point of intersection of L and K.

Solution:

Point of intersection of two lines, $\therefore$ use simultaneous equations.
First write both equations in the form $ax + by = k$.

$$5x + 2y = 8 \quad \textcircled{L}$$
$$x - 3y = 5 \quad \textcircled{K}$$
$$\overline{15x + 6y = 24} \quad \textcircled{L} \times 3$$
$$2x - 6y = 10 \quad \textcircled{K} \times 2$$
$$\overline{17x = 34} \quad \text{(add)}$$
$$x = 2$$

Put $x = 2$ into $\textcircled{L}$ or $\textcircled{K}$

$$5x + 2y = 8 \quad \textcircled{L}$$
$$5(2) + 2y = 8$$
$$10 + 2y = 8$$
$$2y = -2$$
$$y = -1$$

$$\therefore \text{ the coordinates of } q \text{ are } (2, -1).$$

When the point of intersection contains fractions

If the point of intersection contains fractions, a very useful method is to:

> **Step 1:** Remove the y's and get a value for x.
>
> **Step 2:** Remove the x's and get a value for y.

Note: This method can be used even if the point of intersection contains whole numbers only.

Example 12

L: $2x - 3y + 2 = 0$ and M: $4x - y - 2 = 0$ are the equations of two lines.
Find the coordinates of p, the point of intersection of L and M.

Solution:

Point of intersection of two lines, $\therefore$ use simultaneous equations.
First, write both equations in the form $ax + by = k$.

$2x - 3y = -2$ (L)	$2x - 3y = -2$ (L)
$\underline{4x - y = 2}$ (M)	$\underline{4x - y = 2}$ (M)
$2x - 3y = -2$ (L)	$-4x + 6y = 4$ (L) × −2
$\underline{-12x + 3y = -6}$ (K) × −3	$\underline{4x - y = 2}$ (K)
$-10x = -8$ (add)	$5y = 6$ (add)
$10x = 8$	$y = \dfrac{6}{5}$
$x = \dfrac{8}{10}$	
$x = \dfrac{4}{5}$	

$\therefore$ the coordinates of p are $\left(\dfrac{4}{5}, \dfrac{6}{5}\right)$.

Example 13

The equation of the line K is $2x - 5y + 10 = 0$.
K cuts the x-axis at p and the y-axis at q.

(i) Find the coordinates of p and the coordinates of q.

(ii) Graph the line K.

(iii) Calculate the area of the triangle opq, where o is the origin.

Solution:

On the x-axis, $y = 0$. On the y-axis, $x = 0$.

(i)

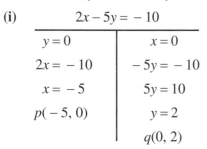

$$2x - 5y = -10$$

$y = 0$	$x = 0$
$2x = -10$	$-5y = -10$
$x = -5$	$5y = 10$
$p(-5, 0)$	$y = 2$
	$q(0, 2)$

(ii)

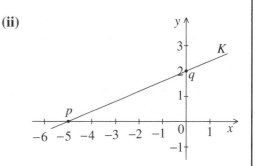

Plot the points $p(-5, 0)$, $q(0, 2)$
and draw a line through these points.

(iii) Area of the triangle $opq = \frac{1}{2}$ (base) (perpendicular height)

$$= \frac{1}{2}|op|.|oq| = \frac{1}{2}(5)(2) = 5$$

Example 14

Graph the line $3x + 4y = 0$.

Solution:

1. Let $x = 4$ (number in front of y).

$$3x + 4y = 0$$
$$\downarrow$$
$$3(4) + 4y = 0$$
$$12 + 4y = 0$$
$$4y = -12$$
$$y = -3$$

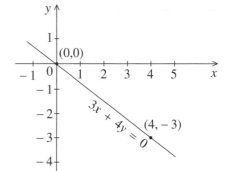

2. Plot the point $(4, -3)$.

3. Draw the line through the points $(4, -3)$ and $(0, 0)$.

Example 15

$L: x + 2y - 2 = 0$ and $K: x + 2y - 7 = 0$
are the equations of two lines.

The lines L and K, together with the line
$x = 5$ and the y-axis, form a parallelogram.
Find the coordinates of the vertices of the
parallelogram.

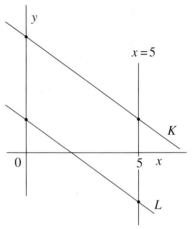

Solution:

We need to find the point of intersection of lines L and the y-axis and the lines K and
the y-axis. On the y-axis, $x = 0$.

$x = 0$

L: $\quad x + 2y - 2 = 0$	K: $\quad x + 2y - 7 = 0$
$0 + 2y - 2 = 0$	$0 + 2y - 7 = 0$
$2y = 2$	$2y = 7$
$y = 1$	$y = \dfrac{7}{2}$
Thus, the line L meets the y-axis at the point $(0, 1)$.	Thus, the line K meets the y-axis at the point $\left(0, \dfrac{7}{2}\right)$.

We need to find the point of intersection of the lines L and $x = 5$ and the lines K and $x = 5$.

$x = 5$

L: $\quad x + 2y - 2 = 0$	K: $\quad x + 2y - 7 = 0$
$5 + 2y - 2 = 0$	$5 + 2y - 7 = 0$
$2y + 3 = 0$	$2y - 2 = 0$
$2y = -3$	$2y = 2$
$y = -\dfrac{3}{2}$	$y = 1$
Thus, the line L meets the line $x = 5$ at the point $\left(5, -\dfrac{3}{2}\right).$	Thus, the line K meets the line $x = 5$ at the point $(5, 1).$

Thus, the required coordinates of the parallelogram are $(0, 1)$, $\left(0, \dfrac{7}{2}\right)$, $(5, 1)$, $\left(5, -\dfrac{3}{2}\right)$.

Example 16

$a(5, 3)$, $b(-1, 1)$ and $c(1, 5)$ are three points.

(i) Calculate the area of the triangle abc.

(ii) The diagonals of the square $bahg$ intersect at c.

Find the coordinates of h and the coordinates of g.

Solution:

(i) Move the point $(-1, 1)$ to $(0, 0)$.

$a(5, 3)$	$b(-1, 1)$	$c(1, 5)$
↓	↓	↓
$(6, 2)$	$(0, 0)$	$(2, 4)$
(x_1, y_1)		(x_2, y_2)

Rule: 'add 1 to x, subtract 1 from y'

Area of triangle

$$= \frac{1}{2}|x_1 y_2 - x_2 y_1|$$

$$= \frac{1}{2}|(6)(4) - (2)(2)|$$

$$= \frac{1}{2}|24 - 4|$$

$$= \frac{1}{2}|20|$$

$$= 10 \text{ square units}$$

(ii) Rough diagram (keep cyclic order)

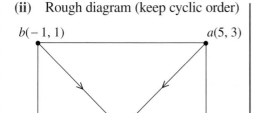

$bahg$ is a square.

$\therefore$ c is the midpoint of $[bh]$ and $[ag]$.

Thus, h is the image of b and g is the image of a under a central symmetry in c.

$b(-1, 1)$	$c(1, 5)$	$g(3, 9)$
●———→	●———→	●
	$(x + 2, y + 4)$	

$a(5, 3)$	$c(1, 5)$	$h(-3, 7)$
●———→	●———→	●
	$(x - 4, y + 2)$	

Thus, the required coordinates are $g(3, 9)$ and $h(-3, 7)$.

Example 17

$p(-2, -1)$, $q(2, -2)$, $r(a, b)$ and $s(2, -4)$ are the vertices of the parallelogram $pqrs$.

Find the coordinates of r.

Solution:

Make a rough diagram (keep cyclic order).

Since $pqrs$ is a parallelogram, $\overrightarrow{qr} = \overrightarrow{ps}$

(i.e. the movement from q to r is the same as the movement from p to s).

We find the rule that moves p to s.

Then apply this rule to q to find r.

$\overrightarrow{ps}: (-2, -1) \rightarrow (2, -4)$

Rule: add 4 to x, take 3 from y

$\overrightarrow{qr}: (2, -2) \rightarrow (2+4, -2-3) = (6, -5)$.

Thus, the coordinates of r are $(6, -5)$

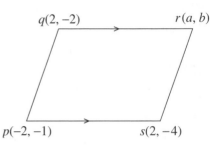

Note: By cyclic order we mean that the points are taken in either clockwise, or anti-clockwise, order.

Example 18

Verify that the point $(3, -4)$ is on the line $7x - 2y - 29 = 0$. Find the equation of the image of the line under the central symmetry in the point $(1, 1)$.

Solution:

$7x - 2y - 29 = 0$

$7(3) - 2(-4) - 29$ (put in $x = 3$ and $y = -4$)

$= 21 + 8 - 29$

$= 29 - 29 = 0$

$\therefore \ (3, -4)$ is on the line $7x - 2y - 29 = 0$

Translation: $(3, -4) \rightarrow (1, 1)$ **Rule:** Take 2 from x, add 5 to y

The image of $(1, 1)$ under this translation will be a point on the image line.

$(1, 1) \rightarrow (1 - 2, 1 + 5) = (-1, 6)$

Thus, the point $(-1, 6)$ will be on the image line.

Slope of the image line will have the same slope as the line $7x - 2y - 29 = 0$

Slope of the line $7x - 2y - 29 = 0$ is $-\dfrac{7}{-2} = \dfrac{7}{2}$

$\therefore$ the slope of image line $= \dfrac{7}{2}$.

Equation of image line: containing $(-1, 6)$ with slope $= \dfrac{7}{2}$

$x_1 = -1,$ $y_1 = 6,$ $m = \dfrac{7}{2}$

$(y - y_1) = m(x - x_1)$

$(y - 6) = \dfrac{7}{2}(x + 1)$

$2(y - 6) = 7(x + 1)$ [multiply both sides by 2]

$2y - 12 = 7x + 7$

$-7x + 2y - 12 - 7 = 0$

$-7x + 2y - 19 = 0$

$7x - 2y + 19 = 0$

$\therefore$ the equation of the image line is $7x - 2y + 19 = 0$

Example 19

$a(-2, 4)$, $b(2, 2)$ and $c(5, 3)$ are three points. Find:

(i) $|ab|$

(ii) the midpoint of $[bc]$

(iii) the area of triangle abc

(iv) the slope of ab

(v) the equation of the line ab

(vi) the equation of the line, L, through the point c where $L \perp ab$

(vii) the coordinates of p the point of intersection of the lines L and ab

(viii) the coordinates of d, the image of c under axial symmetry in the line ab.

Solution:

(i) $|ab|$

$a(-2, 4)$ and $b(2, 2)$

$x_1 = -2 \quad x_2 = 2$

$y_1 = 4 \quad\quad y_2 = 2$

$|ab| = \sqrt{(x_2 - x_1)^2 + (y_2 - y_1)^2}$

$ = \sqrt{(2+2)^2 + (2-4)^2}$

$ = \sqrt{(4)^2 + (-2)^2}$

$ = \sqrt{16 + 4}$

$ = \sqrt{20}$

$\therefore \quad |ab| = \sqrt{20}$

(ii) Midpoint of $[bc]$

$b(2, 2)$ and $c(5, 3)$

$x_1 = 2 \quad\quad x_2 = 5$

$y_1 = 2 \quad\quad y_2 = 3$

$\text{Midpoint} = \left(\dfrac{x_1 + x_2}{2}, \dfrac{y_1 + y_2}{2} \right)$

$\phantom{\text{Midpoint}} = \left(\dfrac{2+5}{2}, \dfrac{2+3}{2} \right)$

$\phantom{\text{Midpoint}} = \left(\dfrac{7}{2}, \dfrac{5}{2} \right)$

$\therefore \quad \left(\dfrac{7}{2}, \dfrac{5}{2} \right)$ is the midpoint of $[bc]$

(iii) Area of triangle abc

$a(-2, 4)$, $b(2, 2)$ and $c(5, 3)$

Map (move) the point $a(-2, 4)$ to $(0, 0)$

$$
\begin{array}{ccc}
(-2, 4) & (2, 2) & (5, 3) \\
\downarrow & \downarrow & \downarrow \\
(0, 0) & (4, -2) & (7, -1) \\
& (x_1, y_1) & (x_2, y_2)
\end{array}
$$

Rule: 'add 2 to x, take 4 from y'

Area of triangle

$= \dfrac{1}{2} |x_1 y_2 - x_2 y_1|$

$= \dfrac{1}{2} |(4)(-1) - (7)(-2)|$

$= \dfrac{1}{2} |-4 + 14|$

$= \dfrac{1}{2} |10|$

$= 5$ square units

(iv) Slope of *ab*

$a(-2, 4)$ and $b(2, 2)$

$x_1 = -2 \qquad x_2 = 2$

$y_1 = 4 \qquad y_2 = 2$

$m = \dfrac{y_2 - y_1}{x_2 - x_1}$

$= \dfrac{2 - 4}{2 + 2}$

$= \dfrac{-2}{4}$

$= -\dfrac{1}{2}$

(v) Equation of *ab*

containing $(-2, 4)$ with slope $= -\dfrac{1}{2}$

$x_1 = -2 \qquad y_1 = 4 \qquad m = -\dfrac{1}{2}$

$(y - y_1) = m(x - x_1)$

$(y - 4) = -\dfrac{1}{2}(x + 2)$

$2(y - 4) = -1(x + 2)$

$2y - 8 = -x - 2$

$x + 2y - 8 + 2 = 0$

$x + 2y - 6 = 0$

(vi) The equation of the line, *L*, through the point *c* where $L \perp ab$

Through $c(5, 3)$ and $L \perp ab$

Slope of $ab = -\dfrac{1}{2}$

$\therefore$ perpendicular slope $= \dfrac{2}{1} = 2$

(turn upside down and change sign)

containing $(5, 3)$ with slope $= 2$

$x_1 = 5 \qquad y_1 = 3 \qquad m = 2$

$(y - y_1) = m(x - x_1)$

$(y - 3) = 2(x - 5)$

$y - 3 = 2x - 10$

$-2x + y - 3 + 10 = 0$

$-2x + y + 7 = 0$

$2x - y - 7 = 0$

(vii) The coordinates of *p*, the point of intersection of the lines *L* and *ab*.

$\therefore$ use simultaneous equations

$x + 2y = 6 \qquad\qquad (ab)$

$2x - y = 7 \qquad\qquad (L)$

$\overline{}$

$x + 2y = 6 \qquad\qquad (ab)$

$4x - 2y = 14 \qquad\quad (L \times 2)$

$\overline{}$

$5x = 20 \qquad\qquad\;\; (\text{add})$

$x = 4$

Put $x = 4$ into L or (ab)

$x + 2y = 6 \qquad\qquad (ab)$

$\downarrow$

$4 + 2y = 6$

$2y = 6 - 4$

$2y = 2$

$y = 1$

Thus, the coordinates of p are $(4, 1)$.

(viii) **The coordinates of *d*, the image of *c* under axial symmetry in the line *ab*.**

In this type of question a rough diagram is very useful.

$c(5, 3)$ is on L, $L \perp ab$ and the point of intersection of L and ab is $p(4, 1)$.

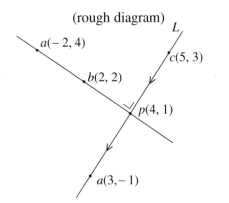

(rough diagram)

Translation from c to p.

$c(5, 3) \rightarrow p(4, 1)$

'Take 1 from x, take 2 from y'.

Apply this translation to the point $p(4, 1)$ to find the coordinates of d.

$p(4, 1) \rightarrow (4 - 1, 1 - 2) \rightarrow d(3, - 1)$.

Thus, the coordinates of d are $(3, - 1)$.

Note: As $L \perp ab$, and the point of intersection of L and ab is $p(4, 1)$, the coordinates of d are simply found by the central symmetry of $c(5, 3)$ in the point $p(4, 1)$.

Example 20

$a(4, 1)$ and $b(7, k)$ are two points. If $|ab| = 5$, find the two values of k.

Solution:

$a(4, 1)$ $b(7, k)$

(x_1, y_1) (x_2, y_2)

Given: $\qquad\qquad\qquad |ab| = 5$

$\therefore \quad \sqrt{(x_2 - x_1)^2 + (y_2 - y_1)^2} = 5$

$\therefore \quad (x_2 - x_1)^2 + (y_2 - y_1)^2 = 25 \qquad$ (square both sides, removes $\sqrt{\ }$)

$\therefore \quad (7 - 4)^2 + (k - 1)^2 = 25 \qquad$ (put in $x_2 = 7$, $x_1 = 4$, $y_2 = k$ and $y_1 = 1$)

$(3)^2 + (k^2 - 2k + 1) = 25 \qquad ((k - 1)^2 = k^2 - 2k + 1)$

$9 + k^2 - 2k + 1 = 25$

$k^2 - 2k + 10 = 25 \qquad$ (simplify the left-hand side)

$k^2 - 2k - 15 = 0 \qquad$ (subtract 25 from both sides)

$(k + 3)(k - 5) = 0$

$k + 3 = 0 \qquad$ or $\qquad k - 5 = 0$

$k = -3 \quad$ or $\qquad k = 5$

Chapter 9. COORDINATE GEOMETRY OF THE CIRCLE

Equation of a Circle

Note: Two quantities are needed to find the equation of a circle:

       1.   Centre   **2.**   Radius

> The equation of a circle, centre (0, 0) and radius r, is
> $$x^2 + y^2 = r^2$$

> The equation of a circle, centre (h, k) and radius r, is
> $$(x - h)^2 + (y - k)^2 = r^2$$

Note: When drawing a circle always make sure the scales are the same on both the x- and y- axes. When tackling problems on the circle a diagram is always very useful.

Points Inside, On or Outside a Circle

Method 1:

To find whether a point is inside, on or outside a circle, calculate the distance from the centre, (0, 0), to the point and compare this distance with the radius. Three cases arise:

Inside

On

Outside

1. Distance from the centre to the point is **less** than the radius.

    ∴   point inside the circle

2. Distance from the centre to the point is **equal** to the radius.

    ∴   point on the circle

3. Distance from the centre to the point is **greater** than the radius.

    ∴   point outside the circle

Method 2:

> If the coordinates of a point satisfy the equation of a circle, then the point is **on** the circle. Otherwise, the point is either **inside** or **outside** the circle. By substituting the coordinates into the equation of the circle, one of the following situations can arise:
>
> > 1. $x^2 + y^2 < r^2$, the point is **inside** the circle.
> > 2. $x^2 + y^2 = r^2$, the point is **on** the circle.
> > 3. $x^2 + y^2 > r^2$, the point is **outside** the circle.

The same applies if the circle is of the form $(x - h)^2 + (y - k)^2 = r^2$.

Equation of a Tangent to a Circle at a Given Point

A tangent is perpendicular to the radius that joins the centre of a circle to the point of tangency.

This fact is used to find the slope of the tangent.

In the diagram on the right, the radius, R, is perpendicular to the tangent, T, at the point of tangency, p.

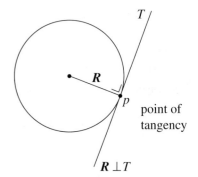

point of tangency

The equation of a tangent to a circle at a given point is found with the following steps:

> 1. Find the slope of the radius to the point of tangency.
>
> 2. Turn this slope upside down and change its sign.
>   This gives the slope of the tangent.
>
> 3. Use the coordinates of the point of contact and the slope of the tangent at this point in the formula:
>
> $$(y - y_1) = m(x - x_1).$$
>
>   This gives the equation of the tangent.

A diagram is often very useful.

Intersection of a Line and a Circle

To find the points where a line and a circle meet, the '**method of substitution**' between their equations is used.

The method involves the following three steps:

1. Get x or y on its own from the equation of the line.
   (Look carefully and select the variable which will make the working easier.)

2. Substitute for this same variable into the equation of the circle and solve the resultant quadratic equation.

3. Substitute **separately** the value(s) obtained in step 2 into the linear equation in step 1 to find the corresponding value(s) of the other variable.

Note: If there is only **one point of intersection** between a line and a circle, then the line is a **tangent** to the circle.

Transformations

Under a central symmetry, axial symmetry or translation a circle will keep the **same** radius. Hence, all that is needed is to find the image of the centre under the particular transformation.

The equation of a circle under a transformation is found with the following steps:

1. Find the **centre** and **radius** of the given circle.

2. Find the image of the centre under the given transformation.

3. Use this new centre and the radius of the original circle in the equation:
$$(x - h)^2 + (y - k)^2 = r^2.$$

As before, a diagram is very useful.

Circle Intersecting the Axes

To find where a circle intersects the axes we use the following:

The circle intersects the x-axis at $y = 0$

The circle intersects the y-axis at $x = 0$

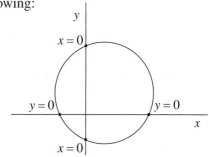

Example 1

Find the radius of each of the following circles:

(i) $x^2 + y^2 = 36$ **(ii)** $x^2 + y^2 = 8$

Solution:

Compare each to $x^2 + y^2 = r^2$

(i) $x^2 + y^2 = 36$

$\quad x^2 + y^2 = r^2$

$\therefore \qquad r^2 = 36$

$\qquad r = \sqrt{36} = 6$

(ii) $x^2 + y^2 = 8$

$\quad x^2 + y^2 = r^2$

$\therefore \qquad r^2 = 8$

$\qquad r = \sqrt{8}$

Example 2

C is a circle with centre $(0, 0)$. It passes through the point $(1, -5)$.

Write down the equation of C.

Solution:

The centre of the circle C is $(0, 0)$. Therefore C is of the form $x^2 + y^2 = r^2$.

Method 1:

Substitute $x = 1$ and $y = -5$ into this equation:

$$x^2 + y^2 = r^2$$
$$(1)^2 + (-5)^2 = r^2$$
$$1 + 25 = r^2$$
$$26 = r^2$$

$\therefore$ C is the circle $x^2 + y^2 = 26$

Method 2:

Find the radius of the circle C.
The radius is the distance from the centre $(0, 0)$ to the point $(1, -5)$.
Using the distance formula:

$$r = \sqrt{(1-0)^2 + (-5-0)^2}$$
$$r = \sqrt{(1)^2 + (-5)^2} = \sqrt{1 + 25} = \sqrt{26}$$
$$x^2 + y^2 = r^2 = \left(\sqrt{26}\right)^2 = 26$$

$\therefore$ C is the circle $x^2 + y^2 = 26$

Example 3

The circle C has equation $x^2 + y^2 = 16$

(i) Write down the centre and radius length of C.

(ii) Find the coordinates of the points where C intersects the x- and y-axes.

(iii) Draw a diagram of C.

Solution:

(i) $x^2 + y^2 = 16$

As the equation is in the form $x^2 + y^2 = r^2$, the centre is $(0, 0)$.

$$r^2 = 16$$
$$r = \sqrt{16} = 4$$

Thus, the radius length is 4.

(ii) $x^2 + y^2 = 16$

On the x-axis, $y = 0$

$$\therefore \quad x^2 = 16$$
$$x = \pm\sqrt{16} = \pm 4$$

Thus, C intersects the x-axis at $(4, 0)$ and $(0, -4)$.

On the y-axis, $x = 0$

$$\therefore \quad y^2 = 16$$
$$y = \pm\sqrt{16} = \pm 4$$

Thus, C intersects the y-axis at $(0, 4)$ and $(0, -4)$.

(iii) Diagram of C

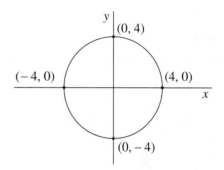

Note: When drawing a circle the scales on the x- and y-axes must be the same.

Example 4

(i) Find the equation of the circle, centre $(3, -2)$ and radius $\sqrt{5}$.

(ii) Find the centre and radius of the circle, $(x-4)^2 + (y+5)^2 = 9$

Solution:

(i) Centre $(3, -2)$, radius $\sqrt{5}$

$h = 3, k = -2, r = \sqrt{5}$

Equation of the circle is:

$(x-h)^2 + (y-k)^2 = r^2$

$(x-3)^2 + (y+2)^2 = \left(\sqrt{5}\right)^2$

$(x-3)^2 + (y+2)^2 = 5$

(ii) $(x-4)^2 + (y+5)^2 = 9$

Compare exactly to:

$(x-h)^2 + (y-k)^2 = r^2$
$\quad\downarrow\qquad\quad\downarrow\qquad\;\downarrow$
$(x-4)^2 + (y+5)^2 = 9$

$\therefore\; h = 4, k = -5, r = 3$

Thus, centre $= (4, -5)$ and radius $= 3$.

Example 5

The circle C has equation $x^2 + y^2 = 17$. Using algebra, verify that the point:

(i) $(2, -3)$ is inside C (ii) $(-4, -1)$ is on C (iii) $(-5, 1)$ is outside of C

Solution:

$C: x^2 + y^2 = 17$

$(2, -3)$	$(-4, -1)$	$(-5, 1)$
put in $x = 2$ and $y = -3$	put in $x = -4$ and $y = -1$	put in $x = -5$ and $y = 1$
$(2)^2 + (-3)^2$	$(-4)^2 + (-1)^2$	$(-5)^2 + (1)^2$
$= 4 + 9$	$= 16 + 1$	$= 25 + 1$
$= 13 < 17$	$= 17$	$= 26 > 17$
$\therefore (2, -3)$ is **inside** C	$\therefore (-4, -1)$ is **on** C	$\therefore (-5, 1)$ is **outside** C

Example 6

The equation of the circle, C, is $(x-3)^2 + (y+2)^2 = 25$.

Determine if the points $(7, -3)$, $(-1, -5)$ and $(9, 2)$ are inside, on, or outside C.

Solution:

$C: (x-3)^2 + (y+2)^2 = 25$

$(7, -3)$	$(-1, -5)$	$(9, 2)$
put in $x = 7$ and $y = -3$	put in $x = -1$ and $y = -5$	put in $x = 9$ and $y = 2$
$(7-3)^2 + (-3+2)^2$	$(-1-3)^2 + (-5+2)^2$	$(9-3)^2 + (2+2)^2$
$= (4)^2 + (-1)^2$	$= (-4)^2 + (-3)^2$	$= (6)^2 + (4)^2$
$= 16 + 1$	$= 16 + 9$	$= 36 + 16$
$= 17 < 25$	$= 25 = 25$	$= 52 > 25$
$\therefore (7, -3)$ is inside C	$\therefore (-1, -5)$ is on C	$\therefore (9, 2)$ is outside C

Example 7

The line $2x + y - 10 = 0$ intersects the circle $x^2 + y^2 = 40$ at the points a and b.

(i) Find the coordinates of a and the coordinates of b.

(ii) Show the line, the circle and the points of intersection on a coordinate diagram.

Solution:

(i) Line $2x + y - 10 = 0$ and circle $x^2 + y^2 = 40$.

1. $2x + y - 10 = 0$

$\qquad\qquad y = 10 - 2x \qquad$ (get x on its own from the line equation)

2. Substitute $(10 - 2x)$ for y into the equation of the circle.

$$x^2 + y^2 = 40$$

$x^2 + (10 - 2x)^2 = 40 \qquad$ (put in $(10 - 2x)$ for y)

$x^2 + 100 - 40x + 4x^2 = 40 \qquad$ ($(10 - 2x)^2 = 100 - 40x + 4x^2$)

$5x^2 - 40x + 100 = 40 \qquad$ ($x^2 + 4x^2 = 5x^2$)

$5x^2 - 40x + 60 = 0 \qquad$ (subtract 40 from both sides)

$x^2 - 8x + 12 = 0 \qquad$ (divide both sides by 5)

$(x - 2)(x - 6) = 0$

$x - 2 = 0 \quad$ or $\quad x - 6 = 0$

$x = 2 \quad$ or $\quad x = 6$

3. Substitute separately, $x = 2$ and $x = 6$, into the equation of the line in step 1 to find the y coordinates.

$$y = 10 - 2x$$

$x = 2$: $\quad y = 10 - 2(2)$

$\quad\quad\quad y = 10 - 4$

$\quad\quad\quad y = 6$

$\quad\quad\quad$ point $(2, 6)$

$$y = 10 - 2x$$

$x = 6$: $\quad y = 10 - 2(6)$

$\quad\quad\quad y = 10 - 12$

$\quad\quad\quad y = -2$

$\quad\quad\quad$ point $(6, -2)$

The line $2x + y - 10 = 0$ intersects the circle $x^2 + y^2 = 40$ at the points a $(2, 6)$ and b $(6, -2)$.

(ii) The diagram illustrates the situation.

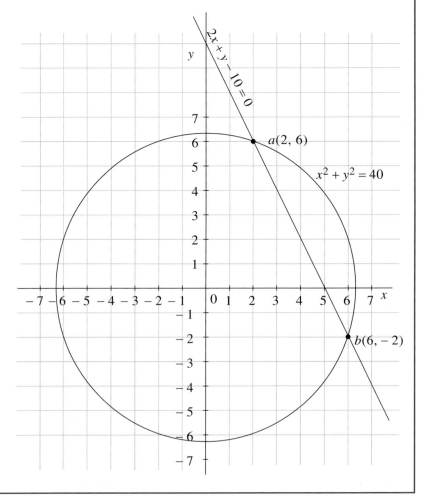

Example 8

Prove that the line $x - 3y + 10 = 0$ is a tangent to the circle with equation $x^2 + y^2 = 10$ and find the coordinates of the point of contact.

Solution:

Line $x - 3y + 10 = 0$ and circle $x^2 + y^2 = 10$

1. $x - 3y + 10 = 0$

                 $x = (3y - 10)$ (*x* on its own from the line)

2. $x^2 + y^2 = 10$

       $(3y - 10)^2 + y^2 = 10$ (put in $(3y - 10)$ for *x*)

    $9y^2 - 60y + 100 + y^2 = 10$ $((3y - 10)^2 = 9y^2 - 60y + 100)$

      $10y^2 - 60y + 100 = 10$ $(9y^2 + y^2 = 10y^2)$

       $10y^2 - 60y + 90 = 0$ (subtract 10 from both sides)

         $y^2 - 6y + 9 = 0$ (divide both sides by 10)

        $(y - 3)(y - 3) = 0$

          $y - 3 = 0$ or $y - 3 = 0$

              $y = 3$

3.   Put in $y = 3$ into the equation of the line in step 1 to find *x*.

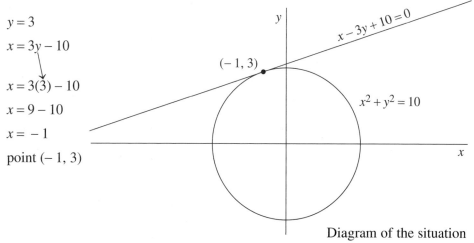

     $y = 3$

     $x = 3y - 10$

     $x = 3(3) - 10$

     $x = 9 - 10$

     $x = -1$

     point $(-1, 3)$

Diagram of the situation

The line $x - 3y + 10 = 0$ meets the circle $x^2 + y^2 = 10$ at the point $(-1, 3)$.
Since there is only **one point of contact** between the line and the circle, the line **is** a tangent to the circle.

181

Example 9

The circle C has equation $(x+2)^2 + (y-1)^2 = 20$.

(i) Write down the radius length and the coordinates of the centre of C.

(ii) C intersects the y-axis at the points a and b.

Find **(a)** the coordinates of the points a and b, an **(b)** $|ab|$.

Draw a coordinate diagram, showing the circle and where the circle intersects the y-axis.

Solution:

(i)

$$(x+2)^2 + (y-1)^2 = 20$$

$$\text{Centre} = (-2, 1) \qquad \text{Radius} = \sqrt{20}$$

(ii) **(a)** $(x+2)^2 + (y-1)^2 = 20$ On the y-axis, $x = 0$.

$(0+2)^2 + (y-1)^2 = 20$ (put in $x = 0$)

$(2)^2 + (y-1)^2 = 20$

$4 + y^2 - 2y + 1 = 20$

$y^2 - 2y + 5 = 20$

$y^2 - 2y - 15 = 0$

$(y+3)(y-5) = 0$

$y + 3 = 0$ or $y - 5 = 0$

$y = -3$ or $y = 5$

∴ the circle intersects the y-axis at -3 and 5.

Thus, the required coordinates are $a\,(0, -3)$ and $b\,(0, 5)$.

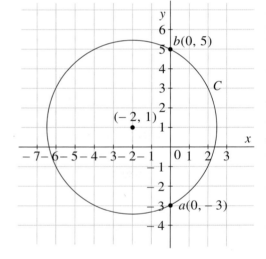

(b) Using the distance formula:

$$|ab| = \sqrt{(0-0)^2 + (5+3)^2} = \sqrt{0^2 + 8^2} = \sqrt{0 + 64} = \sqrt{64} = 8$$

Alternatively, from the diagram the distance between a and b is 8.

Example 10

$a(3, 5)$ and $b(-1, -1)$ are the end points of a diameter of a circle K.
(i) Find the centre and radius length of K.
(ii) Find the equation of K.
(iii) K intersects the x-axis at p and q, where $p < q$. Find the coordinates of p and q.

Solution:

(i) Centre

The centre is the midpoint of $[ab]$

$(3, 5) \qquad\qquad (-1, -1)$

$(x_1, y_1) \qquad\quad (x_2, y_2)$

$$\text{Centre} = \left(\frac{x_1 + x_2}{2}, \frac{y_1 + y_2}{2}\right) = \left(\frac{3-1}{2}, \frac{5-1}{2}\right) = \left(\frac{2}{2}, \frac{4}{2}\right) = (1, 2)$$

Radius

The radius is the distance from the centre $(1, 2)$ to either $(3, 5)$ or $(-1, -1)$.
Distance from $(1, 2)$ to $(3, 5)$.

$\qquad\qquad (x_1, y_1)\ (x_2, y_2)$

$$\text{Radius} = \sqrt{(x_2 - x_1)^2 + (y_2 - y_1)^2}$$

$$= \sqrt{(3-1)^2 + (5-2)^2} = \sqrt{2^2 + 3^2} = \sqrt{4+9} = \sqrt{13}$$

(ii) Centre $(1, 2)$, radius $\sqrt{13}$

$h = 1, k = 2$ and $r = \sqrt{13}$

$(x - h)^2 + (y - k)^2 = r^2$

$(x - 1)^2 + (y - 2)^2 = \left(\sqrt{13}\right)^2$

$K: (x - 1)^2 + (y - 2)^2 = 13$

Diagram of the situation

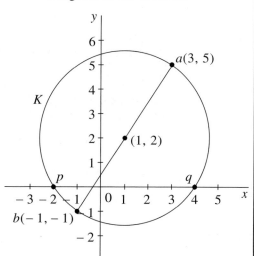

(iii) On the x-axis $y = 0$

$\therefore \quad (x - 1)^2 + (0 - 2)^2 = 13 \quad$ (put in $y = 0$)

$\qquad x^2 - 2x + 1 + 4 = 13$

$\qquad\quad x^2 - 2x - 8 = 0$

$\qquad (x + 2)(x - 4) = 0$

$\qquad x + 2 = 0 \quad$ or $\quad x - 4 = 0$

$\qquad x = -2 \quad$ or $\qquad x = 4$

$\therefore$ K intersects the x-axis at -2 and 4.

Thus, the coordinates where K intersects the x-axis are $p\ (-2, 0)$ and $q\ (4, 0)$.

Example 11

The vertices of a triangle are $p(0, 2)$, $q(5, 1)$ and $r(4, -4)$.

The circle K passes through the points p, q and r.

(i) On a coordinate diagram, draw the triangle pqr.

(ii) Verify that $\angle pqr$ is a right angle.

(iii) Find the coordinates of the point c, the centre of K, and draw K.

(iv) Find the equation of K.

Solution:

(i)

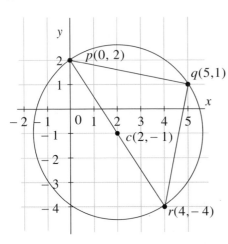

(ii) $p(0, 2)$, $q(5, 1)$, $r(4, -4)$

Using the slope formula: $m = \dfrac{y_2 - y_1}{x_2 - x_1}$

Slope of $pq = \dfrac{1-2}{5-0} = \dfrac{-1}{5} = -\dfrac{1}{5}$

Slope of $qr = \dfrac{-4-1}{4-5} = \dfrac{-5}{-1} = \dfrac{5}{1} = 5$

(Slope of pq) × (Slope of qr)

$= -\dfrac{1}{5} \times 5 = -1$

$\therefore \quad pq \perp qr$

$\therefore \quad \angle pqr$ is a right-angle.

(iii) Triangle pqr is a right-angled triangle and the right angle is a q.

Thus, the centre c, of the circle K is the midpoint of $[pr]$.

$p(0, 2) \qquad r(4, -4)$

$(x_1, y_1) \qquad (x_2, y_2)$

Centre $c = $ midpoint of $[pr] = \left(\dfrac{x_1 + x_2}{2}, \dfrac{y_1 + y_2}{2} \right) = \left(\dfrac{0+4}{2}, \dfrac{2-4}{2} \right)$

$= \left(\dfrac{4}{2}, \dfrac{-2}{2} \right) = (2, -1)$

With $c(2, -1)$ as centre and $|cp|$ as radius, the circle K is drawn on the diagram.

(iv) We have the centre, $c(2, -1)$ of the circle and need the radius.

Radius $= |cp|$

$c(2, -1)$ $p(0, 2)$

(x_1, y_1) (x_2, y_2)

Radius $= \sqrt{(x_2 - x_1)^2 + (y_2 - y_1)^2}$

$\qquad = \sqrt{(0-2)^2 + (2+1)^2}$

$\qquad = \sqrt{(-2)^2 + (3)^2} = \sqrt{4+9} = \sqrt{13}$

Equation of the circle K.

Centre $= (2, -1)$ Radius $= \sqrt{13}$

$h = 2$ $k = -1$ $r = \sqrt{13}$

$(x - h)^2 + (y - k)^2 = r^2$

$(x - 2)^2 + (y + 1)^2 = \left(\sqrt{13}\right)^2$

$K:$ $(x - 2)^2 + (y + 1)^2 = 13$

Example 12

State the centre and radius length of the circle

$$K: (x + 1)^2 + (y - 3)^2 = 4$$

Find the equation of the image of K under the central symmetry in the point $(2, 1)$.

Solution:

$(x + 1)^2 + (y - 3)^2 = 4$

1.   Centre $= (-1, 3)$

Radius $= \sqrt{4} = 2$

Given circle has centre
$(-1, 3)$ and radius 2.

2.   The new centre will be
the image of $(-1, 3)$
under a central symmetry
in $(2, 1)$.

$(-1, 3) \rightarrow (2, 1) \rightarrow (5, -1)$

Thus the image circle has
centre $(5, -1)$ and radius 2.

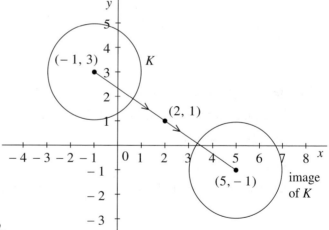

3. $h = 5$, $k = -1$, $r = 2$

$(x - h)^2 + (y - k)^2 = r^2$

$(x - 5)^2 + (y + 1)^2 = 2^2$

$(x - 5)^2 + (y + 1)^2 = 4$

Thus, the equation of the image of K is $(x - 5)^2 + (y + 1)^2 = 4$.

Example 13

The equation of the circle, C, is $(x + 1)^2 + (y - 1)^2 = 13$.

Find the centre and radius of C.

Show that the point $(2, -1)$ is on C and represent C on a diagram.

T is a tangent to C at $(2, -1)$. Find the equation of T.

K is a second tangent to C and $K \parallel T$. Find the equation of K and the distance between T and K.

Solution:

$$(x + 1)^2 + (y - 1)^2 = 13$$

Compare to: $(x - h)^2 + (y - k)^2 = r^2$

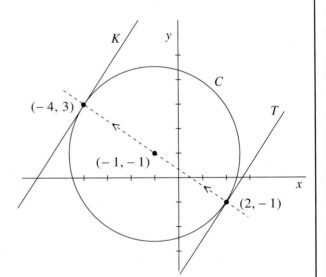

$$h = -1, \quad k = 1, \quad r = \sqrt{13}$$

Thus, the centre of C is $(-1, 1)$ and the radius is $\sqrt{13}$.

$C: (x + 1)^2 + (y - 1)^2 = 13$

Is $(2, -1)$ on the circle?
Put in $x = 2$ and $y = -1$.

$$(2 + 1)^2 + (-1 - 1)^2$$
$$= (3)^2 + (-2)^2$$
$$= 9 + 4$$
$$= 13$$

$\therefore (2, -1)$ is on the circle C.

Equation of T

1. We find the slope of the radius from the centre $(-1, 1)$ to the point $(2, -1)$.

$$\begin{matrix} (-1, 1) & (2, -1) \\ (x_1, y_1) & (x_2, y_2) \end{matrix}$$

Slope of radius $= m = \dfrac{y_2 - y_1}{x_2 - x_1} = \dfrac{-1 - 1}{2 + 1} = \dfrac{-2}{3} = -\dfrac{2}{3}$

2. $\therefore$ Slope of $T = \dfrac{3}{2}$ (turn upside down and change sign)

3. Point $(2, -1)$ and slope $\frac{3}{2}$

$$x_1 = 2, \qquad y_1 = -1, \qquad m = \frac{3}{2}$$

$$(y - y_1) = m(x - x_1)$$

$$(y + 1) = \frac{3}{2}(x - 2)$$

$$2(y + 1) = 3(x - 2) \quad \text{(multiply both sides by 2)}$$

$$2y + 2 = 3x - 6$$

$$-3x + 2y + 2 + 6 = 0$$

$$-3x + 2y + 8 = 0$$

$$3x - 2y - 8 = 0$$

Thus, the equation of T is $3x - 2y - 8 = 0$

$K \parallel T$, $\therefore$ Slope of K is also $\frac{3}{2}$.

The image of $(2, -1)$ under a central symmetry in the centre $(-1, 1)$ will be a point on the tangent K.

$$(2, -1) \rightarrow (-1, 1) \rightarrow (-4, 3)$$

$\therefore$ the image of $(2, -1)$ under central symmetry in $(-1, 1)$ is $(-4, 3)$.

Thus, the point $(-4, 3)$ is on K and K has slope $\frac{3}{2}$.

Point $(-4, 3)$ and slope $= \frac{3}{2}$

$$x_1 = -4, \qquad y_1 = 3, \qquad m = \frac{3}{2}$$

$$(y - y_1) = m(x - x_1)$$

$$(y - 3) = \frac{3}{2}(x + 4)$$

$$2(y - 3) = 3(x + 4)$$

$$2y - 6 = 3x + 12$$

$$-3x + 2y - 6 - 12 = 0$$

$$-3x + 2y - 18 = 0$$

$$3x - 2y + 18 = 0$$

$\therefore$ equation of K is $3x - 2y + 18 = 0$

Distance between T and K

= length of diameter

= 2 (length of radius)

$= 2(\sqrt{13})$

$= 2\sqrt{13}$

Thus, the distance between T and K is $2\sqrt{13}$

[we could also find the distance between the points $(2, -1)$ and $(-4, 3)$]

Example 14

Find the equation of the circle, C, with centre (3, 2) which touches the x-axis at one point only.

T is a tangent to C and T is parallel to the y-axis.

Find the two possible equations for T.

Solution:

Draw a diagram:

The centre $= (3, 2) = (h, k)$

C touches the x- axis at (3, 0) (one point)

Radius $=$ distance from (3, 2) to (3, 0) $= 2$

$h = 3,$ $\quad k = 2,$ $\quad r = 2$

$\quad (x - h)^2 + (y - k)^2 = r^2$

$\quad (x - 3)^2 + (y - 2)^2 = 2^2$

$C: (x - 3)^2 + (y - 2)^2 = 4$

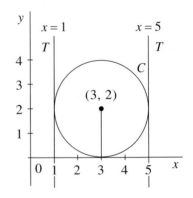

From the diagram the two tangents to C which are parallel to the y-axis are:

$$x = 1 \text{ and } x = 5$$

Example 15

The point (5, k) is on the circle $(x - 2)^2 + (y - 3)^2 = 25$.

Find the two values of k.

Solution:

$$(x - 2)^2 + (y - 3)^2 = 25$$

$\therefore \quad (5 - 2)^2 + (k - 3)^2 = 25$ $\qquad$ (put in $x = 5$ and $y = k$)

$\quad (3)^2 + k^2 - 6k + 9 = 25$ $\qquad\qquad$ $((k - 3)^2 = k - 6k + 9)$

$\quad\quad 9 + k^2 - 6k + 9 = 25$

$\quad\quad\quad k^2 - 6k + 18 = 25$

$\quad\quad\quad\quad k^2 - 6k - 7 = 0$

$\quad\quad\quad (k - 7)(k + 1) = 0$

$\quad\quad k - 7 = 0 \quad$ or $\quad k + 1 = 0$

$\quad\quad\quad k = 7 \quad$ or $\quad k = -1$

Thus, the two values of k are 7 or -1.

Example 16

The point $(t, 2t)$ is on the circle $(x+2)^2+(y-1)^2 = 10$. Find the two possible values of t.

Solution:

The point $(t, 2t)$ is on the circle $(x+2)^2+(y-1)^2 = 10$.

$$(x+2)^2+(y-1)^2 = 10$$

$(t+2)^2+(2t-1)^2 = 10$ (put in $x = t$ and $y = 2t$)

$t^2+4t+4+4t^2-4t+1 = 10$ $((t+2)^2 = t^2+4t+4$ and $(2t-1)^2 = 4t^2-4t+1)$

$5t^2+5 = 10$ $(t^2+4t^2 = 5t^2)$

$5t^2 = 5$ (subtract 5 from both sides)

$t^2 = 1$ (divide both sides by 5)

$t = \pm\sqrt{1}$ (take the square root of both sides)

$t = \pm 1$

Chapter 10. GEOMETRY AND ENLARGEMENTS

Proofs

There are 10 theorems to be proved on our course.
A proof in geometry should consist of five steps:

---

1. **Diagram**
   Draw a clear diagram, if not given, from the information given in the question.

2. **Given**
   State what is given.

3. **To prove**
   State what is to be proved.

4. **Construction**
   If necessary, state any extra lines that have to be added to the diagram to help in the proof. Also at this stage, if necessary, it can simplify the work if the angles are labelled with a number.

5. **Proof**
   Set out each line of the proof, justifying each statement made.

1.

> The sum of the degree-measures of the angles of a triangle is 180°.

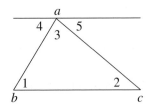

Given:	Triangle abc with angles 1, 2 and 3.
To prove:	$\lvert\angle 1\rvert + \lvert\angle 2\rvert + \lvert\angle 3\rvert = 180°$
Construction:	Draw a line through a, parallel to bc. Label angles 4 and 5.
Proof:	$\lvert\angle 1\rvert = \lvert\angle 4\rvert$ and $\lvert\angle 2\rvert = \lvert\angle 5\rvert$ (alternate angles)
$\therefore$	$\lvert\angle 1\rvert + \lvert\angle 2\rvert + \lvert\angle 3\rvert = \lvert\angle 4\rvert + \lvert\angle 5\rvert + \lvert\angle 3\rvert$
but	$\lvert\angle 4\rvert + \lvert\angle 5\rvert + \lvert\angle 3\rvert = 180°$ (straight angle)
$\therefore$	$\lvert\angle 1\rvert + \lvert\angle 2\rvert + \lvert\angle 3\rvert = 180°$

Corollary 1

The degree-measure of an exterior angle of a triangle is equal to the sum of the degree-measures of the two remote interior angles.

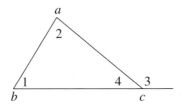

Given:	Triangle *abc* with interior opposite angles 1 and 2 and exterior angle 3.
To prove:	$|\angle 1| + |\angle 2| = |\angle 3|$
Construction:	Label angle 4.
Proof:	$|\angle 1| + |\angle 2| + |\angle 4| = 180°$ (three angles in a triangle)
	$|\angle 3| + |\angle 4| = 180°$ (straight angle)
	$\therefore \quad |\angle 1| + |\angle 2| + |\angle 4| = |\angle 3| + |\angle 4|$
	$\therefore \quad |\angle 1| + |\angle 2| = |\angle 3|$

Corollary 2

An exterior angle of a triangle is greater than either remote (opposite) interior angle.

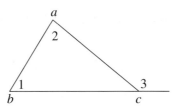

Given:	Triangle *abc* with interior opposite angles 1 and 2 and exterior angle 3.
To prove:	$|\angle 3| > |\angle 1|$ and $|\angle 3| > |\angle 2|$
Proof:	$|\angle 3| = |\angle 1| + |\angle 2|$ (exterior angle)
	but $|\angle 1| > 0$ and $|\angle 2| > 0$
	$\therefore \quad |\angle 3| > |\angle 1|$ and $|\angle 3| > |\angle 2|$

2.

Opposite sides of a parallelogram are equal in length.

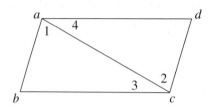

Given:	Parallelogram *abcd*
To prove:	$|ab| = |dc|$ and $|ad| = |bc|$
Construction:	Join *a* to *c*. Label angles 1, 2, 3 and 4.
Proof:	Consider triangle *abc* and triangle *adc*:

        $|\angle 1| = |\angle 2|$ and $|\angle 3| = |\angle 4|$ (alternate angles)

        $|ac| = |ac|$ (common)

∴   triangle *abc* ≡ triangle *adc*   (ASA)

∴ $|ab| = |dc|$ and $|ad| = |bc|$ (corresponding sides)

3.

> If three parallel lines make intercepts of equal length on a transversal, then they will make intercepts of equal length on any other transversal.

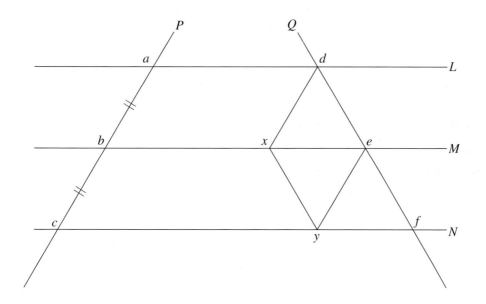

Given:		Three parallel lines *L*, *M* and *N*.	
		Transversal *P*, intersecting the lines at *a, b* and *c* such that $|ab| = |bc|$.	
		Transversal *Q*, intersecting the lines at *d, e* and *f*.	
To prove:		$|de| = |ef|$	
Construction:		Complete parallelograms *badx* and *edxy*.	
Proof:		*edxy* is a parallelogram	(construction)
	∴	$|xy| = |de|$	(opposite sides)
		xy ∥ *ef*	(construction)
	and	*M* ∥ *N*	(given)
	∴	*fexy* is a parallelogram	
	∴	$|xy| = |ef|$	(opposite sides)
	∴	$|de| = |ef|$	

4.

A line which is parallel to one side-line of a triangle and cuts a second side will cut the third side in the same proportion as the second.

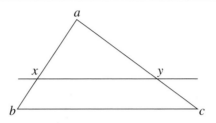

Given: Triangle abc with $xy \parallel bc$.

To prove: $\dfrac{|ax|}{|xb|} = \dfrac{|ay|}{|yc|}$

Proof: Let x divide $[ab]$ in the ratio $m : n$, i.e. $\dfrac{|ax|}{|xb|} = \dfrac{m}{n}$

Let $[ax]$ be divided into m equal parts.

Let $[xb]$ be divided into n equal parts.

Through each point thus obtained on $[ax]$ and $[xb]$ draw lines parallel to bc to meet ac.

∴ $[ay]$ is divided into m equal parts and $[yc]$ is divided into n equal parts.

∴ $\dfrac{|ay|}{|yc|} = \dfrac{m}{n}$

∴ $\dfrac{|ax|}{|xb|} = \dfrac{|ay|}{|yc|}$

5.

> If the three angles of one triangle have degree-measures equal, respectively, to the degree-measures of the angles of a second triangle, then the lengths of the corresponding sides of the two triangles are proportional.

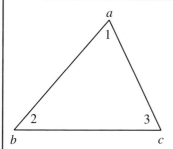 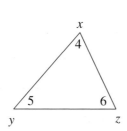 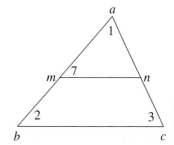

Given: Equiangular triangles abc and xyz in which

$|\angle 1| = |\angle 4|$, $|\angle 2| = |\angle 5|$ and $|\angle 3| = |\angle 6|$

To prove: $\dfrac{|ab|}{|xy|} = \dfrac{|ac|}{|xy|} = \dfrac{|bc|}{|yz|}$

Construction: Mark the point m on $[ab]$ such that $|am| = |xy|$

Mark the point n on $[ac]$ such that $|an| = |xz|$

Join m to n. Label angle 7.

Proof: Consider triangle amn and triangle xyz:

$|am| = |xy|$ and $|an| = |xz|$ (construction)

$|\angle 1| = |\angle 4|$ (given)

$\therefore$ triangle $amn \equiv$ triangle xyz (SAS)

$\therefore$ $|\angle 7| = |\angle 5|$ (corresponding angles)

but $|\angle 2| = |\angle 5|$ (given)

$\therefore$ $|\angle 7| = |\angle 2|$

$\therefore$ $yz \parallel bc$

$\therefore$ $\dfrac{|ab|}{|am|} = \dfrac{|ac|}{|an|}$ $\left(\begin{array}{l}\text{A line parallel to one side} \\ \text{divides the other two sides in} \\ \text{the same proportion.}\end{array}\right)$

$\therefore$ $\dfrac{|ab|}{|xy|} = \dfrac{|ac|}{|xz|}$ $(|am| = |xy|$ and $|an| = |xz|)$

similarly, $\dfrac{|ab|}{|xy|} = \dfrac{|bc|}{|yz|}$

$\therefore$ $\dfrac{|ab|}{|xy|} = \dfrac{|ac|}{|xz|} = \dfrac{|bc|}{|yz|}$

Pythagoras's Theorem

6.

> In a right-angled triangle, the square of the length of the side opposite to the right angle is equal to the sum of the squares of the lengths of the other two sides.

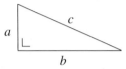

Given:	Right-angled triangle with length of sides a, b and c as shown.
To prove:	$a^2 + b^2 = c^2$
Construction:	Draw a square with sides of length $a + b$.

Draw four congruent right-angled triangles in the square with sides of length a and b and hypotenuse c, as shown.

Label angles 1, 2, 3 and 4.

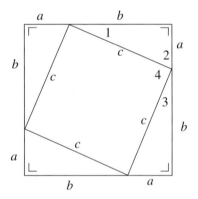

$|\angle 1| + |\angle 2| = 90°$	(remaining angles)
$|\angle 1| = |\angle 3|$	(corresponding angles)

$\therefore \quad |\angle 2| + |\angle 3| = 90°$

$\therefore \quad |\angle 4| = 90°$

Area of square $= (a + b)^2 = 4(\text{area of one triangle}) + c^2$

$$(a + b)^2 = 4\left(\frac{1}{2}ab\right) + c^2$$

$$a^2 + 2ab + b^2 = 2ab + c^2$$

$$a^2 + b^2 = c^2$$

Note: A difficulty with the proof is trying to draw the diagram. One way to do this is to let $a = 2$ cm, $b = 5$ cm and draw a square with each side 7 cm in length. Then simply mark off 2 cm on each side in clockwise direction. Join these points to construct the smaller square.

Alternative Proof

6.

> In a right-angled triangle, the square of the length of the side opposite to the right angle is equal to the sum of the squares of the lengths of the other two sides.

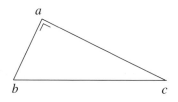 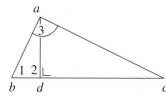 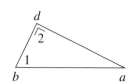

Given:	Triangle abc with $|\angle bac| = 90°$.
To prove:	$|bc|^2 = |ab|^2 + |ac|^2$
Construction:	Draw $ad \perp bc$.
	Label angles 1, 2 and 3.

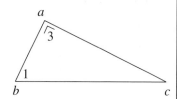

Proof:

Consider triangle abc and triangle dba:

$|\angle 1| = |\angle 1|$ (common angle)

$|\angle 2| = |\angle 3| = 90°$ (construction)

$\therefore$ Triangle abc and triangle dba are similar

$\therefore$ $\dfrac{|ab|}{|bc|} = \dfrac{|bd|}{|ab|}$ (corresponding sides are in proportion)

$|ab|^2 = |bc|.|dc|$ ① (cross-multiply)

Similarly, triangle abc and triangle dac are similar

and $|ac|^2 = |bc|.|dc|$ ②

Adding ① and ②:

$|ab|^2 + |ac|^2 = |bc|.|bd| + |bc|.|dc|$

$= |bc|(|bd| + |dc|)$

$= |bc|.|bc|$

$= |bc|^2$

$\therefore$ $|bc|^2 = |ab|^2 + |ac|^2$

Converse of Pythagoras's Theorem

7.

If the square of the length of one side of a triangle is equal to the sum of the squares of the lengths of the other two sides, then the triangle has a right angle, and this is opposite the longest side.

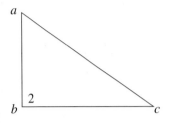

Given: Triangle abc with $[ac]$ the longest side and $|ac|^2 = |ab|^2 + |bc|^2$

To prove: $|\angle abc| = 90°$

Construction: Draw triangle pqr such that $|\angle pqr| = 90°$,

$|pq| = |ab|$ and $|qr| = |bc|$.

Label angles 1 and 2.

Proof:

$|ab|^2 + |bc|^2 = |ac|^2$ (given)

but $|pq|^2 + |qr|^2 = |pr|^2$ (as $|\angle 1| = 90°$)

$\therefore$ $|pr| = |ac|$

$\therefore$ triangle $abc \equiv$ triangle pqr (SSS)

$\therefore$ $|\angle 2| = |\angle 1| = 90°$ (corresponding angles)

$\therefore$ $|\angle abc| = 90°$ and is opposite the longest side $[ac]$

8.

> The products of the lengths of the sides of a triangle by the corresponding altitudes are equal.

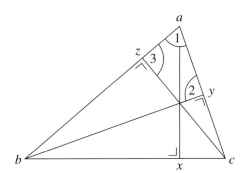

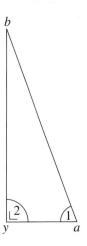

Given:	Triangle abc with altitudes $[ax]$, $[by]$ and $[cz]$.
To prove:	$\lvert ab \rvert . \lvert cz \rvert = \lvert ac \rvert . \lvert by \rvert = \lvert bc \rvert . \lvert ax \rvert$
Construction:	Mark angles 1, 2 and 3.
Proof:	Consider triangle aby and triangle acz:

$$\lvert \angle 1 \rvert = \lvert \angle 1 \rvert \qquad \text{(common angle)}$$

$$\lvert \angle 2 \rvert = \lvert \angle 3 \rvert = 90° \qquad \text{(given)}$$

∴   triangles aby and acz are equiangular

∴ $\dfrac{\lvert ab \rvert}{\lvert ac \rvert} = \dfrac{\lvert by \rvert}{\lvert cz \rvert}$ (corresponding sides are in proportion)

∴ $\lvert ab \rvert . \lvert cz \rvert = \lvert ac \rvert . \lvert by \rvert$ (cross-multiply)

Similarly, $\lvert ab \rvert . \lvert cz \rvert = \lvert bc \rvert . \lvert ax \rvert$

∴ $\lvert ab \rvert . \lvert cz \rvert = \lvert ac \rvert . \lvert by \rvert = \lvert bc \rvert . \lvert ax \rvert$

9.

> If the lengths of two sides of a triangle are unequal, then the degree-measures of the angles opposite to them are unequal, with the greater angle opposite the longer side.

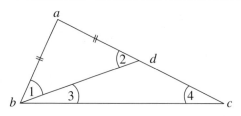

Given:	Triangle *abc* with $|ac| > |ab|$.
To prove:	$|\angle abc| > |\angle acb|$
Construction:	Construct point *d* on [*ac*] such that $|ad| = |ab|$.
	Join *b* to *d*. Mark angles 1, 2, 3 and 4.
Proof:	In triangle *abd*,

$$|ab| = |ad| \qquad \text{(construction)}$$

$$\therefore \quad |\angle 1| = |\angle 2| \qquad \text{(isosceles triangle)}$$

In triangle *bcd*,

$$|\angle 2| > |\angle 4| \qquad \text{(exterior angle)}$$

$$\therefore \quad |\angle 1| > |\angle 4|$$

$$\therefore \quad |\angle 1| + |\angle 3| > |\angle 4|$$

$$\therefore \quad |\angle abc| > |\angle acb|$$

10.

> The sum of the lengths of any two sides of a triangle is greater than that of the third side.

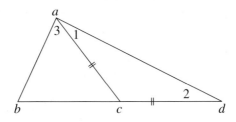

Given:	Triangle *abc*	
To prove:	$\|bc\| + \|ac\| > \|ab\|$	
Construction:	Produce $[bc]$ to d such that $\|cd\| = \|ac\|$.	
	Join *a* to *d*. Mark angles 1, 2 and 3.	
Proof:	In triangle *acd*,	
	$\|ac\| = \|cd\|$	(construction)
∴	$\|\angle 1\| = \|\angle 2\|$	(isosceles triangle)
∴	$\|\angle 1\| + \|\angle 3\| > \|\angle 2\|$	
∴	$\|bd\| > \|ab\|$	(side opposite greater angle)
but	$\|bd\| = \|bc\| + \|cd\|$	
	$\quad = \|bc\| + \|ac\|$	
∴	$\|bc\| + \|ac\| > \|ab\|$	

Angles

Example 1

Calculate the value of:

(i) x **(ii)** y

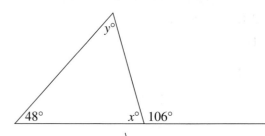

Solution:

(i) $x° + 106° = 180°$ (straight angle)

   $\therefore$ $x + 106 = 180$

        $x = 74$ (subtract 106 from both sides)

(ii) $x° + y° + 48° = 180$ (three angles in a triangle)

   $\therefore$ $74 + y + 48 = 180$ (put in $x = 74$)

        $y + 122 = 180$

            $y = 58$ (subtract 122 from both sides)

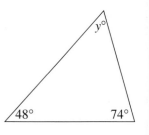

Example 2

Calculate the value of a in the diagram.

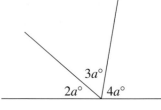

Solution:

    $2a° + 3a° + 4a° = 180°$ (straight angle)

   $\therefore$ $2a + 3a + 4a = 180$

            $9a = 180$

             $a = 20$ (divide both sides by 9)

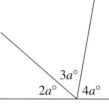

Example 3

Calculate the value of

(i) x **(ii)** y

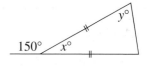

Solution:

(i) $x° + 150° = 180°$ (straight angle)

$\therefore\ x + 150 = 180$

$x = 30$

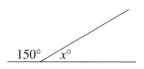

(ii)   Redraw the triangle.
        The marks indicate that the triangle is isosceles.

$\therefore$ the two base angles are equal to $y°$

Thus, $y° + y° + 30° = 180°$ (three angles in a triangle)

$\therefore$ $y + y + 30 = 180$

$2y + 30 = 180$

$2y = 150$

$y = 75$

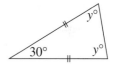

Example 4

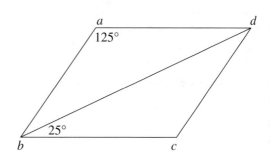

$abcd$ is a parallelogram, with
$|\angle bad| = 125°$ and $|\angle cbd| = 25°$.

Find   **(i)** $|\angle bcd|$ **(ii)** $|\angle adb|$ **(iii)** $|\angle abd|$ **(iv)** $|\angle cdb|$

Solution:

(i)

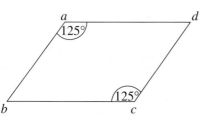

$|\angle bcd| = |\angle bad| = 125°$

(opposite angles of the parallelogram)

(ii)

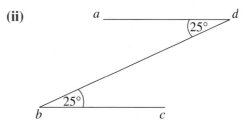

$|\angle adb| = |\angle cbd| = 25°$

(alternate angles)

(iii)

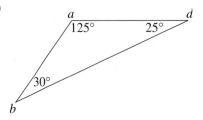

$$|\angle abd| + |\angle bad| + |\angle adb| = 180°$$

(Three angles in a triangle add to 180°)

$$|\angle abd| + 125° + 25° = 180°$$

$$|\angle abd| + 150° = 180°$$

$$|\angle abd| = 30°$$

(iv)

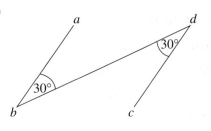

$$|\angle cdb| = |\angle abd| = 30°$$

(alternate angles)

Examples of Pythagoras's Theorem

Example 1

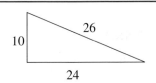

(i) Prove that the triangle with sides of lengths 10 units, 24 units and 26 units is right-angled.

(ii) abc is a triangle with $|ab| = 8$, $|ac| = 4$ and $|\angle acb| = 90°$.

Calculate $|bc|$, correct to two places of decimals.

Solution:

(i)

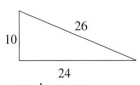

$10^2 + 24^2$	26^2
$= 100 + 576$	$= 676$
$= 676$	

Thus, $10^2 + 24^2 = 26^2$

∴ triangle is right-angled

(according to Pythagoras's Theorem)

(ii)

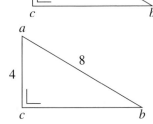

Using Pythagoras's Theorem:

$$|bc|^2 + |ac|^2 = |ab|^2$$

$$|bc|^2 + 4^2 = 8^2$$

$$|bc|^2 + 16 = 64$$

$$|bc|^2 = 48$$

$$|bc| = \sqrt{48}$$

$$|bc| = 6.92820323$$

∴ $|bc| = 6.91$ (correct to two places of decimals)

Example 2

In the triangle *abc*,

$|ab| = 8$, $|ac| = 17$ and $|\angle abc| = 90°$.

Find **(i)** $|bc|$ **(ii)** area of triangle *abc*.

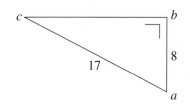

Solution:

(i)   Using Pythagoras's Theorem:

$$|bc|^2 + |ab|^2 = |ac|^2$$
$$|bc|^2 + 8^2 = 17^2$$
$$|bc|^2 + 64 = 289$$
$$|bc|^2 = 225$$
$$|bc| = \sqrt{225}$$
$$|bc| = 15$$

(ii)   Area of triangle *abc*

$$= \tfrac{1}{2} \text{ (base) (perpendicular height)}$$
$$= \tfrac{1}{2}\,|ab| \times |bc|$$
$$= \tfrac{1}{2} \times 8 \times 15$$
$$= 60 \text{ square units}$$

Example 3

Find the values of *x* and *y*.

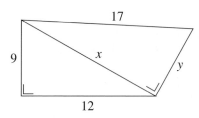

Solution:

Redraw both right-angled triangles separately and apply Pythagoras's theorem twice.

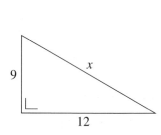

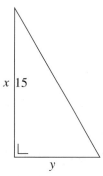

$$x^2 = 12^2 + 9^2$$
$$x^2 = 144 + 81$$
$$x^2 = 225$$
$$x = \sqrt{225}$$
$$x = 15$$

$$x^2 + y^2 = 17^2$$
$$15^2 + y^2 = 17^2$$
$$225 + y^2 = 289$$
$$y^2 = 64$$
$$y = \sqrt{64}$$
$$y = 8$$

Examples of Parallel Lines and Eqilateral Triangles

Example 1

In the diagram, *L*, *M* and *N* are parallel lines. They make intercepts of the indicated lengths on *J* and *K*. *bd* is parallel to *J*.

(i)   Write down the length of [*bd*]

(ii) Write down the length of [*bc*]

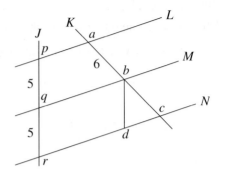

Solution:

(i)   Given: *qbdr* is a parallelogram

$\therefore \qquad |bd| = |qr|$

$\therefore \qquad |bd| = 5$

(ii) $\dfrac{|pq|}{|qr|} = \dfrac{|ab|}{|bc|}$

(because *L* || *M* || *N*)

$\therefore \qquad \dfrac{5}{5} = \dfrac{6}{|bc|}$

$\therefore \qquad |bc| = 6 \qquad \left(\text{as } \dfrac{5}{5} = \dfrac{6}{6}\right)$

Example 2

In the diagram *L* || *K*.

Find the value of *x*.

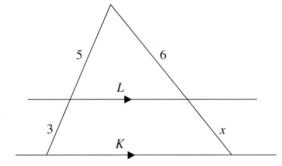

Solution:

$\dfrac{x}{6} = \dfrac{3}{5}$ (as *L* || *K*)

$5x = 18$ (multiply both sides by 30)

$x = \dfrac{18}{5}$ or 3.6 (divide both sides by 5)

206

Enlargements

Properties of Enlargements

1. The shape of the image is the same as the shape of the object (only size has changed).

2. The amount by which a figure is enlarged is called the 'scale factor' and is denoted by k.

3. image length = k(object length)   or $k = \dfrac{\text{image length}}{\text{object length}}$

4. area of image = k^2(area object)   or $k^2 = \dfrac{\text{area of image}}{\text{area of object}}$

Notes:

1. The scale factor can be less than one (i.e. $0 < k < 1$). In these cases, the image will be smaller than the object. Though smaller, the image is still called an enlargement.

2. The centre of enlargement can be a vertex on the object figure or inside it.

Example 1

The triangle *ors* is the image of the triangle *opq* under an enlargement, centre *o*.

$|op| = 4$, $|pr| = 6$.

Find:

(i)   the scale factor of the enlargement

(ii) $|qs|$ if $|oq| = 3.2$

(iii) $|pq| : |rs|$

(iv)   the area of the triangle *ors* given the area of $\triangle opq$ to be 6 square units.

Solution:

Divide the figure into two separate similar triangles. Mark in known lengths.

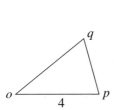 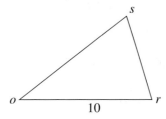

(i)   Scale factor = $k = \dfrac{\text{image length}}{\text{object length}} = \dfrac{|or|}{|op|} = \dfrac{10}{4} = 2.5$

(ii) $|qs|$

$$|os| = k|oq| = (2.5)(3.2) = 8$$

$$|qs| = |os| - |oq| = 8 - 3.2 = 4.8$$

(iii) $|pq| : |rs| = |op| : |or| = 4 : 10 = 2 : 5$

(iv) area of image $= k^2$ (area of object)

$$\therefore \quad \text{area of } \triangle ors = k^2 \ (\text{area of } \triangle opq)$$

$$= (2.5)^2(6)$$

$$= (6.25)(6)$$

$$= 37.5$$

Thus, the area of $\triangle ors = 37.5$ square units

Example 2

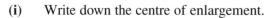
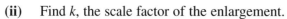

The rectangle *aefg* is an enlargement of the rectangle *abcd* with $|ac| = 5$, $|cf| = 3$.

(i) Write down the centre of enlargement.

(ii) Find k, the scale factor of the enlargement.

(iii) If the area of the rectangle *aefg* is 62.72 square units, find the area of the rectangle *abcd*.

(iv) A further enlargement will map rectangle *aefg* back onto rectangle *abcd*.

Find the scale factor, if the centre of enlargement remains the same.

Solution:

(i) The centre of enlargement is *a* (as *a* is common to both rectangles)

(ii) Divide the figure into two separate similar rectangles. Mark in known lengths.

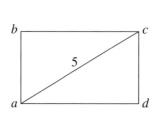
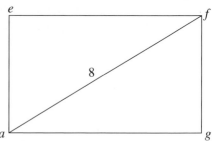

$$\text{Scale factor} = k = \frac{\text{image length}}{\text{object length}} = \frac{|af|}{|ac|} = \frac{8}{5} = 1.6$$

(iii) $\qquad$ (area of image) $= k^2$(area of object)

$\therefore \qquad$ area of rectangle $aefg = k^2$(area of rectangle $abcd$)

$\therefore \qquad\qquad\qquad 62.72 = (1.6)^2$(area of rectangle $abcd$)

$\qquad\qquad\qquad\qquad 62.72 = 2.56$(area of rectangle $abcd$)

$$\frac{62.72}{2.56} = \text{area of rectangle } abcd$$

$\qquad$ (divide both sides by 2.56)

$\qquad\qquad\qquad\qquad 24.5 = \text{area of rectangle } abcd$

Thus, the area of rectangle $abcd$ is 24.5 square units.

(iv) rectangle $aefg$ is mapped onto rectangle $abcd$ under an enlargement of scale factor $\frac{1}{k}$.

$$k = \frac{8}{5}, \ \therefore \ \frac{1}{k} = \frac{5}{8} \quad \text{(turn upside down)}$$

Thus, rectangle $aefg$ is mapped onto rectangle $abcd$ under an enlargement of scale factor $\frac{5}{8}$.

Example 3

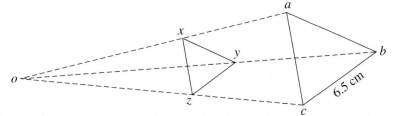

$\triangle xyz$ is the image of $\triangle abc$, under an enlargement, centre o.
If area of $\triangle abc = 40$ cm^2 and the area of $\triangle xyz = 25.6$ cm^2, find:

(i) the scale factor of enlargement, k

(ii) $|yz|$ if $|bc| = 6.5$ cm.

Solution:

(i) $\qquad$ area of image $= k^2$(area of object)

$\therefore \qquad$ area of $\triangle xyz = k^2$(area of $\triangle abc$)

$\therefore \qquad\qquad 25.6 = k^2(40)$

$$\frac{25.6}{40} = k^2 \quad \text{(divide both sides by 40)}$$

$\qquad\qquad 0.64 = k^2$

$\qquad\qquad 0.8 = k$

Thus, the scale factor of enlargement is 0.8

(ii) $\qquad$ image length $= k$(object length)

$\qquad\qquad |yz| = k|bc|$

$\qquad\qquad\qquad = (0.8)(6.5)$

$\qquad\qquad\qquad = 5.2$

Thus, $|yz| = 5.2$ cm

Chapter 11. TRIGONOMETRY

Notation

The diagram shows the **usual notation**
for a triangle in trigonometry:

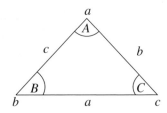

Vertices: a, b, c

Angles: A, B, C

Length of sides: a, b, c

The lengths of the sides are denoted by a lower-case letter, and named after the angle they
are opposite, i.e. a is opposite angle A, b is opposite angle B, and c is opposite angle C.

Using the terminology, we also have the following:

$A = |\angle bac|,$	$B = |\angle abc|,$	$C = |\angle acb|$
$a = |bc|,$	$b = |ac|,$	$c = |ab|$

Solving Right-angled Triangles

We can use a trigonometric ratio to calculate the length of a side in a right-angled triangle if
we know the length of one side and one angle (other than the right angle). We can also find the
size of an angle in a right-angled triangle if we know the lengths of two of its sides.

Summary of which trigonometric ratio to choose linking the given sides and angles:

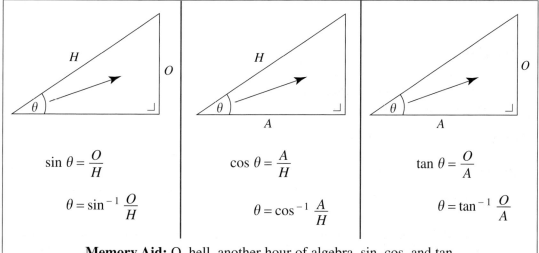

$$\sin \theta = \frac{O}{H}$$

$$\theta = \sin^{-1} \frac{O}{H}$$

$$\cos \theta = \frac{A}{H}$$

$$\theta = \cos^{-1} \frac{A}{H}$$

$$\tan \theta = \frac{O}{A}$$

$$\theta = \tan^{-1} \frac{O}{A}$$

Memory Aid: <u>O</u>, <u>h</u>ell, <u>a</u>nother <u>h</u>our <u>o</u>f <u>a</u>lgebra, sin, cos, and tan.

Notes:

1. The side opposite the right angle is called the **hypotenuse, H**. The side opposite the angle θ is called the **opposite, O**. The other side near the angle θ is called the **adjacent, A**.

2. If the lengths of any two sides are known, the third side can be found using Pythagoras's theorem: $A^2 + O^2 = H^2$, where A, O and H are the lengths of the sides.

3. The three angles of a triangle add up to $180°$.

4. sin, cos and tan are short for sine, cosine, and tangent, respectively.

5. The arrow points to the side opposite the angle under consideration.

6. θ is a Greek letter, pronounced theta, often used to indicate an angle.

Practical Applications

Mark on your triangle the angles and lengths you know, and label what you need to calculate, using the correct ratio to link the angle or length required with the known angle or length.

Angles of elevation, depression and compass directions

Angle of elevation
The **angle of elevation** of an object as seen by an observer is the angle between the horizontal line from the object to the observer's eye (upwards from the horizontal).

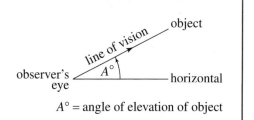

$A°$ = angle of elevation of object

Angle of depression

If the object is below the level of the observer, the angle between the horizontal and the observer's line of vision is called the **angle of depression** (downwards from the horizontal).

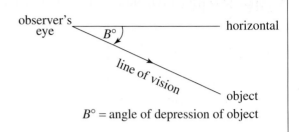

$B°$ = angle of depression of object

Compass directions

> The direction of a point is stated as a number of degrees East or West of North and South.

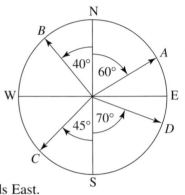

A is N 60° E

B is N 40° W

C is S 45° W (or SW)

D is S 70° E

Note: N 60° E means start at North and turn 60° towards East.

Solving Non-right-angled Triangles

Area of a Triangle

Area of triangle abc

$$= \frac{1}{2}ab \sin C = \frac{1}{2}ac \sin B = \frac{1}{2}bc \sin A$$

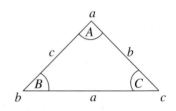

To use this formula to find the area of a triangle we need:
The length of two sides **and** the size of the angle between these sides.

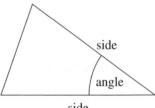

Area of triangle

$= \frac{1}{2}$(length of side) × (length of side) × (sine of the angle between these sides)

Sine Rule

In any triangle abc:

$$\frac{a}{\sin A} = \frac{b}{\sin B} = \frac{c}{\sin C}$$

or:

$$\frac{\sin A}{a} = \frac{\sin B}{b} = \frac{\sin C}{c}$$

(The first form is given on page 9 of the tables)

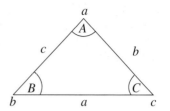

This is known as the '**sine rule**' and it applies to any triangle, including a right-angled triangle.

The sine rule can be used to:

1. Find an unknown side, a. Using the sine rule we need: Two angles and one side.	**2.** Find an unknown angle, $A°$. Using the sine rule we need: Two sides and the size of one angle opposite one of these sides.
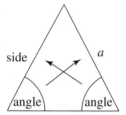	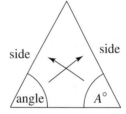
If we know two angles we can calculate the third angle, as the three angles add up to $180°$.	The unknown angle, $A°$, must be opposite a known side.

The sine rule connects each side with the angle opposite in a triangle.

Notes: 1. In practice we put only two fractions equal to each other, e.g.:

$$\frac{a}{\sin A} = \frac{b}{\sin B}$$

2. Put the required quantity, side or angle, on the top of the first fraction.

To find a, use $\quad \dfrac{a}{\sin A} = \dfrac{b}{\sin B}$

To find B, use $\quad \dfrac{\sin B}{b} = \dfrac{\sin A}{a}$

213

Cosine Rule

In any triangle *abc:*

$$a^2 = b^2 + c^2 - 2bc \cos A$$

or $\quad b^2 = a^2 + c^2 - 2ac \cos B$

or $\quad c^2 = a^2 + b^2 - 2ab \cos C$

(The first form is given on page 9 of the tables)

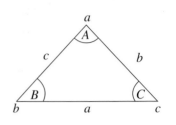

This is known as the '**cosine rule**' and it applies to any triangle, including a right-angled triangle.

The cosine rule can be used to:

1. Find the length of the third side, *a*, of a triangle when given the lengths of the other two sides and the angle contained between these sides.

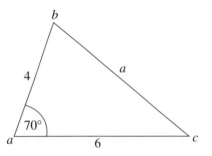

2. Find the measure of an angle, *A*, of a triangle when given the lengths of the three sides.

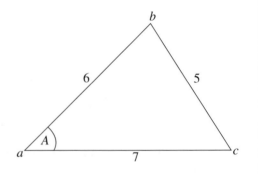

Note: In 1 and 2 above the sine rule would not work.
If the unknown angle is between 90° and 180° its cosine is negative.

For example, $\cos 120° = -\frac{1}{2}$

The largest angle of a triangle is opposite the largest side and the smallest angle is opposite the shortest side. There can be only one obtuse angle in a triangle.

As a general rule, if you cannot use the sine rule then use the cosine rule.

Special Angles: 45°, 30° and 60°

There are three special angles whose sine, cosine and tangent ratios can be expressed as simple fractions or surds.

$$\sin 45° = \frac{1}{\sqrt{2}}$$

$$\cos 45° = \frac{1}{\sqrt{2}}$$

$$\tan 45° = 1$$

$$\sin 60° = \frac{\sqrt{3}}{2} \qquad \sin 30° = \frac{1}{2}$$

$$\cos 60° = \frac{1}{2} \qquad \cos 30° = \frac{\sqrt{3}}{2}$$

$$\tan 60° = \sqrt{3} \qquad \tan 30° = \frac{1}{\sqrt{3}}$$

These ratios can be used instead of a calculator.

These ratios are tabulated on page 9 of the maths tables. However, on this page the angles are measured in radians. To use this table we can convert radians to degrees by using the fact that:

$$\pi \text{ radians} = 180°$$

Thus

$\frac{\pi}{2}$ radians = 90°	$\frac{\pi}{3}$ radians = 60°	$\frac{\pi}{4}$ radians = 45°	$\frac{\pi}{6}$ radians = 30°

Example 1

$\sin \theta = \frac{3}{5}$ where $0° < \theta < 90°$.

(i) Find, as fractions, the value of $\cos \theta$ and $\tan \theta$.

(ii) Find the value of $\sin \theta \cos \theta$, as a fraction.

(iii) Find the value of $\cos 2\theta$, as a fraction. (**Note:** $\cos 2\theta = \cos^2\theta - \sin^2\theta$).

(iv) Verify that $\sin \theta + \cos \theta > \tan \theta$.

(v) Find the measurement of the angle θ, correct to nearest degree.

Solution:

(i) From the trigonometric ratio given, sketch a right-angled triangle to represent the situation and use Pythagoras's theorem to find the missing side.

Given: $\sin \theta = \frac{3}{5}$

Opposite $= 3$, Hypotenuse $= 5$, let the Adjacent $= x$.

$x^2 + 3^2 = 5^2$ (Pythagoras's Theorem)

$x^2 + 9 = 25$

$x^2 = 16$

$x = \sqrt{16} = 4$

$\cos \theta = \dfrac{A}{H} = \dfrac{4}{5}$

$\tan \theta = \dfrac{O}{A} = \dfrac{3}{4}$

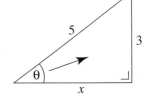

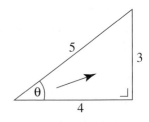

(ii) $\sin \theta \cos \theta$

$= (\sin \theta) \times (\cos \theta)$

$= \dfrac{3}{5} \times \dfrac{4}{5}$

$= \dfrac{12}{25}$

(iii) $\cos 2\theta = \cos^2\theta - \sin^2\theta$

$= (\cos \theta)^2 - (\sin \theta)^2$

$= \left(\dfrac{4}{5}\right)^2 - \left(\dfrac{3}{5}\right)^2$

$= \dfrac{16}{25} - \dfrac{9}{25}$

$= \dfrac{7}{25}$

(iv) $\sin\theta + \cos\theta > \tan\theta$

$$\frac{3}{5} + \frac{4}{5} > \frac{3}{4}$$

$$\frac{7}{5} > \frac{3}{4}$$

$$1.4 > 0.75 \quad \text{true}$$

$$\therefore \sin\theta + \cos\theta > \tan\theta$$

(v) Given: $\sin\theta = \dfrac{3}{5}$

$$\therefore \qquad \theta = \sin^{-1}\left(\frac{3}{5}\right)$$

$$\theta = 36.86989765°$$

$$\theta = 37° \quad \text{(nearest degree)}$$

 2nd F | sin | (| 3 | ÷ | 5 |) | =

Example 2

The diagram shows a vertical wall which stands on level ground.

A cable joins the top of the wall to a point on the ground which is 5 m from the base of the wall.

The cable makes an angle of 66.2° with the ground.

(i) Find the height of the wall, correct to two decimal places.

(ii) Find the length of the cable, correct to one decimal place.

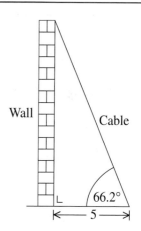

Solution:

(i) Represent the situation with a right-angled triangle.
Let h represent the height of the wall.
We know the adjacent and require the opposite.
$\therefore$ use the tan ratio.

$$\tan\theta = \frac{O}{A}$$

$$\tan 66.2° = \frac{h}{5} \qquad \text{(put in known values)}$$

$$5\tan 66.2° = h \qquad \text{(multiply both sides by 5)}$$

$$11.33651756 = h \qquad \left(\begin{array}{l} 5\ \boxed{\tan}\ 66.2\ \boxed{=} \end{array}\right)$$

$$11.34 = h \qquad \text{(correct to two decimal places)}$$

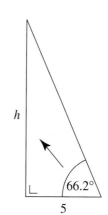

Thus, the height of the wall is 11.34 m (correct to two decimal places).

(ii) Using Pythagoras's Theorem

Let the length of the cable be l metres

$$l^2 = 11.34^2 + 5^2$$
$$l^2 = 128.5956 + 25$$
$$l^2 = 153.5956$$
$$l = \sqrt{153.5956}$$
$$l = 12.39336919$$
$$l = 12.4 \qquad \text{(correct to one decimal place)}$$

Thus, the length of cable is 12.4 m.

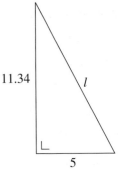

11.34

l

5

Example 3

$|ad| = 6$ cm, $|db| = 9$ cm,

$|\angle cad| = 35°$ and $cd \perp ab$.

Find,

(i) $|cd|$, correct to one decimal place.

(ii) $|\angle cbd|$, correct to the nearest degree.

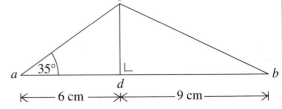

a   35°   d   b   c

←— 6 cm —※— 9 cm —→

Solution:

Redraw both right-angled triangles separately.

(i)

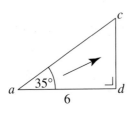

a   35°   6   d   c

$$\tan 35° = \frac{|cd|}{6}$$

$$6 \tan 35° = |cd|$$

(multiply both sides by 6)

$$4.201245229 = |cd|$$

$$4.2 \text{ cm} = |cd|$$

(correct to one decimal place)

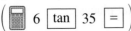

(ii)

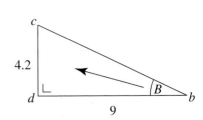

c   4.2   d   9   B   b

$$\tan B = \frac{4.2}{9}$$

$$B = \tan^{-1}\left(\frac{4.2}{9}\right)$$

$$B = 25.01689348°$$

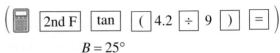

$$B = 25°$$

(nearest degree)

Example 4

A garden *pqrs* is in the shape of a quadrilateral.

$|pq| = 15$ m, $|ps| = 8$ m, $|rs| = 9$ m, $pq \perp ps$

and $|\angle qrs| = 80°$.

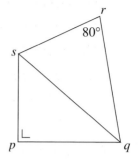

Find the value of:

(i) $|qs|$.

(ii) $|\angle rqs|$ to the nearest degree.

Solution:

Divide figure into two separate triangles.

(i)

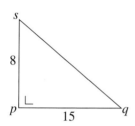

Use Pythagoras's Theorem to find $|qs|$

$$|qs|^2 = |pq|^2 + |ps|^2$$
$$|qs|^2 = (15)^2 + (8)^2$$
$$|qs|^2 = 225 + 64$$
$$|qs|^2 = 289$$
$$|qs| = \sqrt{289} = 17$$

Thus, $|qs| = 17$ m

(ii)

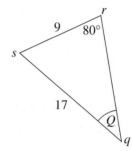

Using the sine rule:

$$\frac{\sin Q}{q} = \frac{\sin R}{r}$$

$$\frac{\sin \angle rqs}{|rs|} = \frac{\sin \angle qrs}{|qs|}$$

$$\frac{\sin \angle rqs}{9} = \frac{\sin 80°}{17}$$

$$\sin \angle rqs = \frac{9 \sin 80°}{17}$$

$$\therefore \quad |\angle rqs| = \sin^{-1}\left(\frac{9 \sin 80°}{17}\right)$$

 2nd F | sin | (| 9 | sin | 80 | ÷ | 17 |) | =)

$$|\angle rqs| = 31.42411346$$
$$|\angle rqs| = 31° \quad \text{(nearest degree)}$$

Example 5

A plot of land has a triangular shape *pqr*, as shown.

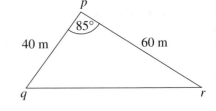

Find:

(i) the area of triangle *pqr*, correct to the nearest m^2

(ii) $|qr|$, correct to the nearest metre.

Solution:

(i) Area of triangle *pqr*

$= \frac{1}{2} qr \sin P$

$= \frac{1}{2} |pr|.|pq| \sin \angle qpr$

$= \frac{1}{2} \times 60 \times 40 \sin 85°$

$= 1{,}195.433638$

$= 1{,}195 \text{ m}^2 \quad (\text{nearest m}^2)$

(ii) We know two sides and the included angle

$\therefore$ Use the cosine rule:

$p^2 = q^2 + r^2 - 2qr \cos P$

$|qr|^2 = |pr|^2 + |pq|^2 - 2|pr|.|qr| \cos \angle qpr$

$|qr|^2 = (60)^2 + (40)^2 - 2(60)(40)(\cos 85°)$

$|qr|^2 = 3{,}600 + 1{,}600 - 418.3475652$

$|qr|^2 = 4{,}781.652435$

$|qr| = \sqrt{4{,}781.652435}$

$|qr| = 69.14949338$

$\therefore |qr| = 69 \text{ m} \quad (\text{nearest m})$

Example 6

In the triangle *abc*, *d* is a point on [*bc*].

$|bd| = 5$ cm, $|ac| = 7$ cm,

$|\angle dca| = 82°$ and $|\angle cad| = 50°$.

(i) Find $|dc|$, correct to one decimal place.

(ii) Find $|ab|$, correct to the nearest cm.

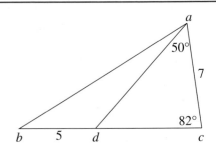

Solution:

(i) $|\angle adc| = 180° - 82° - 50° = 48°$

Using the sine rule:

$$\frac{a}{\sin A} = \frac{d}{\sin D}$$

$$\frac{|dc|}{\sin \angle cad} = \frac{|ac|}{\sin \angle adc}$$

$$\frac{|dc|}{\sin 50°} = \frac{7}{\sin 48°}$$

$$|dc| = \frac{7 \sin 50°}{\sin 48°} \qquad \text{(multiply both sides by } \sin 50°\text{)}$$

$|dc| = 7.215701325 \qquad \left(\boxed{} \; 7 \; \boxed{\sin} \; 50° \; \boxed{\div} \; \boxed{\sin} \; 48 \; \boxed{=} \right)$

$|dc| = 7.2$ cm \qquad (one decimal place)

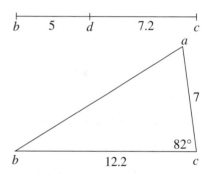

(ii) $|dc| = 7.2$ \qquad (from part **(i)**)

$\therefore |bc| = |bd| + |dc| = 5 + 7.2 = 12.2$

Using the cosine rule:

$$c^2 = a^2 + b^2 - 2ab \cos C$$

$$|ab|^2 = |bc|^2 + |ac|^2 - 2|bc|.|ac| \cos \angle bac$$

$$|ab|^2 = (12.2)^2 + (7)^2 - 2(12.2)(7) \cos 82°$$

$$|ab|^2 = 148.84 + 49 - 23.77076564$$

$$|ab|^2 = 174.0692344$$

$$|ab| = \sqrt{174.0692344}$$

$$|ab| = 13.19353002$$

$$|ab| = 13 \text{ cm} \qquad \text{(nearest cm)}$$

Example 7

A lighthouse, *h*, is observed from a ship sailing a straight course due North.
The distance from *p* to *h* is 2 km and the bearing of the lighthouse from *p* is N 41.3° E.
The distance from *q* to *h* is 2.64 km.

(i) Find the bearing of the lighthouse from *q*, correct to the nearest degree.

(ii) The ship is sailing at a speed of 19 km/h. Find, correct to the nearest minute, the time taken to sail from *p* to *q*.

Solution:

(i) We need to find $|\angle hqp|$.

Using the sine rule:

$$\frac{\sin Q}{q} = \frac{\sin P}{p}$$

$$\frac{\sin \angle hqp}{|hp|} = \frac{\sin \angle hpq}{|hq|}$$

$$\frac{\sin \angle hqp}{2} = \frac{\sin 41.3°}{2.64}$$

$$\sin \angle hqp = \frac{2 \sin 41.3°}{2.64}$$

$$\therefore \quad |\angle hqp| = \sin^{-1}\left(\frac{2 \sin 41.3°}{2.64}\right)$$

$$|\angle hqp| = 30.0000836°$$

$$\left(\boxed{\blacksquare}\;\left(\boxed{\text{2nd F}}\;\boxed{\sin}\;\boxed{(}\;2\;\boxed{\sin}\;41.3\;\boxed{\div}\;2.64\right)\;\boxed{=}\;\right)$$

$$\therefore \quad |\angle hqp| = 30° \text{ (nearest degree)}$$

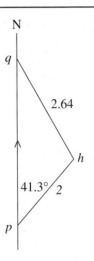

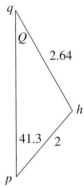

Thus, the bearing of the lighthouse, *h*, from *q* is:

S 30° E

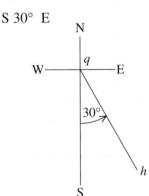

(ii) $|\angle qhp| = H = 180° - 30° - 41.3° = 108.7°$.

We need to find $|pq|$.

Using the cosine rule:

$$h^2 = p^2 + q^2 - 2pq \cos H$$

$$|pq|^2 = |hq|^2 + |hp|^2 - 2|hq|.|hp| \cos \angle phq$$

$$|pq|^2 = (2.64)^2 + (2)^2 - 2(2.64)(2) \cos 108.7°$$

$$|pq|^2 = 6.9696 + 4 + 3.385673181$$

$$|pq|^2 = 14.35527318$$

$$|pq| = \sqrt{14.35527318}$$

$$|pq| = 3.788835333 \text{ km}$$

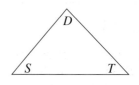

$$\text{Time} = \frac{\text{Distance}}{\text{Speed}}$$

$$= \frac{|pq|}{19}$$

$$= \frac{3.788835333}{19}$$

$$= 0.199412385 \text{ hours}$$

$$= 0.199412385 \times 60 \text{ minutes}$$

$$= 11.96474316$$

$$= 12 \text{ minutes}$$

(nearest minute)

Note: The sine rule could also have been used to find $|pq|$.

Example 8

In the triangle abc,

$|ab| = 3$ cm, $|bc| = 7$ and $|ac| = 5$.

Find the measure of largest angle
in triangle abc.

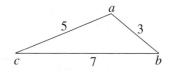

Solution:

The largest angle is opposite the largest side.
We know the lengths of the three sides but we
do not know any angles.

$\therefore$ Use the cosine rule:

$$a^2 = b^2 + c^2 - 2bc \cos A$$

$$|bc|^2 = |ac|^2 + |ab|^2 - 2|ac|.|ab| \cos \angle bac$$

$$7^2 = 5^2 + 3^2 - 2(5)(3) \cos \angle bac \qquad \text{(put in known values)}$$

$$49 = 25 + 9 - 30 \cos \angle bac$$

$$49 = 34 - 30 \cos \angle bac$$

$$30 \cos \angle bac = 34 - 49$$

$$30 \cos \angle bac = -15$$

$$\cos \angle bac = -\frac{15}{30} \qquad \text{(divide both sides by 30)}$$

$$\cos \angle bac = -\frac{1}{2}$$

$$\therefore \quad |\angle bac| = \cos^{-1}\left(-\frac{1}{2}\right)$$

$$|\angle bac| = 120° \qquad \left(\boxed{\text{2nd F}} \ \boxed{\cos} \ \boxed{(} \ \boxed{+/-} \ 1 \ \boxed{\div} \ 2 \ \boxed{)} \ \boxed{=} \right)$$

Thus, the largest angle is 120°.

Example 9

In the triangle abc, $|ab| = 5$ cm and $|bc| = 8$ cm.
The area of the triangle is 16.58 cm^2.

Find $|\angle abc|$, correct to the nearest degree.

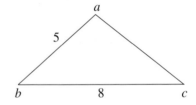

Solution:

Equation given in disguise:

$$\text{Area of triangle } abc = 16.58 \text{ cm}$$

$$\therefore \qquad \frac{1}{2} ac \sin B = 16.58$$

$$\therefore \quad \frac{1}{2} |bc| \times |ab| \sin \angle abc = 16.58$$

$$\frac{1}{2} \times 8 \times 5 \sin \angle abc = 16.58 \qquad \text{(put in } |bc| = 8 \text{ and } |ab| = 5)$$

$$20 \sin \angle abc = 16.58$$

$$\sin \angle abc = 0.829 \qquad \text{(divide both sides by 20)}$$

$$\therefore \qquad |\angle abc| = \sin^{-1}(0.829)$$

$$|\angle abc| = 55.99615045° \qquad \left(\boxed{\text{2nd F}} \ \boxed{\sin} \ 0.829 \ \boxed{=} \right)$$

$$|\angle abc| = 56° \qquad \text{(nearest degree)}$$

Example 10

A circle has centre o and radius 7 cm. The two points b and c are on the circle and $|\angle boc| = 140°$.

(i) Find the area of the sector obc, correct to the nearest cm^2.

(ii) Find the area of the triangle obc, correct to the nearest cm^2.

(iii) Taking the areas correct to the nearest cm^2, express the area of the shaded region as a fraction of the total area enclosed by the circle. Give your answer as a fraction in its simplest form.

(iv) Find the length of the shorter arc bc, correct to the nearest cm.

Solution:

(i)

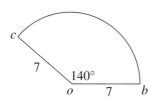

Area of sector obc

$$= \frac{\theta}{360} \times \pi r^2$$

$$= \frac{140}{360} \times \pi \times 7 \times 7$$

$$= 59.86479334$$

$$= 60 \text{ cm}^2 \qquad \text{(nearest cm}^2\text{)}$$

(ii)

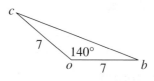

Area of triangle obc

$$= \frac{1}{2} |ob|.|oc| \sin \angle boc$$

$$= \frac{1}{2} \times 7 \times 7 \sin 140°$$

$$= 15.74829644$$

$$= 16 \text{ cm}^2 \qquad \text{(nearest cm}^2\text{)}$$

(iii) Area of shaded region

= Area of sector obc − Area of triangle obc

= 60 − 16

= 44 cm^2

Area of circle

= πr^2

= $\pi \times 7 \times 7$

= 153.93804

= 154 cm^2 (nearest cm^2)

$$\frac{\text{Area of shaded region}}{\text{Area of circle}} = \frac{44}{154} = \frac{2}{7}$$

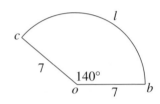

(iv) Let the length of the shorter arc $bc = l$.

$$l = \frac{\theta}{360} \times 2\pi r$$

$$l = \frac{140}{360} \times 2 \times \pi \times 7$$

$$l = 17.10422667$$

$$l = 17 \text{ cm} \qquad \text{(nearest cm)}$$

Compound Angles

A **compound angle** is an angle which is written as the sum or difference of two angles. For example, $(A + B)$ and $(A - B)$ are compound angles.

Compound angle formulas:

> **1.** $\cos(A + B) = \cos A \cos B - \sin A \sin B$
>
> **2.** $\cos(A - B) = \cos A \cos B + \sin A \sin B$
>
> **3.** $\sin(A + B) = \sin A \cos B + \cos A \sin B$
>
> **4.** $\sin(A - B) = \sin A \cos B - \cos A \sin B$

1 and 3 are on page 9 of the tables.

Example 1

A and *B* are acute angles where $\sin A = \frac{4}{5}$ and $\cos B = \frac{5}{13}$.

Find, as fractions, the value of: **(i)** $\cos A$ **(ii)** $\sin B$ **(iii)** $\sin (A + B)$.

Show that $\sin^2 A + \cos^2 A = 1$.

Solution:

Draw two right-angled triangles from the given information and use Pythagoras's theorem to find the missing sides.

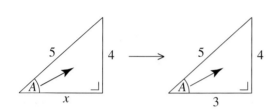 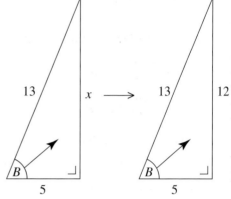

Given: $\sin A = \frac{4}{5}$

$$x^2 + 4^2 = 5^2$$
$$x^2 + 16 = 25$$
$$x^2 = 9$$
$$x = 3$$

Given: $\cos B = \frac{5}{13}$

$$x^2 + 5^2 = 13^2$$
$$x^2 + 25 = 169$$
$$x^2 = 144$$
$$x = 12$$

(i) $\cos A = \frac{3}{5}$

(ii) $\sin B = \frac{12}{13}$

(iii) $\sin (A + B) = \sin A \cos B + \cos A \sin B$

$$= \frac{4}{5} \times \frac{5}{13} + \frac{3}{5} \times \frac{12}{13}$$

$$= \frac{20}{65} + \frac{36}{65}$$

$$= \frac{56}{65}$$

$\sin^2 A + \cos^2 A$

$$= \left(\frac{4}{5}\right)^2 + \left(\frac{3}{5}\right)^2$$

$$= \frac{16}{25} + \frac{9}{25}$$

$$= \frac{25}{25} = 1$$

Example 2

Write cos 75° in surd form.

Solution:

We first express 75° as a combination of 30°, 45° or 60° and use page 9 of the tables.

$$75° = 45° + 30°$$

$$\cos (A + B) = \cos A \cos B - \sin A \sin B \qquad \text{(page 9 of the tables)}$$

$$\cos 75°$$

$$= \cos (45° + 30°)$$

$$= \cos 45° \cos 30° - \sin 45° \sin 30° \qquad \text{(let } A = 45° \text{ and } B = 30°)$$

$$= \frac{1}{\sqrt{2}} \cdot \frac{\sqrt{3}}{2} - \frac{1}{\sqrt{2}} \cdot \frac{1}{2} \qquad \left(\frac{\pi}{4} = 45° \text{ and } \frac{\pi}{6} = 30°, \text{ page 9}\right)$$

$$= \frac{\sqrt{3}}{2\sqrt{2}} - \frac{1}{2\sqrt{2}}$$

$$= \frac{\sqrt{3} - 1}{2\sqrt{2}} \qquad \text{(same denominator)}$$

Trigonometric Ratios for Angles Between 0° and 360°

Method for finding the trigonometric ratio for any angle between 0° and 360°:

1. Draw a rough diagram of the angle.

2. Determine in which quadrant the angle lies and use $\left(\begin{array}{c|c} S & A \\ \hline T & C \end{array}\right)$ to find its sign.

3. Find its **related** angle (the acute angle to the nearest horizontal).

4. Use the trigonometric ratio of the related angle with the sign in step 2.

Example

Find cos 210°, leaving your answer in surd form.

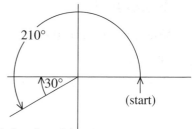

Solution:

Surd form, ∴ cannot use calculator.

1. The diagram shows the angle 210°.

2. 210° is in the 3rd quadrant.
   cos is negative in the 3rd quadrant.

3. Related angle is 30°.

4. ∴ $\cos 210° = -\cos 30° = -\frac{\sqrt{3}}{2}$ (page 9 of tables)

Solving Trigonometric Equations

Between 0° and 360° there may be two angles with the same trigonometric ratios.
For example, $\cos 120° = -\frac{1}{2}$ and $\cos 240° = -\frac{1}{2}$.

To solve a trigonometric equation, do the following:

1. Ignore the sign and calculate the related angle.
2. From the sign of the given ratio, decide in which quadrants the angles lie.
3. Using a rough diagram, state the angles between 0° and 360°.

Example

If $\sin \theta = -\dfrac{1}{\sqrt{2}}$, find the two values of θ, $0° \leqslant \theta \leqslant 360°$.

Solution:

1. Find the related angle (ignore sign).

   If $\sin \theta = \dfrac{1}{\sqrt{2}}$

   $\theta = \sin^{-1}\left(\dfrac{1}{\sqrt{2}}\right) = 45°$

   The related angle is $45°$.

2. sin is negative in the 3rd and 4th quadrant.

   $$\begin{array}{c|c} S & A \\ \hline T & C \end{array}$$

3. Rough diagram.

   θ in the 3rd quadrant

   θ in the 4th quadrant

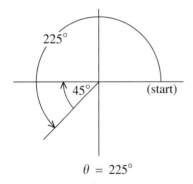

$\theta = 225°$

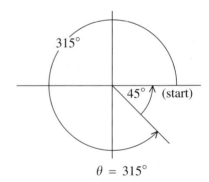

$\theta = 315°$

Thus, if $\sin \theta = -\dfrac{1}{\sqrt{2}}$, $\theta = 225°$ or $315°$, $0° \leqslant \theta \leqslant 360°$.

Values of sin, cos and tan for 0°, 90°, 180°, 270° and 360°

Both diagrams following represent the unit circle, but using two different notations to describe any point p on the circle.

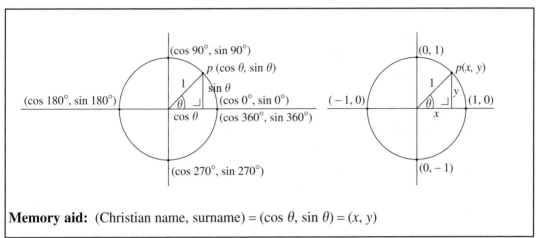

Memory aid: (Christian name, surname) $= (\cos \theta, \sin \theta) = (x, y)$

By comparing corresponding points on both unit circles, the values of sin, cos and tan for 0°, 90°, 180°, 270° and 360° can be read directly.

Example

(i) Find the value of A for which $\cos A = -1$, $0° \leqslant A \leqslant 360°$.

(ii) If $0° \leqslant A \leqslant 360°$, find the value of A for which $\sin A = 1$.

(iii) If $0° \leqslant A \leqslant 360°$, find the values of A for which $\cos A = 0$.

(iv) Evaluate $\sin^2 270$.

Solution:

Draw the unit circle.

Remember: (Christian name, surname) $= (\cos \theta, \sin \theta) = (x, y)$.

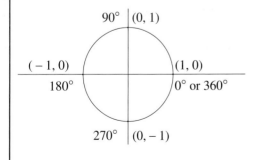

(i) $\cos A = -1$

$A = 180°$

(ii) $\sin A = 1$

$A = 90°$

(iii) $\cos A = 0$

$A = 90°$ or $270°$

(iv) $\sin^2 270$

$= (\sin 270)^2$

$= (-1)^2 = 1$

Chapter 12. PERMUTATIONS, COMBINATIONS AND PROBABILITY

Factorials and $\binom{n}{r}$ notation

Factorials

Definition:

> The product of all the positive whole numbers from n down to 1 is called '**factorial n**' and is denoted by $n!$
>
> $$\text{Thus, } n! = n(n-1)(n-2) \dots \times 3 \times 2 \times 1.$$

$\binom{n}{r}$ gives the number of ways of choosing r objects from n different objects.

Its value can be calculated in two ways:

> **1.** $\binom{n}{r} = \dfrac{n!}{r!(n-r)!}$ $\qquad$ (definition)
>
> **2.** $\binom{n}{r} = \dfrac{n(n-1)(n-2) \dots (n-r+1)}{r!}$ $\qquad$ (in practice)

Note: $\binom{n}{r}$ is pronounced 'n-c-r' or 'n-choose-r'.

Example

Evaluate   **(i)**   6!   **(ii)** $\begin{pmatrix} 12 \\ 3 \end{pmatrix}$ **(iii)** $5\begin{pmatrix} 8 \\ 3 \end{pmatrix} - 4\begin{pmatrix} 8 \\ 4 \end{pmatrix}$.

Solution:

(i) $6! = 6 \times 5 \times 4 \times 3 \times 2 \times 1 = 720$

(ii) $\begin{pmatrix} 12 \\ 3 \end{pmatrix} = \dfrac{12 \times 11 \times 10}{3 \times 2 \times 1} = 220$

 6 | 2nd F | | n! | | = |

 12 | 2nd F | | nCr | 3 | = |

(iii) $5\begin{pmatrix} 8 \\ 3 \end{pmatrix} - 4\begin{pmatrix} 8 \\ 4 \end{pmatrix}$

$= 5(56) - 4(70)$

$= 280 - 280$

$= 0$

$\begin{pmatrix} 8 \\ 3 \end{pmatrix} = \dfrac{8 \times 7 \times 6}{3 \times 2 \times 1} = 56$

$\begin{pmatrix} 8 \\ 4 \end{pmatrix} = \dfrac{8 \times 7 \times 6 \times 5}{4 \times 3 \times 2 \times 1} = 70$

 5 | × | 8 | 2nd F | | nCr | 3 | − | 4 | × | 8 | 2nd F | | nCr | 4 | = |

Note: With some calculators n! and nCr can be used directly without having to use the | 2nd F | key.

Permutations (Arrangements)

> A permutation is an arrangement of a number of objects in a definite order.

Consider the three letters *P*, *Q* and *R*. If these letters are written down in a row, there are six different possible arrangements:

> *PQR* or *PRQ* or *QPR* or *QRP* or *RPQ* or *RQP*

The first letter can be written down in 3 ways, the second letter can then be written down in 2 ways and the third letter can be written down in only 1 way.
Thus the three operations can be performed in $\boxed{3} \times \boxed{2} \times \boxed{1} = 6$ ways.
The boxes are an aid in helping to fill in the number of ways each choice can be made at each position.
In an arrangement, or permutation, the order of the objects chosen is important.

Example 1

A number plate is to consist of three letters of the English alphabet followed by two digits. If no letter or digit can be repeated and 0 can never be used as the first digit, how many different plates can be manufactured?

| B | A | T | 4 | 5 |

(an example)

Solution:

Represent each choice with a box.

The first place can be filled in 26 ways, the second in 25 ways and the third in 24 ways.

The fourth place can be filled in 9 ways (0 not allowed) and the last place can also be filled in 9 ways (one digit used in the fourth place and 0 allowed in the last place).

∴ number of number plates = $\boxed{26} \times \boxed{25} \times \boxed{24} \times \boxed{9} \times \boxed{9}$ = 1, 263, 600

Example 2

How many different arrangements, taking 3 letters at a time, can be formed from the word *P H O E N I X*.

Solution:

Represent each choice with a box. We only use 3 boxes because our choice is restricted to 3 letters at a time.

The first place can be filled in 7 ways, the second in 6 ways and the third place in 5 ways.

∴ number of arrangements = $\boxed{7} \times \boxed{6} \times \boxed{5}$ = 210

Example 3

There are 6 horses – *A, B, C, D, E* and *F* – in a race. Each horse takes a different time to complete the race. On completing the race:

(i) In how many different placing arrangements can the 6 horses finish?

(ii) If *A* is placed first and *B* last, in how many different placing arrangements can the other horses finish?

Solution:

(i)   In how many different placing arrangements can the 6 horses finish?

The first place can be filled in 6 ways, the second in 5 ways, the third in 4 ways, the fourth in 3 ways, the fifth in 2 ways and the last in 1 way.

$$\boxed{6} \times \boxed{5} \times \boxed{4} \times \boxed{3} \times \boxed{2} \times \boxed{1} = 720$$

(ii)   If *A* is placed first and *B* last, in how many different placing arrangements can the other horses finish?

The first place can be filled in only 1 way, with *A*, and the last place can be filled also in only 1 way (fill these in first). Then the second place can be filled in 4 ways, the third in 3 ways, the fourth in 2 ways and the fifth place in 1 way.

A   *B*

$$\boxed{1} \times \boxed{4} \times \boxed{3} \times \boxed{2} \times \boxed{1} \times \boxed{1} = 24$$

Example 4

N I A M H uses a password formed from one letter of her name followed by four of the digits from 1 to 9. She does not use any digit more than once.

 (i)   How many such passwords can be formed?

 (ii)   How many of the passwords begin with N?

(iii)   How many of the passwords end in an even digit?

(iv)   How many of the passwords begin with N or M and use only odd digits?

Solution:

Represent each choice with a box. Always start with the choice which is most restrictive.

  N I A M H   1, 2, 3, 4, 5, 6, 7, 8, 9

In each case we use 1 letter followed by 4 digits, $\therefore$ use 5 boxes.

There are 5 letters and 9 digits (no digit can be used more than one).

(i)   How many such passwords can be formed?

The first place (letters) can be filled in 5 ways. Then the second place can be filled in 9 ways, the third place in 8 ways, the fourth place in 7 ways and the last place in 6 ways.

$\therefore$ number of passwords = $\boxed{5} \times \boxed{9} \times \boxed{8} \times \boxed{7} \times \boxed{6} = 15{,}120$

(ii)   How many of the passwords begin with N?

Begin with N. Thus the first place can only be filled in one way, with N. Then the second place can be filled in 9 ways, the third place in 8 ways, the fourth place in 7 ways and the last place in 6 ways.

$\therefore$ number of passwords = $\boxed{1} \times \boxed{9} \times \boxed{8} \times \boxed{7} \times \boxed{6} = 3{,}024$

(iii) **How many of the passwords end in an even digit?**

The **first** place can be filled in 5 ways, with N, I, A, M or H (fill that place first). The **last** place can only be filled in 4 ways, with 2, 4, 6 or 8 (fill that place next). Then the second place can be filled in 8 ways (one even number used in the last place), the third place in 7 ways and the fourth place in 6 ways.

$\therefore$ number of passwords = $\boxed{5} \times \boxed{8} \times \boxed{7} \times \boxed{6} \times \boxed{4} = 6,720$

(iv) **How many of the passwords begin with N or M and use only odd digits?**

Begin with N or M. Thus, the first place can only be filled in 2 ways (fill this in). The other restriction is that we can only use the 5 odd digits, 1, 3, 5, 7 and 9. Then the second place can be filled in 5 ways, the third place in 4 ways, the fourth place in 3 ways and the last place in 2 ways.

$\therefore$ number of passwords = $\boxed{2} \times \boxed{5} \times \boxed{4} \times \boxed{3} \times \boxed{2} = 240$

Example 5

How many different five digit numbers can be formed from the digits, 1, 2, 3, 4 and 5, if no digit can be repeated and:

(i) there are no restrictions on digits

(ii) the number is odd

(iii) the number is even

(iv) the number is greater than 30,000

Solution:

Represent each choice with a box.

(i) no restrictions

$\boxed{5} \times \boxed{4} \times \boxed{3} \times \boxed{2} \times \boxed{1}$

$= 120$

(ii) must be odd.

Thus, the last place can be filled in only 3 ways (1, 3 or 5). Fill this in first, then fill in the other places.

$\boxed{4} \times \boxed{3} \times \boxed{2} \times \boxed{1} \times \boxed{3}$

$= 72$

(iii) must be even.

Thus, the last place can be filled in only 2 ways (2 or 4). Fill this in first, then fill in the other places.

$\boxed{4} \times \boxed{3} \times \boxed{2} \times \boxed{1} \times \boxed{2}$

$= 48$

(iv) must be greater than 30,000. Thus, the first place can be filled in only 3 ways (3, 4 or 5). Fill this in first, then fill in the other places.

$\boxed{3} \times \boxed{4} \times \boxed{3} \times \boxed{2} \times \boxed{1}$

$= 72$

Combinations (Selections)

> A combination is a selection of a number of objects in any order.

In making a selection of a number of objects from a given set, only the contents of the group selected are important, not the order in which the items are selected.

For example, *AB* and *BA* represent the same selection.
However, *AB* and *BA* represent different arrangements.

Note: What is called a 'combination lock' should really be called a 'permutation lock', as the order of the digits is essential.

Example 1

Seven people take part in a chess competition. How many games will be played if each person must play each of the others?

Solution:

We **have** 7 people to choose from, of whom we want to **choose** 2 (as 2 people play in each game).

$$\therefore\ n = 7 \text{ and } r = 2$$

$$\therefore\quad \text{Number of games} = \binom{7}{2} = \frac{7 \times 6}{2 \times 1} = 21$$

Example 2

Ten points are taken on the circumference of a circle (as shown). A chord is a line segment joining any two of these points. Calculate the number of such chords that can be drawn. With these points as vertices, how many triangles can be drawn?

Solution:

Number of chords.	Number of triangles.
We **have** 10 points.	We **have** 10 points.
Each chord **uses** 2 points.	Each triangle **uses** 3 points.
$\therefore\quad n = 10 \text{ and } r = 2$	$\therefore\quad n = 10 \text{ and } r = 3$
$\binom{10}{2} = \dfrac{10 \times 9}{2 \times 1} = 45$	$\binom{10}{3} = \dfrac{10 \times 9 \times 8}{3 \times 2 \times 1} = 120$
$\therefore\quad$ number of chords is 45	$\therefore\quad$ number of triangles is 120

Example 3

(i) In how many ways can a selection of 3 books be made from 8?

(ii) If a certain book must always be chosen, in how many ways can the selection be made?

(iii) If a certain book must never be chosen, in how many ways can the selection be made?

Solution:

(i) **In how many ways can a selection of 5 books be made from 12?**

We **have** 8 books to choose from and we need to **choose** 3.

$$\therefore \quad n = 8 \text{ and } r = 3$$

$$\text{Number of selections} = \binom{8}{3} = \frac{8 \times 7 \times 6}{3 \times 2 \times 1} = 56$$

(ii) **If a certain book must always be chosen, in how many ways can the selection be made?**

One particular book **must always** be chosen.

Thus, we **have** 7 books to choose from and we need to **choose** 2 (one book already chosen).

$$\therefore \quad n = 7 \text{ and } r = 2$$

$$\text{Number of selections} = \binom{7}{2} = \frac{7 \times 6}{2 \times 1} = 21$$

(iii) **If a certain book must never be chosen, in how many ways can the selection be made?**

One particular book **must never** be chosen.

Thus, we **have** 7 books to choose from (one book cannot be chosen) and we need to **choose** 3.

$$\therefore \quad n = 7 \text{ and } r = 3$$

$$\text{Number of selections} = \binom{7}{3} = \frac{7 \times 6 \times 5}{3 \times 2 \times 1} = 35$$

Example 4

A committee of 4 people is to be formed from a group of 6 women and 5 men.

(i) How many different committees can be formed?

(ii) On how many of these committees is there an equal number of men and of women?

(iii) On how many of these committees are there more women than men?

Solution:

(i) How many different committees can be formed?

We **have** 11 different people to choose from, 6 women and 5 men.

A committee must consist of 4 people.

$$\therefore \quad n = 11 \text{ and } r = 4$$

$$\text{Number of different committees} = \binom{11}{4} = \frac{11 \times 10 \times 9 \times 8}{4 \times 3 \times 2 \times 1} = 330$$

(ii) On how many of these committees is there an equal number of men and of women?

$$\boxed{\text{and} = \times}$$

A committee must consist of 4 people. If there are to be an equal number of women and men then each committee must consist of 2 women and 2 men.

Thus, from the 6 women we have to choose 2, **and** from the 5 men we have to choose 2.

$$\text{Number of ways of choosing 2 women from 6 women} = \binom{6}{2} = \frac{6 \times 5}{2 \times 1} = 15$$

$$\text{Number of ways of choosing 2 men from 5 men} = \binom{5}{2} = \frac{5 \times 4}{2 \times 1} = 10$$

Thus, the number of committees with an equal number of women **and** men $= 15 \times 10 = 15$.

(iii) On how many of these committees are there more women than men?

$$\boxed{\text{and} = \times} \qquad \boxed{\text{or} = +}$$

A committee must consist of 4 people. If there are to be more women than men, then each committee must consist of:

4 women and 0 men   or   3 women and 1 man.

Thus, we need to choose '4 women **and** 0 men' **or** '3 women **and** 1 man', from 6 women and 5 men.

Let W stand for women and let M stand for men.

We have 6 women and 5 men and these are **always** the upper numbers.

$$
\begin{array}{ccccccc}
4W & \text{and} & 0M & \text{or} & 3W & \text{and} & 1M \quad \text{(lower numbers in each case)}\\
\downarrow & & \downarrow & \downarrow & \downarrow & & \downarrow \\
\binom{6}{4} & \times & \binom{5}{0} & + & \binom{6}{3} & \times & \binom{5}{1} \\
= 15 & \times & 1 & + & 20 & \times & 5 \\
= 15 & & & + & 100 \\
= 115
\end{array}
$$

Probability

Probability involves the study of the laws of chance. It is a measure of the chance, or likelihood, of something happening.

If E is an event, then $P(E)$ stands for the probability that the event occurs.

$P(E)$ is read as 'the probability of E'.

Definition:

> The measure of the probability of an event, E, is given by:
>
> $$P(E) = \frac{\text{number of successful outcomes}}{\text{number of possible outcomes}}$$

The probability of an event is a number between 0 and 1, including 0 and 1.

$$0 \leqslant P(E) \leqslant 1$$

The value of $P(E)$ can be given as a fraction, decimal or percentage.

Note: $P(E) = 0$ means that an event is **impossible**.

$P(E) = 1$ means that an event is **certain**.

Addition Rule (OR)

> The probability that two events, A or B, can happen is given by:
> $$P(A \text{ or } B) = P(A) + P(B) - P(A \text{ and } B)$$
> $$\uparrow$$
> (removes double counting)

It is often called the **or** rule. It is important to remember that $P(A \text{ or } B)$ means A occurs, or B occurs, or both occur. By subtracting $P(A \text{ and } B)$, the possibility of double counting is removed.

Probability of an event not happening

If E is any event, then 'not E' is the event that E does not occur. Clearly E and 'not E' cannot occur at the same time. Either E or not E must occur. Thus, we have the following relationship between the probabilities of E and not E:

> $$P(E) + P(\text{not } E) = 1$$
> or
> $$P(\text{not } E) = 1 - P(E)$$

Multiplication Rule (AND)

Successive events

> The probability that two events, A and then B, both happen, and in that order is given by:
> $$P(A \text{ and } B) = P(A) \times P(B)$$
> where $P(B)$ has been worked out assuming that A has already occurred.

Order must be taken into account. Also, be very careful where the outcome at one stage does affect the outcome at the next stage.

> When the question says **and**, then **multiply**

The multiplication rule helps reduce the need to make out a sample space diagram.

Example 1

A letter is selected at random from the letters of the word $M I S S I S S I P P I$.

Find the probability that the letter is:

(i) M **(ii)** S or P **(iii)** a vowel

Solution:

There are 11 letters in the word $M I S S I S S I P P I$.

(i) There is just one M

$$\therefore \quad P(M) = \frac{1}{11}$$

(ii) There are 4 S's and 2 P's (6 altogether)

$$\therefore \quad P(S \text{ or } P) = \frac{6}{11}$$

(iii) There is just one vowel, I. However, I occurs 4 times.

$$\therefore \quad P(\text{vowel}) = P(I) = \frac{4}{11}$$

Example 2

Two unbiased six-sided dice are thrown, one red and the other black, and the scores are added.

The faces of the red die are numbered 1, 2, 3, 4, 5 and 6.

The faces of the black die are numbered 1, 1, 2, 3, 3 and 4.

Find the probability of obtaining:

(i) a score of 5   **(ii)** a score of 6 or more   **(iii)** a score less than 4.

Solution:

Make out a sample space diagram: Number of possible outcomes $= 6 \times 6 = 36$

black die						
④	5	6	7	8	9	10
③	4	5	6	7	8	9
③	4	5	6	7	8	9
②	3	4	5	6	7	8
①	2	3	4	5	6	7
①	2	3	4	5	6	7
■	①	②	③	④	⑤	⑥

red die

(i) $P \text{ (a score of 5)} = \dfrac{6}{36} = \dfrac{1}{6}$

(ii) $P \text{ (a score of 6 or more)} = \dfrac{20}{36} = \dfrac{5}{9}$

(iii) $P \text{ (a score less than 4)} = \dfrac{5}{36}$

Example 3

A bag contains 12 red, 8 blue and 4 yellow discs. A disc is selected at random from the bag. What is the probability that the disc selected is:

(i) red   **(ii)** red or blue   **(iii)** yellow   **(iv)** not yellow?

Solution:

There are $12 + 8 + 4 = 24$ discs in the bag.

(i) $P(\text{red disc}) = \dfrac{\text{number of red discs}}{\text{total number of discs}} = \dfrac{12}{24} = \dfrac{1}{2}$

(ii) $P(\text{red or blue disc}) = \dfrac{\text{number of red discs} + \text{number of blue discs}}{\text{total number of discs}}$

$$= \dfrac{12 + 8}{24} = \dfrac{20}{24} = \dfrac{5}{6}$$

(iii) $P(\text{yellow disc}) = \dfrac{\text{number of yellow discs}}{\text{total number of discs}} = \dfrac{4}{24} = \dfrac{1}{6}$

(iv) We are certain that the disc selected is yellow or not yellow.

$$P(\text{yellow disc}) + P(\text{not a yellow disc}) = 1$$

$$P(\text{not a yellow disc}) = 1 - P(\text{yellow disc})$$

$$= 1 - \dfrac{1}{6} = \dfrac{5}{6}$$

Alternatively:

$$P(\text{not a yellow disc}) = \dfrac{\text{number of non-yellow discs}}{\text{total number of discs}}$$

$$= \dfrac{\text{number of red discs} + \text{number of blue discs}}{\text{total number of discs}} = \dfrac{12 + 8}{24} = \dfrac{20}{24} = \dfrac{5}{6}$$

Example 4

In a class, there are 18 boys and 12 girls. Two boys wear glasses and three girls wear glasses. A pupil is picked at random from the class.

(i) What is the probability that the pupil is a boy?

(ii) What is the probability that the pupil wears glasses?

(iii) What is the probability that the pupil is a boy who wears glasses?

A girl is picked at random from the class.

(iv) What is the probability that she does not wear glasses?

A pupil wearing glasses is picked at random from the class.

(v) What is the probability that it is a boy?

Solution:

It is good practice to represent the information in a table (including the totals for each column and row).

	Boy	Girl	Total
Does not wear glasses	16	9	25
Wears glasses	2	3	5
Total	18	12	30

There are $18 + 12 = 30$ pupils in the class.

(i) $P(\text{boy}) = \dfrac{\text{number of boys}}{\text{number of pupils in the class}} = \dfrac{18}{30} = \dfrac{3}{5}$

(ii) $P(\text{pupil wears glasses}) = \dfrac{\text{number of pupils who wear glasses}}{\text{number of pupils in the class}} = \dfrac{5}{30} = \dfrac{1}{6}$

(iii) P(boy who wears glasses) $= \dfrac{\text{number of boys who wear glasses}}{\text{number of pupils in the class}} = \dfrac{2}{30} = \dfrac{1}{15}$

(iv) We are certain that the pupil picked is a girl. There are 12 girls in the class. 9 of these do not wear glasses.

P(when a girl is picked she does not wear glasses)

$= \dfrac{\text{number of girls in the class who do not wear glasses}}{\text{number of girls in the class}} = \dfrac{9}{12} = \dfrac{3}{4}$

(v) We are certain that the pupil picked wears glasses. There are 5 pupils who wear glasses. 2 of these pupils are boys.

P(when a pupil who wears glasses is picked, the pupil is a boy)

$= \dfrac{\text{number of boys in the class who wear glasses}}{\text{number of pupils in the class who wear glasses}} = \dfrac{2}{5}$

Example 5

A bag contains twelve counters, numbered 1 to 12 inclusive. A counter is chosen at random. What is the probability that the counter chosen has a number that is even or divisible by 3?

Solution:

There are 12 possible outcomes : 1, 2, 3, 4, 5, 6, 7, 8, 9, 10, 11, 12

Even numbers are
2, 4, 6, 8, 10 or 12 $\therefore$ P(even number) $= \dfrac{6}{12}$

Numbers divisible by 3 are
3, 6, 9 or 12 $\therefore$ P(number divisible by 3) $= \dfrac{4}{12}$

Even numbers and numbers
divisible by 3, are 6 or 12 $\therefore$ P(even number and a number divisible by 3) $= \dfrac{2}{12}$

P(even number or divisible by 3)

$= P$(even number) $+ P$(divisible by 3) $- P$(even number and a number divisible by 3)

$= \qquad \dfrac{6}{12} \qquad + \qquad \dfrac{4}{12} \qquad - \qquad \dfrac{2}{12}$

$\qquad\qquad\qquad\qquad\qquad\qquad\qquad\qquad\qquad\qquad\qquad \uparrow$

$= \dfrac{8}{12} = \dfrac{2}{3} \qquad\qquad\qquad\qquad$ (removes double counting)

Note: The numbers 6 and 12 are common to both events and if the probabilities were simply added, then the numbers 6 and 12 would have been counted twice.

Example 6

A bag contains 2 red and 3 yellow discs only. When a disc is drawn from the bag, it is returned before the next draw. What is the probability that two draws will yield both discs the same colour?

Solution:

Method 1: Using a sample space diagram.

Let R represent that a red disc is chosen and let Y represent that a yellow disc is chosen.

sample space diagram

There are 25 possible outcomes
(5 for the first draw and 5 for the second draw).
The dots indicate where the colours are the same, successful outcome, either two reds or two yellows. There are 13 dots.

P(both discs the same colour) $= \dfrac{13}{25}$

Method 2: Using the rules of probability.

Let R_1 represent that a red disc is chosen first, Y_2 represent that a yellow disc is chosen second, and so on.

P(both discs the same colour)

$= P(R_1 \text{ and } R_2) \quad \text{or} \quad P(Y_1 \text{ and } Y_2)$

$= P(R_1) \times P(R_2) \quad + \quad P(Y_1) \times P(Y_2)$

$= \dfrac{2}{5} \times \dfrac{2}{5} + \dfrac{3}{5} \times \dfrac{3}{5}$

$= \dfrac{4}{25} + \dfrac{9}{25}$

$= \dfrac{13}{25}$

> red and then a red
>
> or
>
> yellow and then a yellow

Example 7

Two women, Ann and Bríd, and two men, Con and Declan, sit in a row for a photograph.

(i) How many different arrangements of the four people are possible?

(ii) Write out the four possible arrangements that have the two women in the middle.

(iii) If the arrangement of the four people is chosen at random from all of the possible arrangements, what is the probability that the two women will be in the middle?

Solution:

(i) **How many different arrangements of the four people are possible?**

The first place can be filled in 4 ways, the second place in 3 ways, the third place in 2 ways and the last place in 1 way.

Number of different arrangements = $\boxed{4} \times \boxed{3} \times \boxed{2} \times \boxed{1} = 24$

(ii) **Write out the four possible arrangements that have the two women in the middle.**

Let A = Ann, B = Bríd, C = Con and D = Declan.

The four arrangements are:

C A B D   or   C B A D   or   D A B C   or   D B A C

(iii) **If the arrangement of the four people is chosen at random from all of the possible arrangements, what is the probability that the two women will be in the middle?**

Using the answers from parts (i) and (ii)

P(two women will be in the middle)

$$\frac{\text{Number of arrangements that have the two women in the middle}}{\text{Total number of different arrangements}} = \frac{4}{24} = \frac{1}{6}$$

Example 8

Sarah and Jim celebrate their birthdays in a particular week (Monday to Sunday inclusive). Assuming that the birthdays are equally likely to fall on any day of the week, what is the probability that:

(i) both people were born on a Friday,

(ii) one was born on a Monday and the other was born on a Wednesday.

Solution:

Note: P(any person born on a particular day of the week) $= \frac{1}{7}$.

Method 1: Using a sample space diagram.

Jim (vertical axis), Sarah (horizontal axis)

S							
S							
F					•		
T							
W	×						
T							
M			×				
	M	T	W	T	F	S	S

Sarah

There are $7 \times 7 = 49$ possible outcomes.

• represents both people born on Friday

× represents one person born on Monday and the other person born on Wednesday.

(i) P(both people born on Friday) $= \frac{1}{49}$

(ii) P(one person born on Monday and the other born Wednesday) $= \frac{2}{49}$

Method 2: Using the rules of probability.

Let S_M stand for Sarah was born on Monday, J_W stand for Jim was born on Wednesday etc.

(i) P(both people were born on a Friday)

$= P(S_F \text{ and } J_F)$

$\downarrow$

$= P(S_F) \times P(J_F)$ ('and' means multiply)

$= \frac{1}{7} \times \frac{1}{7}$

$= \frac{1}{49}$

(ii) P(one was born on Monday and the other was born on Wednesday)

$= P(S_M \text{ and } J_W \quad \text{or} \quad S_W \text{ and } J_M)$

$= P(S_M \text{ and } J_W) \quad \text{or} \quad P(S_W \text{ and } J_M)$

$\downarrow \qquad \downarrow \qquad \downarrow$

$= P(S_M) \times P(J_W) \; + \; P(S_M) \times P(J_W)$ ('and' means multiply, 'or' means add)

$= \frac{1}{7} \times \frac{1}{7} \; + \; \frac{1}{7} \times \frac{1}{7}$

$= \frac{1}{49} + \frac{1}{49}$

$= \frac{2}{49}$

Example 9

Twelve blood samples are tested in a laboratory. Of these it is found that five blood samples are of type A, four of type B and the remaining three are of type O.

Two blood samples are selected at random from the twelve.

What is the probability that:

(i) the two samples are of type A

(ii) one sample is of type B and the other sample is of type O

(iii) the two samples are of the same blood type?

Solution:

Picking two blood samples at a time is the same as picking one after another **without replacement**.

Method 1: Using the rules of probability.

Let A_1 represent that blood Sample A is chosen first, B_2 that blood sample B is chosen second and so on.

(i) P(the two samples are of type A) $= P(A_1) \times P(A_2)$

$$= \frac{5}{12} \times \frac{4}{11} = \frac{5}{33}$$

> A first and then A second
>
> (no replacement)

(ii) P(one sample is of type B and the other sample is of type O)

$= P(B_1 \text{ and } O_2) \quad \text{or} \quad P(O_1 \text{ and } B_2)$

$= P(B_1) \times P(O_2) \quad + \quad P(O_1) \times P(B_2)$

$= \dfrac{4}{12} \quad \times \quad \dfrac{3}{11} \quad + \quad \dfrac{3}{12} \quad \times \quad \dfrac{4}{11}$

$= \dfrac{1}{11} \quad + \quad \dfrac{1}{11} \quad = \quad \dfrac{2}{11}$

> B first and then O second
>
> or
>
> O first and then B second
>
> (no replacement)

(iii) P(the two samples are of the same blood type)

$= P(A_1 \text{ and } A_2) \text{ or } P(B_1 \text{ and } B_2) \text{ or } P(O_1 \text{ and } O_2)$

$= P(A_1) \times P(A_2) + P(B_1) \times P(B_2) + P(O_1) \times P(O_2)$

$= \dfrac{5}{12} \quad \times \quad \dfrac{4}{11} \quad + \quad \dfrac{4}{12} \quad \times \quad \dfrac{3}{11} \quad + \quad \dfrac{3}{12} \quad \times \quad \dfrac{2}{11}$

$= \dfrac{5}{33} \quad + \quad \dfrac{1}{11} \quad + \quad \dfrac{1}{22} \quad = \quad \dfrac{19}{66}$

> A first and then A second
>
> or
>
> B first and then B second
>
> or
>
> O first and O second
>
> (no replacement)

Method 2: Using a sample space diagram.

Picking two blood samples at a time is the same as picking one after another **without** replacement.

The shaded regions indicate that you can't pick the same blood sample again.

	A	A	A	A	A	B	B	B	B	O	O	O
O						×	×	×	×	✓	✓	■
O						×	×	×	×	✓	■	✓
O						×	×	×	×	■	✓	✓
B						✓	✓	✓	■	×	×	×
B						✓	✓	■	✓	×	×	×
B						✓	■	✓	✓	×	×	×
B						■	✓	✓	✓	×	×	×
A	✓	✓	✓	✓	■							
A	✓	✓	✓	■	✓							
A	✓	✓	■	✓	✓							
A	✓	■	✓	✓	✓							
A	■	✓	✓	✓	✓							

Number of possible outcomes $= 12 \times 11 = 132$

- • represents the two samples are of type A
- × represents one sample is of type B and the other sample is of type O
- ✓ represents the two samples are of the same blood type?

(i) P(the two samples are of

type A) $= \dfrac{20}{132} = \dfrac{5}{33}$

(ii) P(one sample is of type B and the other sample

is of type O) $= \dfrac{24}{132} = \dfrac{2}{11}$

(iii) P(the two samples are of the same blood type)

$= \dfrac{20 + 12 + 6}{132} = \dfrac{38}{132} = \dfrac{19}{66}$

Example 10

The probability that a woman will hit the target with a single shot at a rifle range is $\frac{2}{5}$.
Find the probability that she first hits the target with her third shot.

Solution:

$P(\text{hit}) + P(\text{miss}) = 1$ (either she hits the target or she misses it)

$$P(\text{hit}) = \frac{2}{5}$$

$$\therefore \quad P(\text{miss}) = 1 - P(\text{hit}) = 1 - \frac{2}{5} = \frac{3}{5}$$

(she first hits the target on the third shot)

$= P(\text{misses on 1st shot}) \times P(\text{misses on 2nd shot}) \times P(\text{hits target on 3rd shot})$

$$= \frac{3}{5} \times \frac{3}{5} \times \frac{2}{5} = \frac{18}{125}$$

Example 11

A bag contains 16 marbles, 7 of which are white and the remainder black.
Three marbles are removed at random, one at a time, without replacement.
Find the probability that:
(i) all are black   **(ii)** at least one is white.

Solution:

Let B_1 represent that a black marble is chosen first, B_2 that a black marble is chosen
second, and B_3 that a black marble is chosen third.
There are 16 marbles, 7 white, 9 black.

(i) $P(\text{all are black}) = P(B_1) \times P(B_2) \times P(B_3)$

$$= \frac{9}{16} \times \frac{8}{15} \times \frac{7}{14}$$

$$= \frac{3}{20}$$

$P(B_1) = \frac{9}{16}$

$P(B_2) = \frac{8}{15} \begin{pmatrix} 1 \text{ black removed,} \\ 8 \text{ black and 7 white left} \end{pmatrix}$

$P(B_3) = \frac{7}{14} \begin{pmatrix} 2 \text{ black removed,} \\ 7 \text{ black and 7 white left} \end{pmatrix}$

(ii) In every other case there is **at least** one white.

$P(\text{at least one white}) = 1 - P(\text{none is white})$

$$= 1 - P(\text{all are black})$$

$$= 1 - \frac{3}{20}$$

$$= \frac{17}{20}$$

Chapter 13. STATISTICS

Median, Mean and Standard Deviation of an Array of Numbers

Median

> When the values are arranged in ascending, or descending, order of size, then the median is the middle value. If the number of values is even, then the median is the average of the two middle values.

Note: Half the values lie below the median and half the values lie above the median.

Mean

> The mean of a set of values is defined as the sum of all the values divided by the number of values.

$$\text{Mean} = \frac{\text{Sum of all the Values}}{\text{Number of Values}} \qquad \text{or} \qquad \bar{x} = \frac{\Sigma x}{n}$$

Example 1

Find: **(i)** the mean **(ii)** the median of the array of numbers: 10, 4, 5, 4, 12, 2, 8, 5, 4.

Solution:

(i) $\text{Mean} = \bar{x} = \frac{\Sigma x}{n} = \frac{10 + 4 + 5 + 4 + 12 + 2 + 8 + 5 + 4}{9} = \frac{54}{9} = 6$

(ii) Median: First write the numbers in ascending order:

2, 4, 4, 4, ⑤, 5, 8, 10, 12

The middle number is 5 $\quad \therefore$ the median = 5

Example 2

Find the median of the array of numbers: 15, 5, 6, 3, 17, 11, 2, 8

Solution:

First write the numbers in ascending order: 2, 3, 5, ⑥, ⑧, 11, 15, 17

Since there is an even number of numbers we take the average of the two middle ones, 6 and 8.

$$\therefore \quad \text{the median} = \frac{6+8}{2} = \frac{14}{2} = 7$$

Standard Deviation

> The standard deviation is a measure of the spread of the values about the mean.

In other words, it gives us an indication of how the values we have are spread out. The higher the standard deviation, the more spread out around the mean is the data, and vice versa. The Greek letter σ, sigma, is used to denote the standard deviation.

To calculate the standard deviation, σ, of a set of values we use the following formula:

$$\sigma = \sqrt{\frac{\sum d^2}{n}}$$

where $d = |x - \bar{x}|$

x represents the values.

d, the deviation, is the difference between a single value, x, and the mean, $\bar{x}$.

n is the number of values of x.

Note: When calculating σ, it is good practice to lay out the data in vertical columns in a table.

Example

Calculate the standard deviation, correct to one decimal place, of the following array of numbers: 2, 4, 7, 8, 9.

Solution:

First calculate the mean, $\bar{x}$:

$$\bar{x} = \frac{2+4+7+8+9}{5}$$

$$= \frac{30}{5}$$

$$= 6$$

Now make out a table:

x	d	d^2
2	4	16
4	2	4
7	1	1
8	2	4
9	3	9

$d = |x - \bar{x}|$

$$\Sigma d^2 = 34$$

Standard deviation $= \sigma = \sqrt{\dfrac{\Sigma d^2}{n}} = \sqrt{\dfrac{34}{5}} = 2.607680962$

$$\therefore \quad d = 2.6 \text{ (correct to one decimal place)}$$

Mean and Standard Deviation of a Frequency Distribution

$$\text{Mean} = \bar{x} = \frac{\Sigma fx}{\Sigma f}$$

$$\sigma = \sqrt{\frac{\Sigma fd^2}{\Sigma f}}$$

where $d = |x - \bar{x}|$

f is the frequency attached to each value of x.

Example

20 pupils were given a problem to solve. The following grouped frequency distribution table gives the number of pupils who solved the problem in the given time interval.

Time (minutes)	0 – 4	4 – 12	12 – 24	24 – 40
Frequency	3	8	7	2

Assuming the data can be taken at the mid-interval values, calculate:

(i)   the mean   (ii)   the standard deviation, correct to one place of decimals.

Solution:

The table can be rewritten using the mid-interval values.

Time (minutes)	2	8	18	32
Frequency	3	8	7	2

(i) $\text{Mean} = \bar{x} = \dfrac{\Sigma fx}{\Sigma f} = \dfrac{3(2) + 8(8) + 7(18) + 2(32)}{3 + 8 + 7 + 2}$

$$= \frac{6 + 64 + 126 + 64}{20} = \frac{260}{20} = 13$$

(ii)   Make out a table:

f	x	d	d^2	fd^2
3	2	11	121	363
8	8	5	25	200
7	18	5	25	175
2	32	19	361	722

$d = |x - \bar{x}|$

$\Sigma f = 20$ $\Sigma d^2 = 1{,}460$

$$\sigma = \sqrt{\frac{\Sigma fd^2}{\Sigma f}} = \sqrt{\frac{1{,}460}{20}} = 8.544003745$$

$\therefore$ $\sigma = 8.5$ (correct to one decimal place)

Weighted Mean

A weighted mean is one where the **frequencies** are replaced by **weights**. The weights are a **measure of importance** of a particular value, i.e. each value has a **statistical weight** attached to it.

Note: Calculating a weighted mean is exactly the same as finding the mean of a frequency distribution, except that the frequencies are replaced by weights.

We calculate the weighted mean using the formula:

$$\text{Weighted mean} = \bar{x}_w = \frac{\Sigma wx}{\Sigma w}$$

(**Note:** The weights are often given in the form of a ratio or proportion.)

Example

Subject	Physics	Chemistry	Mathematics	Irish
Mark	74	65	82	58
Weight	3	4	5	2

The table shows a student's marks and the weights given to these marks.

Calculate the weighted mean mark for the student.

Solution:

$$\text{Weighted mean} = \bar{x}_w = \frac{\Sigma wx}{\Sigma w} = \frac{3(74) + 4(65) + 5(82) + 2(58)}{3 + 4 + 5 + 2}$$

$$= \frac{222 + 260 + 410 + 116}{14}$$

$$= \frac{1{,}008}{14}$$

$$= 72$$

Thus, the student had a weighted mean mark of 72.

Histogram

A histogram is constructed with the following steps:

1. Let the base of the rectangle which represents the class interval of smallest width have a length of 1 unit (or of length 2 units, 3 units, etc.).

2. Express the bases of the other rectangles, depending on the width of the class intervals, in terms of this base (i.e. are they one and a half times the base? double it? treble it? etc.).

3. Divide each frequency by its corresponding base in step 2 to find the height of each rectangle.

   That is: $\text{Height} = \dfrac{\text{Frequency}}{\text{Base}}$

4. With the values on the horizontal axis and the frequencies on the vertical axis, construct the rectangles beside each other.

When given a grouped frequency distribution and asked to represent the distribution with a histogram, it is good practice to rewrite the table again with extra rows to show the base and height of each rectangle.

Example

The following frequency distribution gives the marks obtained, out of 120, by students in an examination.

Marks	0 – 30	30 – 40	40 – 60	60 – 100	100 – 120
No. of students	21	8	12	20	8

(**Note:** 0 – 30 means 0 is included but 30 is not, etc.)
Represent the data with a histogram.

Solution:

The smallest interval is the 30 – 40, i.e. it has a range of 10 marks. The rectangle that represents this interval will have a base of 1. The bases of the other rectangles are expressed in terms of this.

The rectangle representing the   0 – 30   interval will have a base of 3 (range 30).

The rectangle representing the   40 – 60   interval will have a base of 2 (range 20).

The rectangle representing the   60 – 100   interval will have a base of 4 (range 40).

The rectangle representing the 100 – 120   interval will have a base of 2 (range 20).

New table:

Marks	0 – 30	30 – 40	40 – 60	60 – 100	100 – 120
No. of students	21	8	12	20	8
Base	3	1	2	4	2
Height	7	8	6	5	4
	↑	↑	↑	↑	↑
	21 ÷ 3	8 ÷ 1	12 ÷ 2	20 ÷ 4	8 ÷ 2

The last row, height, is simply obtained by dividing the base into the number of students.

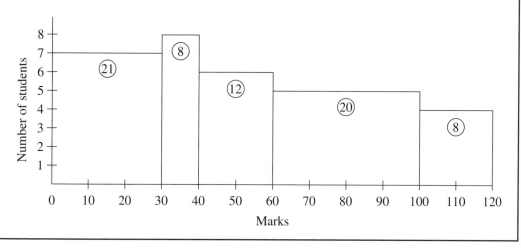

Note: It makes the distribution clearer if we label each rectangle with its frequency. A neat way to do this is to put the frequencies into each rectangle and put a circle around them. The horizontal axis is marked in units of the '**smallest class interval**'.

Given the Histogram

Sometimes we are given the histogram already drawn and we need to calculate the frequencies represented by the rectangles. We are usually given the area of one of the rectangles (which represents the frequency) and its height (read directly from the diagram). From this we can work out the width of the base of the rectangle whose area we are given. We can then calculate the width of the bases of the other rectangles. The heights of the other rectangles can be read directly from the diagram.

> We then use the formula: Frequency = Area of rectangle = base × height

257

We use the following steps:

1. Divide the area of the rectangle whose area we are given by its height. This gives the base of the rectangle.

$$\text{Base} = \frac{\text{Area}}{\text{Height}}$$

2. Express the base of each of the other rectangles in terms of this base (i.e. is it half this base, double it, treble it, etc.?)

3. Multiply the given height of each rectangle by its base to find its area.
   The area of a rectangle is equal to the frequency it represents.

Example

The histogram shows the distribution of the distances, in km, that some students have to travel to school:

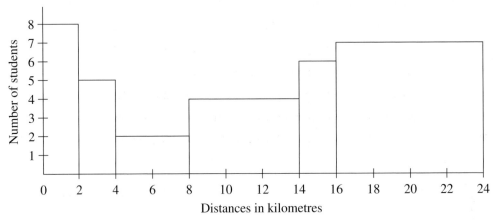

Complete the corresponding frequency distribution table:

Distances (km)	0 – 2	2 – 4	4 – 8	8 – 14	14 – 16	16 – 24
No. of students				24		

Calculate the total number of students.

Solution:

1. Given: Area of the rectangle representing the distances between 8 and 14 km = 24

   The height of this rectangle = 4

   $$(\text{base}) \times (\text{height}) = \text{area}$$

   ∴ $$(\text{base})(4) = 24$$

   ∴ $$\text{base} = \frac{24}{4} = 6$$

   This rectangle uses three marked units on the horizontal axis.

   ∴ each marked unit on the horizontal axis has a measurement of 2 (i.e. 6 ÷ 3 = 2)

2. Thus, the base of the other rectangles can be worked out.

0 – 2 km: base = 2	2 – 4 km: base = 2	4 – 8 km: base = 4
14 – 16 km: base = 2	16 – 24 km: base = 8	

3. Area of each rectangle = base × height = frequency

   0 – 2 km: Area = frequency = base × height = 2 × 8 = 16

   2 – 4 km: Area = frequency = base × height = 2 × 5 = 10

   4 – 8 km: Area = frequency = base × height = 4 × 2 = 8

   14 – 16 km: Area = frequency = base × height = 2 × 6 = 12

   16 – 24 km: Area = frequency = base × height = 8 × 7 = 56

We could also work out the frequencies from the given histogram.

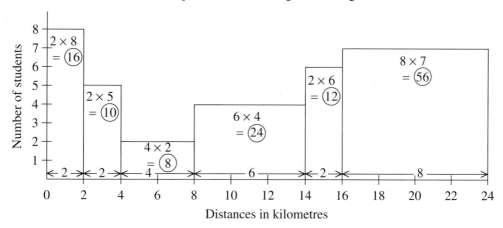

The area (frequencies) are circled in each rectangle.

Completed table:

Distance (km)	0 – 2	2 – 4	4 – 8	8 – 14	14 – 16	16 – 24
No. of students	16	10	8	24	12	56

Total number of students = 16 + 10 + 8 + 24 + 12 + 56 = 126

Cumulative Frequency

In a cumulative frequency the frequencies are accumulated. Each accumulated frequency is the combined total of all the previous frequencies up to that particular value. If we fill in the accumulated frequencies in tabular form, we have what is called a **cumulative frequency table**. The graph of a cumulative frequency is called a **cumulative frequency curve** or **ogive**. It has a distinctively lopsided S-shape.

To draw a cumulative frequency curve do the following:

> 1. Construct a cumulative frequency table (if not given).
>
> 2. Put the values on the horizontal axis and cumulative frequency on the vertical axis.
>
> 3. Plot the points (value, cumulative frequency).
>
> 4. Join the points with a smooth curve.

Note: If the data is given as a grouped frequency distribution, always make sure that in step 3 the **upper class limits** (not the mid-interval value or lower class limit) are plotted against the cumulative frequencies.

Median and interquartile range

How to calculate the median and the interquartile range from a cumulative frequency curve is shown below:

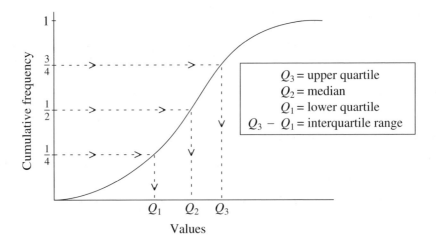

A cumulative frequency curve can be used to estimate the number of values that lie **below,** or **above,** a particular value or to estimate the number of values that lie **between** two values.

Note: Readings from a cumulative frequency curve are only estimates.

Example 1

The following table shows the distribution of the amounts spent by 40 customers in a shop:

Amount spent	€0 – €20	€20 – €40	€40 – €60	€60 – €80	€80 – €100
Number of customers	3	5	17	13	2

(**Note:** 0–20 means 0 is included but 20 is not, etc.)

(**i**)   Construct a cumulative frequency table.

(**ii**) Draw a cumulative frequency curve (ogive).

Use the curve to estimate:

(**iii**) the median

(**iv**) the upper quartile mark

(**v**) the lower quartile mark

(**vi**) the interquartile range

(**vii**) the percentage of customers who spent €70 or more.

Solution:

(**i**)   **Cumulative frequency table:**

Amount spent	< €20	< €40	< €60	< €80	< €100
Number of customers	3	8	25	38	40

(**ii**) **Cumulative frequency curve:**

Plot the points (0, 0), (20, 3), (40, 8), (60, 25), (80, 38) and (100, 40) and join them with a smooth curve.

(**Note:** Always use the upper class limits where plotting the points.)

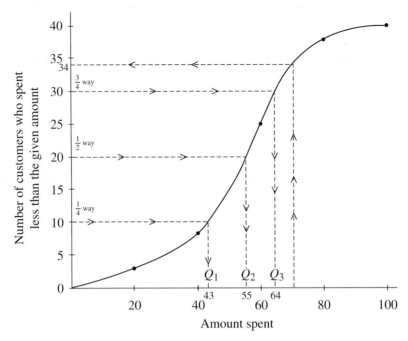

Amount spent

(iii) Median:
The middle value on the cumulative frequency axis is 20.

Draw a horizontal line from 20 to meet the curve and then straight down to the horizontal axis.

This line meets the horizontal axis at 55.

Thus, we estimate the median $= Q_2 = €55$.

(iv) Upper quartile:
The three-quarter-way value on the cumulative frequency axis is 30.

Draw a horizontal line from 30 to meet the curve and then straight down to the horizontal axis.

This line meets the horizontal axis at 64.

Thus, we estimate the upper quartile $= Q_3 = €64$.

(v) Lower quartile:
The quarter-way value on the cumulative frequency axis is 10.

Draw a horizontal line from 10 to meet the curve and then straight down to the horizontal axis.

This line meets the horizontal axis at 43.

Thus, we estimate the lower quartile $= Q_1 = €43$.

(vi) Interquartile range:
The interquartile range $= Q_3 - Q_1 = 64 - 43 = €21$.

(vii) The percentage of customers who spent €70 or more:
From 70 on the horizontal axis draw a vertical line to meet the curve and then straight across to the vertical axis.

This line meets the vertical axis at 34.

Thus we estimate that $40 - 34 = 6$ customers spent more than €70.

$\therefore$ percentage of customers who spent €70 or more

$$= \frac{6}{40} \times 100\% = 15\%$$

Example 2

The cumulative frequency table below shows the ages of people attending a swimming pool on a particular day:

Ages of people (years)	< 10	< 20	< 40	< 50	< 70
Number of people	2	4	19	39	50

(i) Represent the data with a cumulative frequency curve (ogive) putting the number of people on the vertical axis.

Use your graph to estimate:

(ii) the number of people aged less than 36.

(iii) the percentage of people between the ages of 44 and 56.

(iv) Complete the corresponding grouped frequency distribution:

Ages of people (years)	0–10	10–20	20–40	40–50	50–70
Number of people					

(**Note:** 0–10 means that 0 is included but 10 is not, etc.)

Solution:

(i) **cumulative frequency curve:**

Plot the points (0, 0), (10, 2), (20, 4), (40, 19), (50, 39) and (70, 50) and join them with a smooth curve.

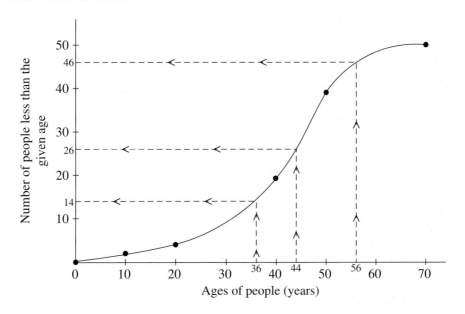

263

(ii) the number of people aged less than 36:

From 36 on the horizontal axis draw a vertical line to meet the curve and then straight across to the vertical axis.
This line meets the vertical axis at 14.
Thus we estimate that 14 people are aged less than 36.

(iii) the percentage of people between the ages of 44 and 56:

First work out the numbers.
From 44 and 56 on the horizontal axis draw vertical lines to meet the curve and then straight across to the vertical axis.
These lines meet the vertical axis at 26 and 46, respectively.

$$46 - 26 = 20$$

$$20 \text{ as a percentage of } 50 = \frac{20}{50} \times 100\% = 40\%$$

Thus we estimate that 40% of the people are between the ages 44 and 56.

(iv) Corresponding grouped frequency table:

When the cumulative frequency table was constructed the frequencies were added. Therefore, to construct a corresponding grouped frequency table we simply do the reverse:

> Subtract the frequencies.

50–70	$50 - 39 = 11$

40–50	$39 - 19 = 20$

20–40	$19 - 4 = 15$

10–20	$4 - 2 = 2$

0–10	$= 2$, remains the same

Completed grouped frequency table:

Ages of people (years)	0–10	10–20	20–40	40–50	50–70
Number of people	2	2	15	20	11

Example 3

The following table shows the time in minutes spent by customers in a cafeteria.

Time in minutes	0–10	10–20	20–40	40–70
Number of customers	80	100	160	60

[Note that 10–20 means at least 10 but less than 20 minutes etc.]

(i) Find the total number of customers.

(ii) What percentage of the customers spent more than 20 minutes in the cafeteria?

(iii) Name the interval in which the median lies.

(iv) What is the greatest possible number of customers who could have spent more than 30 minutes in the cafeteria?

(vi) What is the least possible number of customers who could have spent more than 30 minutes in the cafeteria?

Solution:

(i)   Find the total number of customers.
Total number of customers $= 80 + 100 + 160 + 60 = 400$

(ii) What percentage of the customers spent more than 20 minutes in the cafeteria?
The number of customers who spent more than 20 minutes in the cafeteria

$= 160 + 60$ (customers in the intervals 20–40 and 40–70)

$= 220$

∴ percentage of customers who spent more than 20 minutes in the cafeteria

$= \frac{220}{400} \times 100\% = 55\%$

(iii) Name the interval in which the median lies.

There are 400 customers (an even number of customers).

∴ $\text{median} = \frac{200 + 201}{2} = \frac{401}{2} = 200.5$

First two intervals

0–10	10–20
80	100

Number of customers $= 80 + 100$
$= 180$

First three intervals

0–10	10–20	20–40
80	100	160

Number of customers $= 80 + 100 + 160$
$= 340$

As the median, 200.5, is between 180 and 340, the median is in the interval 20–40.

(iv) **What is the greatest possible number of customers who could have spent more than 30 minutes in the cafeteria?**

20–40	40–70
160	60

(all spend **more** than 30 minutes in the cafeteria)

The greatest possible number of customers who could have spent **more** than 30 minutes in the cafeteria occurs if all 160 customers in the interval 20–40 spend more than 30 minutes in the cafeteria.

Greatest possible number of customers
= 160 + 60 = 220

(v) **What is the least possible number of customers who could have spent more than 30 minutes in the cafeteria?**

20–40	40–70
160	60

(all spend **less** than 30 minutes in the cafeteria)

The least possible number of customers who could have spent **less** than 30 minutes in the cafeteria occurs if all 160 customers in the interval 20–40 spend less than 30 minutes in the cafeteria.

Least possible number of customers
= 0 + 60 = 60

Given the Mean

Often we are given the mean and we need to find one of the values or frequencies. Essentially, we are given an equation in disguise and by solving this equation we can calculate the missing value or frequency.

Example 1

The mean of the five numbers 7, x, 8, 12 and 2 is 7. Calculate the value of x.

Solution:

Method 1:

Equation given in disguise: mean = 7

$$\therefore \quad \frac{7 + x + 8 + 12 + 2}{5} = 7$$

$$\frac{x + 29}{5} = 7$$

$$x + 29 = 35$$

$$x = 6$$

Method 2:

The mean of the five numbers is 7.

$\therefore$ the numbers must add up to 35

$\left(\text{because } 5 \times 7 = 35 \text{ or } \frac{35}{5} = 7\right)$

$\therefore \ 7 + x + 8 + 12 + 2 = 35$

$$x + 29 = 35$$

$$x = 6$$

Example 2

The result of a survey of the number of passengers carried by taxi in a town was recorded as follows:

Number of passengers	1	2	3	4	5
Number of taxis	3	x	9	6	4

If the mean number of passengers carried per taxis was 3, find the value of x.

Solution:

Equation given in disguise: mean = 3

$$\therefore \quad \frac{3(1) + x(2) + 9(3) + 6(4) + 4(5)}{3 + x + 9 + 6 + 4} = 3$$

$$\frac{3 + 2x + 27 + 24 + 20}{x + 22} = 3$$

$$\frac{2x + 74}{x + 22} = 3$$

$$2x + 74 = 3(x + 22) \quad \text{[multiply both sides by } (x + 22)\text{]}$$

$$2x + 74 = 3x + 66$$

$$2x - 3x = 66 - 74$$

$$-x = -8$$

$$x = 8$$

Chapter 14. LINEAR INEQUALITIES AND LINEAR PROGRAMMING

Linear Inequalities

To graph the region (half-plane) represented by a linear inequality of the form $ax + by \geqslant k$ or $ax + by \leqslant k$, do the following:

Step 1: Graph the line $ax + by = k$ by finding two points on the line, and drawing a line through these points.

The usual points are where the line cuts the x- and y-axes.

(**Remember:** on the x-axis, $y = 0$ and on the y-axis, $x = 0$.)

Step 2: Test a point not on the line, usually $(0, 0)$, in the inequality.

    (a) If the inequality is **true** the arrows point towards the point being tested.

    (b) If the inequality is **false** the arrows point away from the point being tested.

Notes:

1. It is usual to select the point $(0, 0)$ if it is not on the line.

2. The required region is usually indicated by arrows or shading.

3. If both sides of an inequality are multiplied or divided by a **negative** number, the direction of the inequality must be **reversed**.

Example

Graph the inequality, $2x + 5y \geqslant 20$ indicating the correct half-plane.

Solution:

1. Graph the line $2x + 5y = 20$

$2x + 5y = 20$	
$y = 0$	$x = 0$
$2x = 20$	$5y = 20$
$x = 10$	$y = 4$
$(10, 0)$	$(0, 4)$

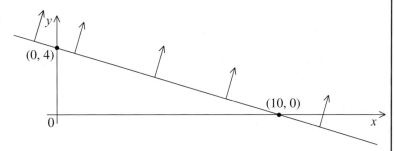

Plot the points $(10, 0)$ and $(0, 4)$ and draw a line through them.

2. Test $(0, 0)$ in $2x + 5y \geqslant 20$

$$2(0) + 5(0) \geqslant 20$$

$$0 \geqslant 20 \qquad \textbf{False}$$

$(0, 0)$ does not satisfy the inequality, hence, all the points on the opposite side of the line $(0, 0)$, indicated by arrows in the diagram, is the required region.

Simultaneous Linear Inequalities

Often it is required to find a region which is common to more than one inequality. This common region is often called the 'feasible region' and is found with the following steps:

> **Step 1:** Complete the calculations to draw the lines and determine the direction of the arrows.
>
> **Step 2:** Draw a diagram and shade in the common region.

Note: If not given in the question, it is good practice to label each inequality with a capital letter, e.g. A, B, C, D, etc. and put these on your diagram.

Example

Illustrate the set of points (x, y) that simultaneously satisfy the three inequalities:

$$y \geqslant 2 \qquad\qquad x + 2y \leqslant 8 \qquad\qquad 5x + y \geqslant -5$$

Solution:

Label the inequalities as A, B, and C:

$$A: y \geqslant 2 \qquad\qquad B: x + 2y \leqslant 8 \qquad\qquad C: 5x + y \geqslant -5$$

$A: y \geqslant 2$ is the set of points on and above the line $y = 2$.

$\therefore$ arrows on the line $y = 2$ and pointing upwards.

$B: x + 2y \leqslant 8$	$C: 5x + y \geqslant -5$
Line: $x + 2y = 8$	Line : $5x + y = -5$

$x + 2y = 8$			$5x + y = -5$	
$y = 0$	$x = 0$		$y = 0$	$x = 0$
$x = 8$	$2y = 8$		$5x = -5$	$y = -5$
$(8, 0)$	$y = 4$		$x = -1$	$(0, -5)$
	$(0, 4)$		$(-1, 0)$	

Test $(0, 0)$ in $x + 2y \leqslant 8$	Test $(0, 0)$ in $5x + y \geqslant -5$
$(0) + 2(0) \leqslant 8$	$5(0) + (0) \geqslant -5$
$0 \leqslant 8$ **True**	$0 \geqslant -5$ **True**
$\therefore$ arrows point **towards** $(0, 0)$	$\therefore$ arrows point towards $(0, 0)$

270

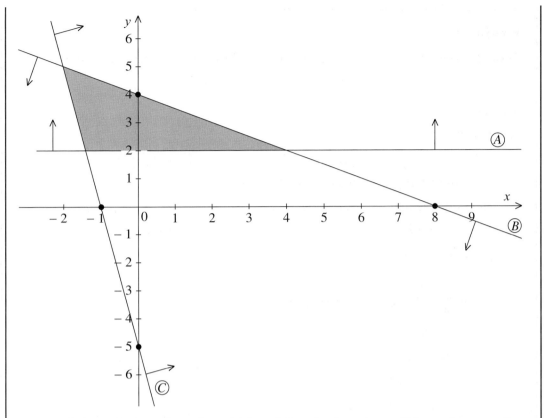

The shaded area is the only region which satisfies the three inequalities at the same time.

Finding the Inequality

Sometimes we are given the graph of a linear inequality and asked to write down, algebraically, the region that the inequality represents.

When this happens do the following:

Step 1: Find the equation of the line in the form $ax + by + c = 0$ (if not given).

Step 2: Pick a point, not on the line, in the required region (indicated by arrows or shading). Pick (0, 0) if possible, otherwise pick a point on the x- or y-axis that you are certain is in the required region.

Step 3: Put the coordinates of the point chosen into $ax + by + c$.

Two possibilities arise:

| < 0, then use $\leqslant 0$ | > 0, then use $\geqslant 0$ |

Note: If you pick a point **not** in the required region then reverse the results of step 3.

| < 0, then use $\geqslant 0$ | > 0, then use $\leqslant 0$ |

Example 1

The line K cuts the x-axis at $(10, 0)$ and the y-axis at $(0, 5)$.

(i) Find the equation of K.

(ii) Write down an inequality which defines the region indicated, by arrows in the diagram.

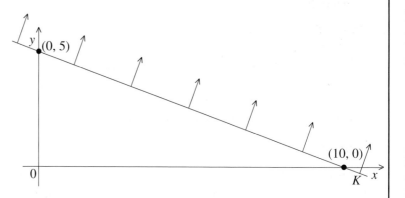

Solution:

(i) We have two points, $(10, 0)$ and $(0, 5)$ on the line K. The **slope** of K is missing.

$(10, 0)$ and $(0, 5)$

(x_1, y_1) (x_2, y_2)

$$\text{Slope} = m = \frac{y_2 - y_1}{x_2 - x_1}$$

$$= \frac{5 - 0}{0 - 10} = \frac{5}{-10} = -\frac{1}{2}$$

Containing $(10, 0)$ with slope $-\frac{1}{2}$:

$$x_1 = 10, \qquad y_1 = 0, \qquad m = -\frac{1}{2}$$

$$(y - y_1) = m(x - x_1)$$

$$(y - 0) = -\frac{1}{2}(x - 10)$$

$$y = -\frac{1}{2}(x - 10)$$

$$2y = -1(x - 10)$$

(multiply both sides by 2)

$$2y = -x + 10$$

$$x + 2y - 10 = 0$$

(ii)

Method 1	Method 2

Method 1

Pick a point **in** the required region.

Given: $x + 2y - 10 = 0$

$(11, 0)$ is **in** the required region.

$(11) + 2(0) - 10 = 11 - 10 = 1 > 0$

$\therefore$ use $\geqslant 0$

as $(11, 0)$ is in the required region.

Thus, the required inequality is:

$$K : x + 2y - 10 \geqslant 0$$

Method 2

Pick a point **not** in the required region.

Given: $x + 2y - 10 = 0$

$(0, 0)$ is **not** in the required region.

$(0) + 2(0) - 10 = -10 < 0$

$\therefore$ use $\geqslant 0$

as $(0, 0)$ is **not** in the required region.

Thus, the required inequality is:

$$K : x + 2y - 10 \geqslant 0$$

Example 2

The equation of the line L is
$5x + 8y + 40 = 0$.
The equation of the line K is
$10x - 7y - 35 = 0$.

Write down the 3 inequalities that
together define the shaded region in the diagram.

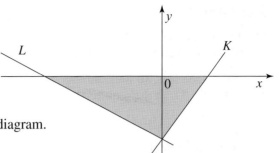

Solution:

The first inequality is $y \leqslant 0$, on the x-axis and below the x-axis.

Given: L: $5x + 8y + 40 = 0$ | Given: K: $10x - 7y - 35 = 0$

   $(0, 0)$ is **in** the required region. | $(0, 0)$ is **in** the required region.

   $5(0) + 8(0) + 40 = 40 > 0$ | $10(0) - 7(0) - 35 = -35 < 0$

   $\therefore$ use $\geqslant 0$ | $\therefore$ use $\leqslant 0$

Thus, the required inequality is: | Thus, the required inequality is:

   L: $5x + 8y + 40 \geqslant 0$ | K: $10x - 7y - 35 \leqslant 0$

Thus, the three inequalities are : $y \leqslant 0$, $5x + 8y + 40 \geqslant 0$ and $10x - 7y - 35 \leqslant 0$

Example 3

The equation of the line L is $x - 2y = 0$.
The equation of the line M is $2x + y = 4$.

Write down the three inequalities that
together define the shaded region in the diagram.

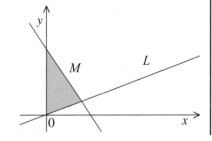

Solution:

The first inequality is $x \geqslant 0$, on the y-axis and to the right of the y-axis.

Given: $L: x - 2y = 0$

$(0, 0)$ is on the line, so pick another point, say $(0, 3)$, **in** the required region.

$$(0) - 2(3) = -6 < 0$$

$\therefore$ use $\leqslant 0$

Thus, the required inequality is:

$$L: x - 2y \leqslant 0$$

Given: $M: 2x + y - 4 = 0$

$(0, 0)$ is **in** the required region.

$$2(0) + (0) - 4 = -4 < 0$$

$\therefore$ use $\leqslant 0$

Thus, the required inequality is:

$$M: 2x + y - 4 \leqslant 0$$

Thus, the three equalities are: $x \geqslant 0$, $x - 2y \leqslant 0$ and $2x + y - 4 \leqslant 0$

Linear Programming

Linear inequalities can be used to solve practical problems. When used in this way we call it **Linear Programming**. Linear programming deals with trying to find the best solution, usually the maximum or minimum, to a wide range of problems within certain limitations called **constraints**. When solving a problem in linear programming, read the question carefully a few times and do the following:

1. Let x equal one unknown number and let y equal the other unknown number that is required (unless given in the question).
2. Using the information in the question, convert the constraints into linear inequalities in terms of x and y (using a table can be useful).
3. Graph each of the inequalities and shade in the feasible region.
4. Find the coordinates of the vertices of this common region.
5. Write the objective function, the expression to be maximised or minimised, in terms of x and y.
6. Substitute, separately, the coordinates of the vertices of the feasible region (obtained in **step 4**) into the objective function, using a table, to find the maximum or minimum values.

    (maximum or minimum values always occur at one of the vertices)

Note: In certain questions the inequalities $x \geqslant 0$ and $y \geqslant 0$ will be given in disguise. This is because it is physically impossible for x and y to be negative.
Make sure that both sides of the inequality are measured in the same units.

Example 1

A shopowner displays videos and DVDs in his shop.

Each video requires 720 cm^3 of display space and each DVD requires 360 cm^3 of display space. The available display space cannot exceed 108,000 cm^3. The shopowner buys each video for €6 and each DVD for €8. He does not wish to spend more than €1,200.

(i) Taking x as the number of videos and y as the number of DVDs, write down two inequalities in x and y and illustrate these on a graph.

During a DVD promotion the selling price of a video is €11 and of a DVD is €10. Assuming that the shopowner can sell all the videos and DVDs:

(ii) How many of each type should he display in order to maximise his income? What is the maximum income?

(iii) How many of each type should he display in order to maximise his profit? What is the maximum profit?

Solution:

Given: x = the number of videos

$\qquad y$ = the number of DVDs

(i) Two inequalities given in disguise are $x \geqslant 0$ and $y \geqslant 0$.

(It is impossible to sell a negative number of videos or DVDs.)

We use a table to help us write down the other two inequalities.

There are two constraints: **1.** Space and **2.** Cost.

	x	y	
Space	720	360	$\leqslant$ 108,000
Cost	6	8	$\leqslant$ 1,200

Space Constraint: $720x + 360y \leqslant 108,000$

$\qquad\qquad\qquad 2x + y \leqslant 300$

$\qquad$ (divide both sides by 360)

Cost Constraint: $6x + 8y \leqslant 1,200$

$\qquad\qquad\qquad 3x + 4y \leqslant 600$

$\qquad$ (divide both sides by 2)

Thus, the four inequalities are:

$A: x \geqslant 0 \qquad\qquad B: y \geqslant 0 \qquad\qquad C: 2x + y \leqslant 300 \qquad\qquad D: 3x + 4y \leqslant 600$

A: $x \geqslant 0$, is the set of points on and to the right of the y-axis,

∴ arrows on the y-axis and pointing right.

B: $y \geqslant 0$, is the set of points on and above the x-axis,

∴ arrows on the x-axis and pointing upwards.

C: $2x + y \leqslant 300$

Line: $2x + y = 300$

$$2x + y = 300$$

$y = 0$	$x = 0$
$2x = 300$	$y = 300$
$x = 150$	$(0, 300)$
$(150, 0)$	

Test $(0, 0)$ in $2x + y \leqslant 300$

$$(0) + 2(0) \leqslant 300$$

$$(0) \leqslant 300 \quad \textbf{True}$$

∴ arrows point towards $(0, 0)$.

D: $3x + 4y \leqslant 600$

Line: $3x + 4y = 600$

$$3x + 4y = 600$$

$y = 0$	$x = 0$
$3x = 600$	$4y = 600$
$x = 200$	$y = 150$
$(200, 0)$	$(0, 150)$

Test $(0, 0)$ in $3x + 4y \leqslant 600$

$$3(0) + 2(0) \leqslant 600$$

$$0 \leqslant 600 \quad \textbf{True}$$

∴ arrows point towards $(0, 0)$.

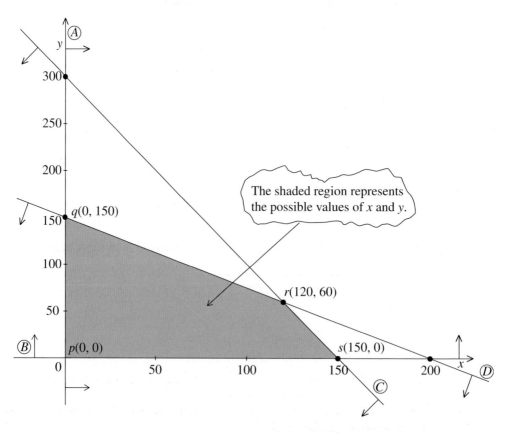

The shaded region represents the possible values of x and y.

Let the vertices of the shaded region be p, q, r and s (as shown).

From the diagram: $p = (0, 0)$, $q = (0, 150)$, $s = (150, 0)$.

We now solve the simultaneous equations $2x + y = 300$ and $3x + 4y = 600$ to find the coordinates of r (cannot be read from the graph).

$$
\begin{array}{ll}
8x + 4y = 1{,}200 \;\textcircled{C} \times 4 & \qquad 2x + y = 300 \;\textcircled{C} \\
-3x - 4y = -600 \;\textcircled{D} \times -1 & \qquad 2(120) + y = 300 \\
\hline
\quad\; 5x = 600 \quad \text{(add)} & \qquad 240 + y = 300 \\
\quad\;\; x = 120 & \qquad\qquad\; y = 60 \\
\text{put } x = 120 \quad \text{into } C \text{ or } D. &
\end{array}
$$

$$\therefore \quad r = (120, 60)$$

(ii) The income on a video is €11 and the income on a DVD is €10.

$\therefore$ the income will be €$(11x + 10y)$.

$\therefore$ the objective function is $11x + 10y$.

Using a table, the coordinates of p, q, r and s are substituted, separately, into $11x + 10y$ to find the maximum value.

Vertex	11x	10y	11x + 10y
$p(0, 0)$	0	0	0
$q(0, 150)$	0	1,500	1,500
$r(120, 60)$	1,320	600	1,920 ← maximum value
$s(150, 0)$	1,650	0	1,650

Thus, to maximise income, the shopowner should display 120 videos and 60 DVDs. The maximum income = €1,920.

(iii) Profit on a video = Income − Cost = €11 − €6 = €5.

Profit on a DVD = Income − Cost = €10 − €8 = €2.

$\therefore$ the profit will be €$(5x + 2y)$ \qquad (during the promotion)

$\therefore$ the objective function is $5x + 2y$

Using a table, the coordinates of p, q, r and s are substituted, separately, into $5x + 2y$ to find the maximum value.

Vertex	5x	2y	5x + 2y
$p(0, 0)$	0	0	0
$q(0, 150)$	0	300	300
$r(120, 60)$	600	120	720
$s(150, 0)$	750	0	750 ← maximum value

Thus, to maximise profits, the shopowner should display 750 videos and no DVDs. The maximum profit = €750.

Example 2

Due to a transport disruption, a bus company is contracted at short notice to carry up to 1,500 passengers to complete their journey. Passengers not carried by this company will be carried by a taxi company.

The bus company has available standard buses and minibuses. Each standard bus carries 60 passengers and each minibus carries 30 passengers.

Each bus is operated by one driver and there are at most 30 drivers available.

(i) Taking x as the number of standard buses and y as the number of minibuses, write down two inequalities in x and y and illustrate them on a graph.

(ii) The operating profit for the journey is €80 for a standard bus and €50 for a minibus. How many of each type of bus should be used in order to maximise the profit?

(iii) If the bus company paid each driver a bonus for working at short notice, the operating profit for each bus would be reduced by €30. By how much would this decrease the maximum profit available to the company?

Solution:

Given: x = number of standard buses

y = number of minibuses

(i) Two inequalities given in disguise are $x \geqslant 0$ and $y \geqslant 0$.

(It is impossible to have a negative number of buses.)

We will use a table to help us write down the other two inequalities.

There are two constraints:

1.   The number of passengers.   2.   The number of drivers.

	x	y	
Number of passengers	60	30	$\leqslant 1{,}500$
Number of drivers	1	1	$\leqslant 30$

Number of passengers constraint:

$$60x + 30y \leqslant 1{,}500$$

$$2x + y \leqslant 50$$

(divide both sides by 30)

Number of drivers constraint:

$$x + y \leqslant 30$$

The four inequalities are:

A: $x \geqslant 0$,　　　　　B: $y \geqslant 0$,　　　　C: $2x + y \leqslant 50$　　D: $x + y \leqslant 30$

A:　$x \geqslant 0$ is the set of points on and to the right of the y-axis,

∴　arrows on the y-axis and pointing right.

B:　$y \geqslant 0$ is the set of points on and above the x-axis,

∴　arrows on the x-axis and pointing upwards.

$2x + y \leqslant 50$

Line: $2x + y = 50$

$2x + y = 50$	
$y = 0$	$x = 0$
$2x = 50$	$y = 50$
$x = 25$	$(0, 50)$
$(25, 0)$	

Test $(0, 0)$ in $2x + y \leqslant 50$

$2(0) + 0 \leqslant 50$

$0 \leqslant 50$　**True**

∴　arrow point toward $(0, 0)$.

D: $x + y \leqslant 30$

Line: $x + y = 30$

$x + y = 30$	
$y = 0$	$x = 0$
$x = 30$	$y = 30$
$(30, 0)$	$(0, 30)$

Test　$(0, 0)$ in $x + y \leqslant 30$

$0 + 0 \leqslant 30$

$0 \leqslant 30$　**True**

∴　arrow point toward $(0, 0)$.

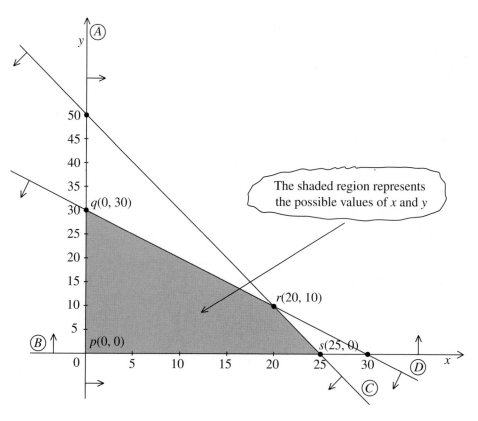

The shaded region represents the possible values of x and y

279

Let the vertices of the shaded region be p, q, r and s (as shown).

From the diagram: $p = (0, 0)$, $q = (0, 30)$, $s = (25, 0)$

We now solve the simultaneous equations $2x + y = 50$ and $x + y = 30$ to find the coordinates of r (cannot be read from the graph).

$$2x + y = 50 \qquad \textcircled{C}$$
$$-x - y = -30 \qquad \textcircled{D} \times -1$$
$$\overline{x = 20 \qquad \text{(add)}}$$

put $x = 20$ into C or D.

$$x + y = 30 \qquad \textcircled{D}$$
$$20 + y = 30$$
$$y = 10$$

$$\therefore r = (20, 10)$$

(ii) The operating profit on a journey is €80 for a standard bus and €50 for a minibus.

∴   the profit will be €$(80x + 50y)$.

∴   the objective function is $80x + 50y$.

Using a table, the coordinates of p, q, r and s are substituted, separately, into $80x + 50y$ to find the maximum value.

Vertex	$80x$	$50y$	$80x + 50y$
$p(0, 0)$	0	0	0
$q(0, 30)$	0	1,500	1,500
$r(20, 10)$	1,600	500	2,100 ← maximum value
$s(25, 0)$	2,000	0	2,000

Thus, to maximise profit, the company should use 20 standard buses and 10 minibuses.

(iii) The maximum profit of €2,100 is obtained when the company uses 20 standard buses and 10 minibuses. Therefore, 30 buses are used in total.

Thus, to obtain this maximum profit the company has to use 30 drivers.

Each driver used reduces the operating profit by €30.

∴   the extra cost = €30 × 30 = €900.

Thus, the maximum profit available is reduced by € 900.

EXAM PAPERS

LEAVING CERTIFICATE EXAMINATION, 2007

MATHEMATICS – ORDINARY LEVEL

PAPER 1 (300 marks)

THURSDAY, 7 JUNE – MORNING, 9.30 to 12.00

Attempt **SIX QUESTIONS** (50 marks each).

WARNING: Marks will be lost if all necessary work is not clearly shown.

Answers should include the appropriate units of measurement, where relevant.

---

1. (a) Convert 164 miles to kilometres, taking 5 miles to be equal to 8 kilometres.

   (b) €8500 was invested for 2 years at compound interest.

   (i) The rate of interest for the first year was 4%.
   Find the amount of the investment at the end of the first year.

   (ii) The amount of the investment at the end of the second year was €9237·80.
   Find the rate of interest for the second year.

   (c) The table shows the hours Alan worked over four days.

Day	Thursday	Friday	Saturday	Sunday
Hours worked	9	9	9·5	h

   Alan's basic rate of pay is €15·60 per hour.
   He is paid one and a half times the basic rate for work on Saturday and Sunday.

   (i) Calculate Alan's total pay for Thursday, Friday and Saturday.

   (ii) Alan was paid a total of €702 for the four days' work.
   Find h, the number of hours Alan worked on Sunday.

2. (a) Find the solution set of $4x - 15 < 1, \quad x \in \mathbf{N}$.

   (b) (i) Find the value of $\dfrac{x + 3y + 5}{2x + 2y}$ when $x = \dfrac{5}{2}$ and $y = \dfrac{1}{3}$.

   (ii) Find the value of x for which $2^{x+3} = 4^x$.

(c) (i) Solve the equation $x - \dfrac{1}{x} = 2$ and write your solutions in the form

$a \pm \sqrt{b}$, where $a, b \in \mathbf{N}$.

(ii) Verify **one** of your solutions.

3. (a) Solve $2x = 3(5 - x)$.

(b) Solve the simultaneous equations

$$\frac{x}{4} - \frac{y}{3} = \frac{5}{6}$$

$$2x - 6 = 3y.$$

(c) Let $f(x) = 2x^3 + 11x^2 + 4x - 5$.

(i) Verify that $f(-1) = 0$.

(ii) Solve the equation

$$2x^3 + 11x^2 + 4x - 5 = 0.$$

4. (a) Given that $i^2 = -1$, simplify

$$3(2 - 4i) + i\,(5 - 6i)$$

and write your answer in the form $x + yi$, where $x, y \in \mathbf{R}$.

(b) Let $z = 5 - 3i$.

(i) Plot z and $-z$ on an Argand diagram.

(ii) Calculate $|z - 1|$.

(iii) Find the value of the real number k such that $k\,i + 4z = 20$.

(c) Let $u = 3 + 2i$.

(i) Find the value of $u^2 + \bar{u}^2$, where $\bar{u}$ is the complex conjugate of u.

(ii) Investigate whether $\dfrac{13}{u} = \bar{u}$.

5. (a) The nth term of a sequence is given by $T_n = 1 - n$.

(i) Find T_5, the fifth term.

(ii) Find $T_5 - T_{10}$ where T_{10} is the tenth term.

(b) The first term of an arithmetic series is 3 and the common difference is 4.

(i) Find, in terms of n, an expression for T_n, the nth term.

(ii) How many terms of the series are less than 200?

(iii) Find the sum of these terms.

(c) The first two terms of a geometric series are $\dfrac{1}{3} + \dfrac{1}{9} + \ldots$

    (i) Find r, the common ratio.

    (ii) Find an expression for S_n, the sum of the first n terms.

        Write your answer in the form $\dfrac{1}{k}\left(1 - \dfrac{1}{3^n}\right)$ where $k \in \mathbf{N}$.

    (iii) The sum of the first n terms of the geometric series $\dfrac{p}{3} + \dfrac{p}{9} + \ldots$ is $1 - \dfrac{1}{3^n}$.

         Find the value of p.

6. (a) Let $g(x) = x^2 - 6x$, $x \in \mathbf{R}$.

    (i) Write down $g'(x)$, the derivative of $g(x)$.

    (ii) For what value of x is $g'(x) = 0$?

(b) A cold object is placed in a warm room.
Its temperature C degrees after time t minutes is shown in the following graph.

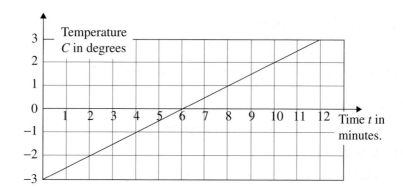

    (i) After what time interval is the temperature of the object 0 degrees?

    (ii) What is the rise in temperature of the object in the first 10 minutes?

    (iii) The relationship between the temperature C and the time t is given by

$$C = \frac{1}{2}(t + k).$$

    Find the value of k.

(c) Let $f(x) = (5x - 2)^4$ for $x \in \mathbf{R}$.

    (i) Find $f'(x)$, the derivative of $f(x)$.

    (ii) Find the co-ordinates of the point on the curve $y = f(x)$ at which the slope of the tangent is 20.

7. **(a)** Differentiate $6x^4 - 3x^2 + 7x$ with respect to x.

(b) **(i)** Differentiate $(x^2 + 9)(4x^3 + 5)$ with respect to x.

(ii) Given that $y = \dfrac{3x}{2x + 3}$, find $\dfrac{dy}{dx}$.

Write your answer in the form $\dfrac{k}{(2x + 3)^n}$, where $k, n \in \mathbf{N}$.

(c) A car starts from rest at the point a.

The distance of the car from a, after t seconds, is given by
$$s = 2t^2 + 2t$$
where s is in metres.

(i) Find the speed of the car after 2 seconds.

(ii) Find the acceleration of the car.

(iii) The distance from a to the point b is 24 metres. After how many seconds does the car reach the point b?

8. **(a)** Let $f(x) = \dfrac{1}{4}(6 - 2x)$ for $x \in \mathbf{R}$.　　　　Evaluate $f(5)$.

(b) Differentiate $x^2 - 3x$ with respect to x from first principles.

(c) Let $f(x) = \dfrac{1}{x + 7}$,　　$x \in \mathbf{R}, \quad x \neq -7$.

(i) Given that $f(k) = 1$, find k.

(ii) Find $f'(x)$, the derivative of $f(x)$.

(iii) Show that the curve $y = f(x)$ has no turning points.

LEAVING CERTIFICATE EXAMINATION, 2007

MATHEMATICS – ORDINARY LEVEL

PAPER 2 (300 marks)

MONDAY, 11 JUNE – MORNING, 9.30 to 12.00

Attempt **FIVE** questions from **Section A** and **ONE** question from **Section B**.

Each question carries 50 marks.

WARNING: Marks will be lost if all necessary work is not clearly shown.

Answers should include the appropriate units of measurement, where relevant.

SECTION A

Attempt FIVE questions from this section.

---

1. **(a)** The right-angled triangle shown in the
    diagram has sides of length 10 cm and 24 cm.

    (i) Find the length of the third side.

    (ii) Find the length of the perimeter of the triangle.

    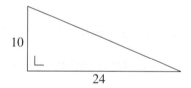

    (b) In order to estimate the area of the irregular shape below, a horizontal line is drawn
    across the widest part of the shape and three offsets (perpendicular lines) are drawn
    at equal intervals along this line.

    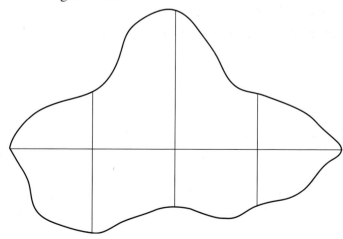

(i) Measure the horizontal line and the offsets, in centimetres.
Make a rough sketch of the shape in your answerbook and record the measurements on it.

(ii) Use Simpson's Rule with these measurements to estimate the area of the shape.

(c) A team trophy for the winners of a football match is in the shape of a sphere supported on a cylindrical base, as shown.
The diameter of the sphere and of the cylinder is 21 cm.

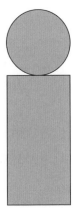

(i) Find the volume of the sphere, in terms of π.

(ii) The volume of the trophy is 6174π cm^3.
Find the height of the cylinder.

21 cm

2. **(a)** Find the co-ordinates of the mid-point of the line segment joining the points $(2, -3)$ and $(6, 9)$.

(b) The line L intersects the x-axis at $(-4, 0)$ and the y-axis at $(0, 6)$.

(i) Find the slope of L.

(ii) Find the equation of L.
The line K passes through $(0, 0)$ and is perpendicular to L.

(iii) Show the lines L and K on a co-ordinate diagram.

(iv) Find the equation of K.

(c) $a(-4, 3)$, $b(6, -1)$ and $c(2, 7)$ are three points.

(i) Find the area of the triangle abc.

(ii) $abcd$ is a parallelogram in which $[ac]$ is a diagonal.
Find the co-ordinates of the point d.

3. **(a)** The circle C has centre $(0, 0)$ and radius 4.

(i) Write down the equation of C.

(ii) Verify that the point $(3, 2)$ lies inside the circle C.

(b) The line $x - 3y = 0$ intersects the circle $x^2 + y^2 = 10$ at the points a and b.

(i) Find the co-ordinates of a and the co-ordinates of b.

(ii) Show that $[ab]$ is a diameter of the circle.

(c) The circle K has equation $(x-5)^2 + (y+1)^2 = 34$.

    (i) Write down the radius of K and the co-ordinates of the centre of K.

    (ii) Verify that the point $(10, -4)$ is on the circle.

    (iii) T is a tangent to the circle at the point $(10, -4)$.
    S is another tangent to the circle and S is parallel to T.
    Find the co-ordinates of the point at which S is a tangent to the circle.

4. (a) In the diagram, two sides of the triangle
are produced.

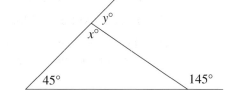

    (i) Find x.

    (ii) Find y.

(b) Prove that the products of the lengths of the
sides of a triangle by the corresponding altitudes are equal.

(c) The triangle ocd is the image of the triangle oab under an enlargement with centre o.
$|oa| = 4$, $|ac| = 7 \cdot 2$ and $|cd| = 7$.

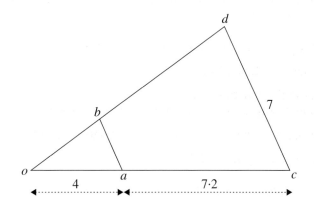

    (i) Find the scale factor of the enlargement.

    (ii) Find $|ab|$.

    (iii) The area of the triangle oab is $4 \cdot 5$ square units.
    Find the area of the triangle ocd.

5. (a) Calculate the area of the triangle shown.

Give your answer correct to one decimal place.

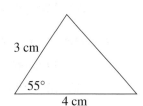

(b) In the right-angled triangle *abc*,
$|ab| = 5$ cm.
The area of the triangle is 15 cm².

    (i) Find $|bc|$.

    (ii) Find $|\angle cab|$, correct to the nearest degree.

    (iii) Find $|\angle bca|$, correct to the nearest degree.

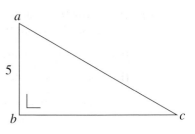

(c) In the triangle *pqr*,
$|pq| = |pr|$, $|qr| = 15$ cm and $|\angle rpq| = 40°$.

    (i) Find $|pr|$, correct to the nearest centimetre.

    (ii) *s* is a point on *qr* such that
$|rs| = 10$ cm.
Find $|ps|$, correct to the nearest centimetre.

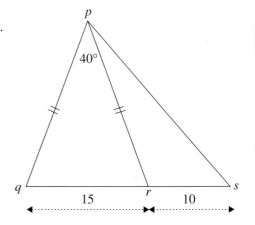

6. **(a)** One letter is chosen at random from the letters of the word EUCLID.

    (i) Find the probability that the letter chosen is D.

    (ii) Find the probability that the letter chosen is a vowel.

(b) The diagram shows two wheels.
The first wheel is divided into four equal segments numbered 1, 2, 3 and 4.
The second wheel is divided into three equal segments labelled *A*, *B* and *C*.

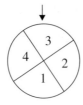 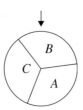

A game consists of spinning the two wheels and noting the segments that stop at the arrows. For example, the outcome shown is (3, *B*).

    (i) Write down all the possible outcomes.

    (ii) What is the probability that the outcome is (2, *C*)?

    (iii) What is the probability that the outcome is an odd number with the letter *A*?

    (iv) What is the probability that the outcome includes the letter *C*?

(c) (i) How many different three-digit numbers can be formed from the digits 2, 3, 4, 5, 6, if each of the digits can be used only once in each number?

(ii) How many of the numbers are less than 400?

(iii) How many of the numbers are divisible by 5?

(iv) How many of the numbers are less than 400 and divisible by 5?

7. (a) Find the median of the numbers

5, 11, 3, 16, 8.

(b) The table below shows the time, in minutes, that customers were waiting to be served in a restaurant.

Time (minutes)	< 5	< 10	< 15	< 20	< 25
Number of customers	5	20	70	110	120

(i) Draw the cumulative frequency curve (ogive).

(ii) Use your curve to estimate the median waiting time.

(iii) Use your curve to estimate the interquartile range.

(c) The age of each person living in one street was recorded during a census. The information is summarised in the following table:

Age (in years)	0 – 20	20 – 30	30 – 50	50 – 80
Number of people	16	12	32	12

(i) How many people were living in the street?

(ii) Using mid-interval values, calculate the mean age.

(iii) What is the greatest number of people who could have been aged under 40 years?

---

8. **(a)** The points a, b, c and d lie on a circle, centre o.
$|\angle aoc| = 110°$.

   (i) Find $|\angle abc|$.

   (ii) Find $|\angle cda|$.

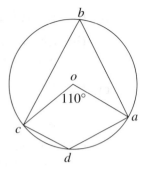

(b) Prove that if $[ab]$ and $[cd]$ are chords of a circle and the lines ab and cd meet at the point k inside the circle, then. $|ak| \cdot |kb| = |ck| \cdot |kd|$.

(c) $[ab]$ and $[cd]$ are chords of the circle, centre o.
$[ab]$ bisects $[od]$ at the point k.
$|ak| = 6$ and $|kb| = 8$.

Find the length of the radius of the circle.

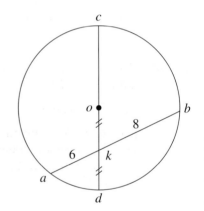

9. **(a)** $oabc$ is a square divided into nine equal squares.
o is the origin and x and y are the points shown.

Copy the diagram and on it show

   (i) the point r such that $\vec{r} = \vec{x} + \vec{y}$

   (ii) the point s such that $\vec{s} = 2\vec{x} + \vec{y}$.

(b) Let $\vec{p} = 2\vec{i} - \vec{j}$ and $\vec{q} = 3\vec{i} + 4\vec{j}$.

   (i) Find $|\vec{p}|$.

   (ii) Express $5\vec{p} - \vec{q}$ in terms of $\vec{i}$ and $\vec{j}$.

   (iii) Express $\vec{pq}$ in terms of $\vec{i}$ and $\vec{j}$.

   (iv) Calculate $\vec{p} \cdot \vec{q}$, the dot product of $\vec{p}$ and $\vec{q}$.

(c) Let $\vec{u} = 2\vec{i} + 5\vec{j}$ and $\vec{v} = 8\vec{i} + 10\vec{j}$.

   (i) Find the scalars h and k such that $\vec{u} + h\vec{v} = k\vec{i}$.

   (ii) Using your values for h and k, verify that $\vec{u}^{\perp} + h\vec{v}^{\perp} = k\vec{i}^{\perp}$.

10. (a) Find the sum to infinity of the geometric series

$$2 + \frac{2}{5} + \frac{2}{25} + \dots$$

(b) (i) Expand $(1 + 2x)^3$ fully.

(ii) Given that $(1 + 2x)^3 + (1 - 2x)^3 = 2(a + bx^2)$, for all x, find the value of a and the value of b.

(c) (i) €2000 is invested at 4% per annum compound interest. Find the value of the investment at the end of six years, correct to the nearest euro.

(ii) An investment account earns 4% per annum compound interest. At the beginning of each year for six consecutive years €2000 is invested in the account. Using the formula for the sum of the first n terms of a geometric series, find the total value of the investment account at the end of the six years, correct to the nearest euro.

11. (a) The line K cuts the x-axis at $(-5, 0)$ and the y-axis at $(0, 2)$.

(i) Find the equation of K.

(ii) Write down the three inequalities that together define the region enclosed by K, the x-axis and the y-axis.

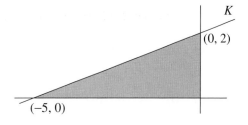

(b) A developer is planning a holiday complex of cottages and apartments. Each cottage will accommodate 3 adults and 5 children and each apartment will accommodate 2 adults and 2 children. The other facilities in the complex are designed for a maximum of 60 adults and a maximum of 80 children.

(i) Taking x as the number of cottages and y as the number of apartments, write down two inequalities in x and y and illustrate these on graph paper.

(ii) If the rental income per night will be €65 for a cottage and €40 for an apartment, how many of each should the developer include in the complex to maximise potential rental income?

(iii) If the construction costs are €200 000 for a cottage and €120 000 for an apartment, how many of each should the developer include in the complex to minimise construction costs?

Answers

Leaving Certificate, Ordinary Level, 2007

Paper 1

1. (a) 262.4 km (b) (i) €8,840 (ii) 4.5% (c) (i) €503.10 (ii) 8.5 hours

2. (a) 0, 1, 2, 3 (b) (i) $\dfrac{3}{2}$ (iii) 3 (c) (i) $1 \pm \sqrt{2}$

3. (a) 3 (b) $x = 6, y = 2$ (c) (ii) $-5, -1, \dfrac{1}{2}$

4. (a) $12 - 7i$ (b) (ii) 5 (iii) 12 (c) (i) 10 (ii) true

5. (a) (i) -4 (ii) 5 (b) (i) $4n - 1$ (ii) 50 (iii) 5050

    (c) (i) $\dfrac{1}{3}$ (ii) $\dfrac{1}{2}\left(1 - \dfrac{1}{3^n}\right)$ (iii) 2

6. (a) (i) $2x - 6$ (ii) 3 (b) (i) 6 mins (ii) $5°$ (iii) -6

    (c) (i) $4(5x - 2)^3$ (5) or $20(5x - 2)^3$ (ii) $\left(\dfrac{3}{5}, 1\right)$

7. (a) $24x^3 - 6x + 7$ (b) (i) $(x^2 + 9)(12x^2) + (4x^2 + 5)(2x)$ or $24x^4 + 108x^2 + 10x$

    (ii) $\dfrac{9}{(2x + 3)^2}$ (c) (i) 10 m/s (ii) 4 m/s^2 (iii) 3 sec

8. (a) -1 (c) (i) -6 (ii) $\dfrac{-1}{(x + 7)^2}$

Paper 2

1. **(a)** **(i)** 26 cm **(ii)** 60 cm **(b)** **(ii)** 50 cm^2 **(c)** **(i)** 1,543.5 π cm^3 **(ii)** 42 cm

2. **(a)** (4, 3) **(b)** **(i)** $\dfrac{3}{2}$ **(ii)** $3x - 2y + 12 = 0$ **(iv)** $2x + 3y = 0$

    (c) **(i)** 32 **(ii)** $(-8, 11)$

3. **(a)** **(i)** $x^2 + y^2 = 16$ **(b)** **(i)** $(3, 1), (-3, -1)$ **(c)** **(i)** $\sqrt{34}$; $(5, -1)$ **(iii)** $(0, 2)$

4. **(a)** **(i)** $x = 100$ **(ii)** $y = 80$ **(c)** **(i)** 2.8 **(ii)** 2.5 **(iii)** 35.28

5. **(a)** 4.9 cm^2 **(b)** **(i)** 6 cm **(ii)** $50°$ **(iii)** $40°$ **(c)** **(i)** 22 cm **(ii)** 27 cm

6. **(a)** **(i)** $\dfrac{1}{6}$ **(ii)** $\dfrac{1}{2}$ **(b)** **(i)** $(1, A), (1, B), (1, C), (2, A), (2, B), (2, C), (3, A),$

    $(3, B), (3, C), (4, A), (4, B), (4, C)$ **(ii)** $\dfrac{1}{12}$ **(iii)** $\dfrac{1}{6}$ **(iv)** $\dfrac{1}{3}$

    (c) **(i)** 60 **(ii)** 24 **(iii)** 12 **(iv)** 6

7. **(a)** 8 **(b)** **(ii)** 14 **(iii)** 6 **(c)** **(i)** 72 **(ii)** 35 **(iii)** 60

8. **(a)** $55°$ **(ii)** $125°$ **(c)** 8

9. **(b)** **(i)** $\sqrt{5}$ **(ii)** $13\vec{i} - 9\vec{j}$ **(iii)** $-5\vec{i} + 5\vec{j}$ **(iv)** -10 **(c)** **(i)** $h = -\dfrac{1}{2}, k = -2$

10. **(a)** $\dfrac{5}{2}$ **(b)** **(i)** $1 + 6x + 12x^2 + 8x^3$ **(ii)** $a = 1, b = 12$

    (c) **(i)** €2,531 **(ii)** €13,797

11. **(a)** **(i)** $2x - 5y + 10 = 0$ **(ii)** $x \leqslant 0, \ y \geqslant 0, \ 2x - 5y + 10 \geqslant 0$

    (c) **(i)** $3x + 2y \leqslant 60, \ 5x + 2y \leqslant 80$ **(ii)** 10 cottages and 15 apartments

    (iii) 16 cottages and 0 apartments

EXAM PAPERS

LEAVING CERTIFICATE EXAMINATION, 2008

MATHEMATICS – ORDINARY LEVEL

PAPER 1 (300 marks)

FRIDAY, 6 JUNE – MORNING, 9:30 to 12:00

Attempt **SIX QUESTIONS** (50 marks each).

WARNING: Marks will be lost if all necessary work is not clearly shown.

Answers should include the appropriate units of measurement, where relevant.

---

1. **(a)** John works from 09:00 hours to 13:00 hours and again from 14:00 hours to 17:30 hours.

    He is paid €18.50 per hour.
    Find his total pay for the day.

   (b) Alice frequently travels from her home to Cork, a distance of 85 km. The journey usually takes 1 hour 15 minutes.

   (i) Find her average speed in kilometres per hour for the journey.

   (ii) On a day of very heavy rain her average speed on a 28 km section of the journey was reduced to 35 km/h.
    How long did this section of the journey take on that day?

   (iii) How much longer did the total journey take on that day, if she completed the rest of the journey at her usual average speed?
    Give your answer correct to the nearest minute.

   (c) A retailer buys an item for €73. She wants to apply a mark-up of 40% of the cost price of the item. She must then add VAT at 21% to this amount to find the price that she would need to charge the customer.

   (i) Find this price, correct to the nearest cent.

    The retailer adjusts the price charged to the customer so that it is 1 cent less than a multiple of €10, while keeping the mark-up as close as possible to 40%.

   (ii) Using this adjusted price, calculate the actual percentage mark-up achieved, correct to the nearest percent.

2. (a) Simplify $3(4x+5) - 2(6x+4)$.

(b) (i) Solve $x^2 - 4x + 1 = 0$.

Write your solutions in the form $a \pm \sqrt{b}$, where $a, b \in \mathbf{N}$.

(ii) Find the value of x for which

$$\frac{5^x}{3} = \frac{5^6}{75}.$$

(c) (i) Factorise $x^2 + 4x + 4$.

(ii) Simplify $\sqrt{x^2 + 4x + 4} + \sqrt{x^2 + 2x + 1}$, given that $x \geq 0$.

(iii) Given that $x \geq 0$, solve for x

$$\sqrt{x^2 + 4x + 4} + \sqrt{x^2 + 2x + 1} = x^2.$$

3. (a) Given that $a(x+5) = 8$, express x in terms of a.

(b) (i) Solve for x and y

$$x - y = 1$$
$$x^2 + y^2 = 25.$$

(ii) Hence, find the two possible values of $x - y^2$.

(c) (i) Let $f(x) = x^2 + bx + c$, $x \in \mathbf{R}$.

The graph of the function f intersects the y-axis at 3 and the x-axis at -1. Find the value of b and the value of c.

(ii) The lengths of the sides of an isosceles triangle are $\sqrt{x^2 + 1}$, $\sqrt{x^2 + 1}$ and $2x$. Taking $2x$ as the base, find the perpendicular height of the triangle.

4. (a) Let $u = 3 - 4i$, where $i^2 = -1$.

Plot on an Argand diagram

(i) u

(ii) $u + 5i$.

(b) Let $w = 2 + 5i$.

(i) Express w^2 in the form $x + yi$, where $x, y \in \mathbf{R}$.

(ii) Verify that $|w^2| = |w|^2$.

(c) Let $z = 6 - 4i$.

   (i) Find the real number k such that

$$k(z + \bar{z}) = 24$$

   where $\bar{z}$ is the complex conjugate of z.

   (ii) Find the real numbers s and t such that

$$\frac{s + ti}{4 + 3i} = z.$$

5. (a) Find the eleventh term of the arithmetic sequence 5, 14, 23 …

  (b) The nth term of a geometric sequence is

$$T_n = \frac{3^n}{27}.$$

   (i) Find a, the first term.

   (ii) Find r, the common ratio.

   (iii) The kth term of the sequence is 243. Find k.

  (c) The sum of the first n terms of an arithmetic series is given by $S_n = n^2 - 16n$.

   (i) Use S_1 and S_2 to find the first term and the common difference.

   (ii) Find T_n, the nth term of the series.

   (iii) Find the values of $n \in \mathbf{N}$ for which $S_n = -63$.

6. (a) Let $g(x) = 2x - 5$, where $x \in \mathbf{R}$.
  Find the value of x for which $g(x) = 19$.

  (b) Differentiate $3x^2 + 5$ with respect to x from first principles.

  (c) Let $f(x) = \dfrac{x^2 - x}{1 - x^3}$, $x \in \mathbf{R}$, $x \neq 1$.

   (i) Find $f'(x)$, the derivative of $f(x)$.

   (ii) Show that the tangent to the curve $y = f(x)$ at the point $(0, 0)$ makes an angle of $135°$ with the positive sense of the x-axis.

7. **(a)** Differentiate with respect to x

    (i) x^7

    (ii) $5x - 3x^4$.

  (b) **(i)** Differentiate $(1 + 3x)(4 - x^2)$ with respect to x.

    (ii) Given that $y = (3x^2 - 4x)^8$, find $\dfrac{dy}{dx}$ when $x = 1$.

  (c) A distress flare is tested by firing it vertically upwards from the top of a tower. The height, h metres, of the flare above the ground is given by

$$h = 20 + 90t - 5t^2$$

where t is the time in seconds from the instant the flare is fired.
The flare is designed to explode 7 seconds after firing.

    (i) Find the height above the ground at which the flare explodes.

    (ii) Find the speed of the flare at the instant it explodes.

    (iii) If the flare failed to explode, find the greatest height above the ground it would
reach before falling back down.

8. Let $f(x) = x^3 - 9x^2 + 24x - 18$, where $x \in \mathbf{R}$.

    (i) Find $f(1)$ and $f(5)$.

    (ii) Find $f'(x)$, the derivative of $f(x)$.

    (iii) Find the co-ordinates of the local maximum point and of the local minimum point of the curve $y = f(x)$.

    (iv) Draw the graph of the function f in the domain $1 \le x \le 5$.

    (v) Use your graph to write down the range of values of x for which $f'(x) < 0$.

    (vi) The line $y = -3x + c$ is a tangent to the curve $y = f(x)$. Find the value of c.

LEAVING CERTIFICATE EXAMINATION, 2008

MATHEMATICS – ORDINARY LEVEL

PAPER 2 (300 marks)

MONDAY, 9 JUNE – MORNING, 9:30 to 12:00

Attempt **FIVE** questions from **Section A** and **ONE** question from **Section B**. Each question carries 50 marks.

WARNING: Marks will be lost if all necessary work is not clearly shown.

Answers should include the appropriate units of measurement, where relevant.

SECTION A

Attempt FIVE questions from this section.

1. **(a)** The semicircular shape shown in the diagram has diameter 16 cm.

    (i) Find the length of the perimeter of the shape, correct to the nearest centimetre.

    (ii) Find the area of the shape, correct to the nearest square centimetre.

    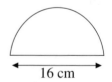
    16 cm

   (b) The sketch shows a piece of land which borders the side of a straight road [*ab*]. The length of [*ab*] is 54 m.
   At equal intervals along [*ab*], perpendicular measurements are made to the boundary, as shown on the sketch.

    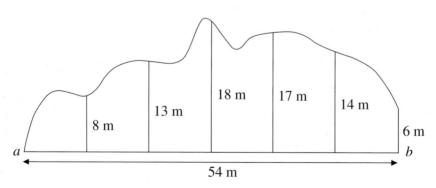

    (i) Use Simpson's Rule to estimate the area of the piece of land.

    (ii) The land is valued at €480 000 per hectare. Find the value of the piece of land.
Note: 1 hectare = 10 000 m².

(c) A wax candle is in the shape of a right circular cone. The height
of the candle is 7 cm and the diameter of the base is 6 cm.

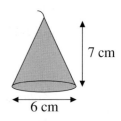

7 cm

    (i) Find the volume of the wax candle, correct to the
nearest cm³.

    (ii) A rectangular block of wax measuring 25 cm by 12 cm
by 12 cm is melted down and used to make a number of
these candles.

6 cm

    Find the maximum number of candles that can be made from the block of wax
if 4% of the wax is lost in the process.

2. **(a)** Find the area of the triangle with vertices $(0, 0)$, $(8, 6)$ and $(-2, 4)$.

  (b) L is the line $y - 6 = -2(x + 1)$.

    (i) Write down the slope of L.

    (ii) Verify that $p(1, 2)$ is a point on L.

    (iii) L intersects the y-axis at t. Find the co-ordinates of t.

    (iv) Show the line L on a co-ordinate diagram.

  (c) $o(0, 0)$, $a(5, 2)$, $b(1, 7)$ and $c(-4, 5)$ are the vertices of a parallelogram.

    (i) Verify that the diagonals $[ob]$ and $[ac]$ bisect each other.

    (ii) Find the equation of ob.

3. **(a)** A circle has equation $x^2 + y^2 = 16$.

    (i) Show the circle on a co-ordinate diagram.

    (ii) Mark the four points at which the circle intersects the axes and label them
with their co-ordinates.

  (b) The diagram shows two circles H and K,
of equal radius. The circles touch at the
point $p(-2, 1)$.
The circle H has centre $(0, 0)$.

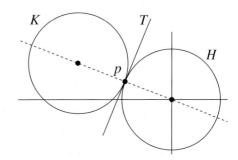

    (i) Find the equation of H.

    (ii) Find the equation of K.

    (iii) T is a tangent to the circles at p.
Find the equation of T.

(c) The circle S has equation $(x-3)^2 + (y+2)^2 = 40$.
S intersects the x-axis at the point a and at the point b.

    (i) Find the co-ordinates of a and the co-ordinates of b.

    (ii) Show that $|ab|$ is less than the diameter of S.

    (iii) Find the equation of the circle with $[ab]$ as diameter.

4. (a) In the triangle abc,

    $|\angle abc| = 90°$, $|bc| = 4{\cdot}5$ and $|ac| = 7{\cdot}5$.

    Find $|ab|$.

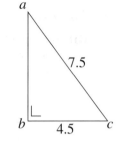

(b) Prove that the opposite sides of a parallelogram have equal lengths.

(c) (i) Construct an equilateral triangle pqr of side 8 cm.

    (ii) Construct the image of the triangle pqr under the enlargement of scale factor $0{\cdot}75$ and centre q.

    (iii) Given that the area of the triangle pqr is $16\sqrt{3}$ cm^2, find the area of the image triangle in the form $k\sqrt{3}$ cm^2.

5. (a) A circle has centre o and radius 21 cm.
s and t are two points on the circle and $|\angle sot| = 120°$.

Find the length of the shorter arc st, correct to the nearest centimetre.

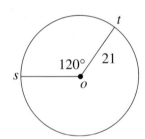

(b) In the right-angled triangle psq, p is joined to a point r on $[sq]$. $|pq| = 8$ cm, $|\angle prq| = 48{\cdot}8°$ and $|\angle psq| = 36°$.

    (i) Find $|pr|$, correct to one decimal place.

    (ii) Find $|sr|$, correct to the nearest centimetre.

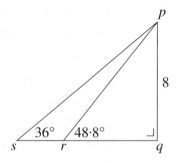

(c) The area of the triangle abc is 33 cm^2. $|ab| = 8$ cm and $|\angle cab| = 55°$.

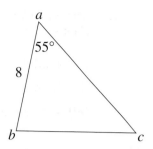

    (i)   Find $|bc|$, correct to one decimal place.

    (ii) Find $|\angle abc|$, correct to the nearest degree.

6. (a) Evaluate $5! + 6!$

    (b) One shelf of a school library has 70 books. The books are on poetry and on drama and are either hardback or paperback.
The following table shows the number of each type.

	Hardback	Paperback
Poetry	23	17
Drama	14	16

A student selects one book at random from the shelf.

Find the probability that the book selected is

    (i)   a paperback poetry book

    (ii) a hardback book

    (iii) a poetry book

    (iv) not a paperback drama book.

    (c) There are 6 junior-cycle students and 5 senior-cycle students on the student council in a particular school.

A committee of 4 students is to be selected from the students on the council.

In how many different ways can the committee be selected if

    (i)   there are no restrictions.

    (ii) a particular student must be on the committee.

    (iii) the committee must consist of 2 junior-cycle students and 2 senior-cycle students.

The committee of 4 students is chosen at random.

    (iv) Find the probability that all 4 students are junior-cycle students.

7. **(a)** The ages of the members of a sports centre were analysed. The results were:

Age	15–25	25–35	35–45	45–55	55–75
Number of members	40	100	60	80	120

[Note: 25–35 means 25 years old or more but less than 35, etc.]

(i) Draw a histogram to represent the data.

(ii) By taking the data at the mid-interval values, calculate the mean age per member.

(iii) What is the greatest possible number of members who could have been over 60 years of age?

(b) The amount of money spent by shoppers in a supermarket over a particular time period was recorded. The results are represented by the ogive below:

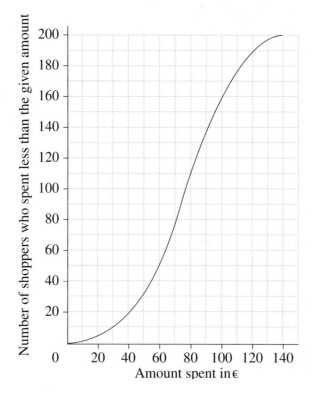

(i) Estimate the median amount spent.

(ii) Estimate the interquartile range.

(iii) Estimate the number of shoppers who spent between €40 and €100.

(iv) Given that the mean amount spent was €80 per shopper, estimate the percentage of shoppers who spent more than the mean amount.

SECTION B

Attempt ONE question from this section.

8. **(a)** The chords [*ab*] and [*cd*] of a circle
intersect at a point *p* inside the circle.
$|ap| = 15$, $|pb| = 6$ and $|pd| = 9$.

Find $|cp|$.

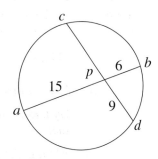

(b) Prove that the degree-measure of an angle subtended at the centre of a circle by a chord
is equal to twice the degree-measure of any angle subtended by the chord at a point of
the arc of the circle which is on the same side of the chordal line as is the centre.

(c) The points *a*, *b*, *c* and *d* lie on a circle.
$|ab| = |bc| = |ac|$ and [*bd*] bisects $\angle abc$.

   (i) Find $|\angle cab|$.

   (ii) Find $|\angle cdb|$.

   (iii) Find $|\angle bcd|$.

   (iv) Is [*bd*] a diameter of the circle?

   Give a reason for your answer.

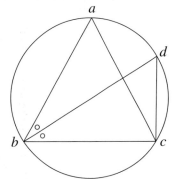

9. **(a)** Let $\vec{v} = 2\vec{i} + 3\vec{j}$ and $\vec{w} = \vec{i} - 4\vec{j}$.

   (i) Express $\vec{v} + 2\vec{w}$ in terms of $\vec{i}$ and $\vec{j}$.

   (ii) Express $\overrightarrow{vw}$ in terms of $\vec{i}$ and $\vec{j}$.

(b) Let $\vec{m} = 4\vec{i} + 3\vec{j}$ and $\vec{n} = 15\vec{i} - 8\vec{j}$.

   (i) Find $\vec{m} \cdot \vec{n}$, the dot product of $\vec{m}$ and $\vec{n}$.

   (ii) Calculate $|\vec{m}|$ and $|\vec{n}|$.

   (iii) Find the measure of the angle between $\vec{m}$ and $\vec{n}$,
   correct to the nearest degree.

(c) *oabc* is a parallelogram. [*cb*] is produced to *d* such that $|bd| = \dfrac{1}{2}|cb|$.

   (i) Express $\overrightarrow{cd}$ in terms of $\vec{a}$.

   (ii) Express $\vec{d}$ in terms of $\vec{a}$ and $\vec{c}$.

   (iii) Express $\overrightarrow{ad}$ in terms of $\vec{a}$ and $\vec{c}$.

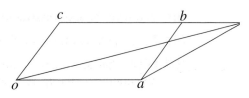

303

10. (a) (i) Write out the first 3 terms in the expansion of $(1 - x)^6$ in ascending powers of x.

   (ii) Calculate the value of the third term when $x = 0.1$.

(b) (i) Find the sum to infinity of the geometric series $\dfrac{7}{10} + \dfrac{7}{100} + \dfrac{7}{1000} + \cdots$.

   (ii) Hence, express the recurring decimal $1.777\ldots$ in the form $\dfrac{a}{b}$, where $a, b \in \mathbf{N}$.

(c) (i) Tom gave a donation of €200 to a charity in 2004.

   Tom agreed to increase his donation by €10 each year for the next 9 years.

   Use the relevant series formula to find the total amount Tom will have donated to the charity after the 10 years.

   (ii) Kate also gave a donation of €200 to the charity in 2004.

   She agreed to increase her donation by a fixed amount each year for the next 9 years. After the 10 years Kate will have donated €3125.

   By how much is Kate increasing her donation each year?

11. (a) (i) Does the point $(18, -15)$ satisfy the inequality $3x + 5y + 11 \geq 0$? Justify your answer.

   (ii) The equation of the line K is $x + 2y + 4 = 0$.

   Write down the inequality which defines the shaded half-plane in the diagram.

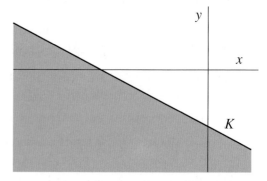

(b) A small restaurant offers two set lunch menus each day: a fish menu and a meat menu.
The fish menu costs €12 to prepare and the meat menu costs €18 to prepare.
The total preparation costs must not exceed €720.
The restaurant can cater for at most 50 people each lunchtime.

   (i) Taking x as the number of fish menus ordered and y as the number of meat menus ordered, write down two inequalities in x and y and illustrate these on graph paper.

   (ii) The price of a fish menu is €25 and the price of a meat menu is €30. How many of each type would need to be ordered each day to maximise income?

   (iii) Show that the maximum income does not give the maximum profit.

Answers

Leaving Certificate, Ordinary Level Maths, 2008

Paper 1

1. (a) €138.75 (b) (i) 68 km/h (ii) 48 min (iii) 23 min
    (c) (i) €123.66 (ii) 36 %

2. (a) 7 (b) (i) $2 \pm \sqrt{3}$ (iii) $x = 4$
    (c) (i) $(x+2)(x+2)$ or $(x+2)^2$ (ii) $2x+3$ (iii) 3

3. (a) $\dfrac{8-5a}{a}$ or $\dfrac{8}{a} - 5$ (b) (i) $x = 4, y = 3$ or $x = -3, y = -4$ (ii) -19 or -5
    (c) (i) $b = 4$ and $c = 3$ (ii) $h = 1$

4. (a) Plot $(3, -4)$ and $(3, 1)$ (b) (i) $-21 + 20i$ (ii) $29 = 29$
    (c) (i) $k = 2$ (ii) $s = 36, t = 2$

5. (a) 95 (b) (i) $\dfrac{1}{9}$ (ii) 3 (iii) $k = 8$
    (c) (i) $a = -15; d = 2$ (ii) $2n - 17$ (iii) 7, 9

6. (a) $x = 12$ (b) $6x$

    (c) (i) $\dfrac{(1 - x^3)(2x - 1) - (x^2 - x)(-3x^2)}{(1 - x^3)^2}$ or $\dfrac{x^4 - 2x^3 + 2x - 1}{(1 - x^3)^2}$

    (ii) $\dfrac{dy}{dx} = -1$, $\therefore$ slope $= -1$, $\therefore$ $\tan \theta = -1$, $\therefore$ $\theta = \tan^{-1}(-1) = 135°$

7. (a) (i) $7x^6$ (ii) $5 - 12x^3$ (b) (i) $(1 + 3x)(-2x) + (4 - x^2)(3)$ or $-9x^2 - 2x + 12$
    (ii) -16 (c) (i) 405 m (ii) 20 m/s (iii) 425 m

8. (i) $-2, 2$ (ii) $3x^2 - 18x + 24$ (iii) max$(2, 2)$, min$(4, -2)$
    (v) $2 < x < 4$ (vi) $c = 9$

Paper 2

1. **(a)** **(i)** 41 cm **(ii)** 101 cm^2 **(b)** **(i)** 678 m^2 **(ii)** €32,544
   (c) **(i)** 66 cm^3 **(ii)** 52

2. **(a)** 22 **(b)** **(i)** -2 **(ii)** $(0, 4)$ **(c)** **(i)** midpoint of $[ob]$ = midpoint of $[a, c] = \left(\dfrac{1}{2}, \dfrac{7}{2}\right)$
   ∴ diagonals bisect each other **(ii)** $7x - y = 0$

3. **(a)** **(ii)** $(4, 0), (0, 4), (-4, 0), (0, -4)$ **(b)** **(i)** $x^2 + y^2 = 5$ **(ii)** $(x + 4)^2 + (y - 2)^2 = 5$
   (iii) $2x - y + 5 = 0$ **(c)** **(i)** $a(-3, 0), b(9, 0)$ **(ii)** $12 < 12.649$ **(iii)** $(x - 3)^2 + y^2 = 36$

4. **(a)** 6 **(c)** **(iii)** $9\sqrt{3}$ cm^2

5. **(a)** 44 cm **(b)** **(i)** 10.6 **(ii)** 4
   (c) using $|ac| = 10.1$ cm, **(i)** 8.6 cm **(ii)** 74°
   using $|ac| = 10.07$ cm, **(i)** 8.5 cm **(ii)** 76°

6. **(a)** 840 **(b)** **(i)** $\dfrac{17}{40}$ **(ii)** $\dfrac{37}{70}$ **(ii)** $\dfrac{40}{70}$ or $\dfrac{4}{7}$ **(ii)** $\dfrac{54}{70}$ or $\dfrac{27}{35}$

   (c) **(i)** 330 **(ii)** 120 **(iii)** 150 **(iv)** $\dfrac{1}{22}$

7. **(a)** **(ii)** 45 **(iii)** 120 **(b)** **(i)** 76 **(ii)** 35 **(iii)** 140 **(iv)** 45%

8. **(a)** 10 **(c)** **(i)** 60° **(ii)** 60° **(iii)** 90° **(iv)** yes, because $|\angle bcd| = 90°$

9. **(a)** **(i)** $4\vec{i} - 5\vec{j}$ **(ii)** $-\vec{i} - 7\vec{j}$ **(b)** **(i)** 36 **(ii)** 5; 17 **(iii)** 65°
   (c) **(i)** $\dfrac{3}{2}\vec{a}$ **(ii)** $\dfrac{3}{2}\vec{a} + \vec{c}$ **(iii)** $\dfrac{1}{2}\vec{a} + \vec{c}$

10. **(a)** **(i)** $1 - 6x + 15x^2$ **(ii)** 0.15 **(b)** **(i)** $\dfrac{7}{9}$ **(ii)** $\dfrac{16}{9}$
    (c) **(i)** €2,450 **(ii)** €25

11. **(a)** **(i)** no, because $-10 \ngeq 0$ **(ii)** $x + 2y + 4 \leq 0$
    (b) **(i)** $12x + 18y \leq 720$; $x + y \leq 50$ **(ii)** 30 fish, 20 meat; max. income of €1,350
    (iii) 50 fish, 0 meat; max. profit of €650, ∴ max. income does not give max. profit